# WINE GROWI
# IN
# GREAT BRITAIN

Stephen Skelton has been growing grapes, making wine and working in the United Kingdom as a viticultural consultant since 1975 and is an expert on its vineyards and wines. He is the author of several editions of the UK Vineyards Guide and of the highly acclaimed book for students: "Viticulture – an introduction to commercial grape growing for wine production".

# WINE GROWING
# IN
# GREAT BRITAIN

A COMPLETE GUIDE TO
GROWING GRAPES FOR WINE PRODUCTION
IN COOL CLIMATES

Published by the Author
May 2014

Copyright © Stephen Skelton 2014
1B Lettice Street,
London,
SW6 4EH.


E-mail: spskelton@btinternet.com
Telephone: 07768 583700

Designed by Geoff Green Book Design, Cambridge

This book, together with:
"Viticulture – An introduction to commercial grape growing for wine production"
"The UK Vineyards Guide 2010"
and
"Vine varieties, clones and rootstocks for UK vineyards"
are available from **www.lulu.com** under the following reference numbers:

Viticulture – 21652909
UK Vineyards Guide 2010 – 14953376
Wine Growing in Great Britain - 21746025
Vine varieties, clones and rootstocks for UK vineyards - 21768956

# Acknowledgements

My thanks go to the following for their help and assistance with some of the content of this book: John Buchan (vineyard nutrition), Chris Cooper (pest and disease control), Jim Newsome (trunk diseases), Mike Paul (wine sales), Julian Searle (pest and disease control and weed control), Richard Smart (trunk diseases), Geoff Taylor (pesticide residue levels), Mike Trought (bird netting and frost prevention), Nick Wenman (organic and bio-dynamic viticulture), and Helen Waite (trunk diseases). My thanks also go to Karen Telford for 'test driving' an early version of the book and for her helpful comments and to Diana Davies for her proof reading skills.

# Introduction

*Wine Growing in Great Britain* has been written not only for anyone interested in growing grapes for winemaking in the British Isles, but also for those attempting to do the same in other ultra-cool climates. It has been written for those who know very little about the subject, but are keen to know more, together with those who have perhaps already whetted their appetites by growing vines on a small scale, but who now wish to move on to bigger things. It has also been written, as far as is possible, in non-scientific terms so that anyone can understand the subject and to relate to the very practical issues surrounding the growing of grapes in challenging climates. It has also been written from a commercial point-of-view and relates the costs of establishing and looking after vineyards to the potential income, something which I do not believe has ever been covered in a book of this type before.

I am not quite sure when I saw my first English vineyard, but it was probably Biddenden Vineyards, the nearest to Headcorn in Kent where we then lived. This would have been in about 1973-4. My interest was sufficiently aroused for me to seek out, and join, the English Vineyards Association and to find out about the small world of English and Welsh wine and we went to see vineyards at Nettlestead and Lamberhurst in Kent and New Hall in Essex. I also attended a one day conference at the National Agricultural Centre at Stoneleigh organised by the British Farmer and Stockbreeder at which several of the then-luminaries in the world of UK-wine spoke and at which Robin Don MW, then owner of Elmham Park Vineyard in Norfolk, said that in order to get a return, you needed to average 2 tonnes per acre and sell wine for between £1.30 and £1.70 per bottle!

By degrees I learnt a bit more about grape growing and wine making and eventually decided that it was something I would like to pursue in a professional capacity. I was aged twenty-six. A visit to Germany in early 1975 took things a stage further and in June 1975 I found myself on a twelve month placement in a vineyard in the Rheingau, to be followed by eight months studying at Geisenheim. All of this was in preparation to taking over a mixed fruit and arable farm which my late father-in-law had bought and generously made available to us for our new enterprise. This farm, then called Spots Farm, and subsequently Tenterden Vineyards (and today Chapel Down) became my base for the next twenty-plus years of grape growing and winemaking.

When I started growing grapes – I planted my first vine on Easter Monday in 1977 – my knowledge was probably better than most, but was still woefully lacking. How I planted, established and managed the vineyard was a combination of my experiences in Germany, what I had learnt at Geisenheim, plus what I could learn from fellow UK vine growers and winemakers and from the very few books on the subject that were written with UK conditions in mind. Nick Poulter's *Wines from Your Vines* published in 1974 was about the best there was. Gillian Pearkes' 1982 book *Vinegrowing in Britain* and Jack Ward's 1984 book *Vine Growing in the British Isles* had yet to be written. Since those early days, I have been a viticulturalist, winemaker both at Tenterden and Lamberhurst and, since 2002, a consultant working with growers to establish vineyards all over the south of England (and one near Calais!) and this book is the culmination of my forty years of growing grapes and making wine in our sometimes exasperating climate.

Sadly, the history of English and Welsh winegrowing is littered with abandoned and grubbed vineyards. Poor site selection, the wrong choice of varieties and a lack of appreciation of the task ahead and of the skills required to manage a successful vineyard in a challenging climate have all played their part. This book has been written with the hope that it will help those who wish to become part of the small, but growing, UK vinegrowing and winemaking industry to avoid some of the pitfalls which wait at every turn.

When I look back at the last sixty-plus years since the first commercial vineyard was planted in the UK and see what was achieved by a very small band of pioneers, the vineyards that were created and the great wines made, and all achieved with very little in the way of official help and guidance, I am filled with a degree of pride and wonder. However, when I look forward to the next forty years (and more), and see the children and grandchildren of those pioneers, and look at the scale of some of the enterprises now planted and yet to be planted and at the skill, professionalism and, above everything else, the enthusiasm of today's winegrowers, I see a future of even better vineyards, better grapes and, of course, better wines.

Stephen Skelton, Fulham, May 2014.

# Contents

# Chapter 1
# A short history of wine growing in the UK

## The early days

Although vines have been grown in the British Isles since before the Romans arrived, and at various times ever since, the revival of viticulture in the 1950s and '60s was based upon very different circumstances. Vineyards prior to then had, almost without exception, been grown to produce wine for consumption in monasteries, palaces and country houses and with perhaps the exception of the third Marquess of Bute's vineyards at Castell Coch in South Wales, never for the production of wine for commercial sale.[1] The experiments carried out by Ray Brock (Raymond Barrington Brock) at his Oxted Viticultural Research Station, which started in 1945, showed that grapes for wine production could be grown in our climate and could be made into wine of something approaching a marketable quality.

*Ray Brock standing in front of his HRG 'Scientific' which he built and raced at Spa in Belgium in 1948*

It was these experiments that led directly to the planting, in 1952, of 0.40-ha (1-acre) of vines at Hambledon in Hampshire by Major-General Sir Guy Salisbury-Jones. This was to be the first modern vineyard, one based upon disease-resistant varieties, and would produce the first harvestable crop of ripe winemaking grapes in the autumn of 1955. What was also changing in these post-war years was the approach to food and wine by

the public. Foreign travel and books such as Elisabeth David's *Mediterranean Cooking* (1950) and *French Country Cooking* (1951) made people more adventurous in their diets and the adoption by new wine drinkers of wines such as light, off-dry, German white wines, helped open the way to English and Welsh wines of a similar style.

Since those early days, UK viticulture has undergone enormous changes. After Hambledon came Jack Ward's vineyards at Horam Manor in 1954 and the Gore-Browne's at Beaulieu in 1958, but together these three amounted to less than 5-ha (12.36-acres). However, their trials and tribulations and the actual production and sale of wines fuelled considerable interest in viticulture and the 1960s and 1970s saw steady expansion in the number of growers, and both the total area and geographical spread of vineyards. By the end of 1975, the total area under vine, as recorded by MAFF[2] in a voluntary survey, was 196-ha (484-acres) and what had been a minute cottage industry, peopled mainly by retired army and navy officers and a few gentleman farmers, was turning into something approaching a mini-industry.

The expansion of the vineyard area continued throughout the '80s and early '90s until it reached a total planted area of 1,065-ha (2,632-acres) with 479 separate vineyards in 1993, after which it started to decline. The main varieties at this time were the German cross-bred varieties (listed in alphabetical order): Bacchus, Huxelrebe, Madeleine x Angevine 7672, Müller-Thurgau, Ortega, Reichensteiner and Schönburger, together with the French-American hybrid, Seyval blanc. Together these eight varieties accounted for around 75 per cent of the UK's vineyard area. Although these varieties could produce interesting and enjoyable wines (this was in the days when wines such as Blue Nun, Golden Oktober and Black Tower were the most popular wines in the UK), their acceptability by both the wine trade and the wine buying public was limited. Although the total planted area started to fall after 1993, the area in production continued to rise (as young vineyards started to crop) rising to 842-ha (2,081-acres) in 1998, after which the area in production started to fall. By 2004, the total area under vine had fallen to 761-ha (1,880-acres), a drop of 304-ha (751-acres) – almost 30 per cent of the planted area – from its peak, with the area in production falling to 697-ha (1,722-acres) by 2007. How much money (let alone the time and effort) went into those grubbed 304-ha (751-acres) one can only wonder at, but it must have been at least £6-7m in vineyards alone, to say nothing of wineries and other costs. Then, following the *über*-warm year of 2003, things started to change. Since the low point in the planted area of 761-ha (1,880-acres) in 2004, the area has risen to where in 2013 it is officially recorded by the Wine Standards Branch (WSB)[3] of the Food Standards Agency as being 1,884-ha (4,655-acres).[4] In 1993 there were 479 vineyards with an average size of 2.22-ha (5.49-acres); in 2013 there were 448 commercial vineyards with an average size of 4.21-ha (10.40-acres), an increase in size of 90 per cent!

Whilst the bravery of the Mosses cannot be denied, it was the change in the climate that made it possible to start growing the Champagne varieties. Chardonnay, Pinot noir and Meunier had already been tried in several different UK vineyards and found wanting.[6] With the summer temperatures between 1952 and 1988 seldom rising above 30°C (1976 being a notable exception) the UK fell well inside the accepted definition of 'cool' (and therefore marginal) for viticulture. However, in the eighteen years between 1989 and 2006, there were only four years when the temperature didn't rise above this magic figure. Met Office figures show that between 1960 and 1991, the mean night-time July temperature in the south-east of England was 11.56°C, whereas between 1981 and 2010 this had risen to 12.24°C. Likewise the day time temperatures for the same month and region rose from 21.19°C to 22.01°C.

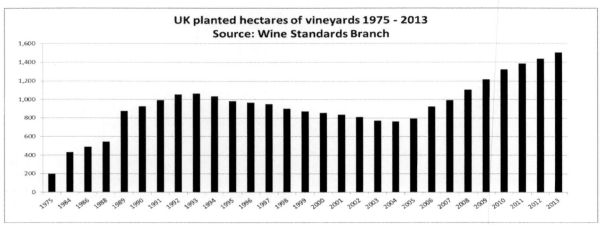

**UK planted hectares of vineyards 1975 - 2013**
**Source: Wine Standards Branch**

*Note: The totals in the above table for 1975-88 are the results from voluntary surveys of farmers and are therefore almost certainly inaccurate. The 1989 and subsequent figures are the result of mandatory surveys and can therefore be assumed to be accurate.*

## The Nyetimber effect

This change in the fortunes of UK vineyards has been dubbed (by me) the 'Nyetimber effect', although in reality it perhaps ought to be called the 'climate change effect'. In 1988, just as the plug was being pulled on the UK's own Liebfraumilch lake, two Americans, Stuart and Sandy Moss, started planting a substantial (for the time) area of Chardonnay, Pinot noir and Meunier solely for the production of bottle-fermented sparkling wines. Most UK winegrowers, who were then happily growing and making still wine, thought they were mad. But, when in 1997 they released their first wine – the 100 per cent Chardonnay *1992 Nyetimber Première Cuvée Blanc de Blancs* – which won an IWSC[5] Gold Medal and that competition's English Wine Trophy, views started to change. When in 1998 their second release, the *1993 Nyetimber Classic Cuvée* (a true Champagne-variety blend) went one better, winning not only an IWSC Gold Medal and the English Wine Trophy, but also the Bottle Fermented Sparkling Wine Trophy, some of us realised that the game was up for German-variety based still wines.

These rises, although seemingly small, in fact take the temperature to the tipping-point where growing these varieties for sparkling wine becomes feasible.

Whilst the higher day time temperatures are obvious in their effect, it is not always appreciated what impact the higher night-time temperatures have had upon UK vineyards. The vine's leaves have to reach a certain temperature[7] before photosynthesis starts and carbo-hydrates are produced. The warmer nights (and if you are a non-believer just ask bedding retailers how many 15-tog duvets they sell these days) mean that the leaves warm up more quickly giving the vine more time in the day in which it can produce sugar. This produces – along with the rest of the vinegrowing world – higher natural alcohol levels. If you take natural sugar levels in UK vineyards for say vintages between 1979 and 1999 and compare them with the sugar levels from the same vine varieties for vintages this century, in many instances they have almost doubled. Whereas UK winemakers were used to harvesting grapes at 6-8 per cent natural alcohol and enriching (chaptalizing) the juice by 4.0 per cent or even 4.5 per cent, since 2000 it has not been unheard of to harvest grapes at 11 per cent, 12 per cent and even 13 per cent and to make wines without any sugar additions at all.

Looking back at my winemaking records for Tenterden Vineyards (today's Chapel Down) I see that between the first vintage in 1979 and 1989, the average potential alcohol level for Müller-Thurgau was 7.1 per cent

(56.8°OE) and for Seyval blanc 6.5 per cent (52.4°OE). 1990 was an exception with Müller-Thurgau rising to 11.1 per cent (82°OE) – the first time the natural alcohol level rose to double figures – and Seyval blanc to 9.2 per cent (70°OE), but for the next eleven years, until I stopped winemaking there in 2000, natural sugar levels for these two varieties were very seldom over 10 per cent (75°OE). (And for the sake of putting these seemingly low sugar levels into a quality context, between 1979 and 1989 the wines I produced from these two varieties won the Gore-Browne Trophy twice, plus two Gold and two Silver medals in the UKVA[8] competition.) In 2013 however, UK winemakers experienced some of the lowest natural sugar levels seen for many years – very few grapes were harvested at over 10 per cent (75°OE) – reminding us (as if any such reminder was really required) that the UK is an unpredictable place to grow grapes and make wine. (It is perhaps also worth putting UK alcohol levels into the context of those in Champagne where up until the late 1980s, the minimum natural alcohol at which grapes could be picked was 7 per cent and even today it is only 9.5 per cent).

Since the early days of the UK winegrowing industry, there have also been other major changes which have had a huge influence upon the quality and marketability of our wines: experience and vine varieties. Those pioneer grapegrowers and winemakers typically had no experience of growing vines (and often no experience of growing anything very much at all) and their winemaking skills were usually gleaned from home winemaking books and they knew nothing of the sterile bottling of wines with residual sugar.[9] Today, there are viticulturalists and winemakers, in some instances the sons and daughters and even the grandsons (I don't know of any granddaughters) of those who started their vineyards, who have been to colleges both overseas and in the UK and have degrees and experience in grapegrowing and winemaking. Whilst no one would pretend that we have got it 100 per cent right yet, we have travelled a long way in sixty years.

In our selection of vine varieties we have also seen some major changes. Hambledon was initially planted with three French-American hybrids: Seyval blanc (Seyve-Villard 5-276), Aurore (Seibel 5279) and Seibel 10-868. Jack Ward and the Gore-Brownes also planted Seyval blanc, but twinned it with what was then often called Riesling Sylvaner, but which we know today as Müller-Thurgau (or occasionally Rivaner) and these two became the default varieties for almost all the early vineyards. Jack Ward, who spoke fluent German, also imported vines and introduced UK growers to Bacchus, Huxelrebe, Reichensteiner, and Schönburger and these, together with a Brock special, Madeleine x Angevine 7672 (cuttings were sent to him from Alzey, Germany in 1957), became the foundation of almost all UK vineyards. In 1984, these seven varieties accounted for 74 per cent of the planted area of 430-ha (1,063-acres). Pinot noir accounted for only 11-ha (27-acres) or just 2.6 per cent of the total and Chardonnay was not separately recorded as it was barely planted at all.

Thirty years later, the spectrum of vine varieties grown in UK vineyards is very different. Chardonnay and Pinot noir – the top two varieties – and Meunier together account for 46.6 per cent of the planted area; Bacchus, Madeleine x Angevine 7672, Müller-Thurgau, Ortega, Reichensteiner, Rondo, Schönburger and Seyval blanc (listed in alphabetical order) account for another 35 per cent. Together these eleven varieties account for 81 per cent of the recorded vine variety area of 1,503-ha (3,714-acres).

**Note:** The vine variety data differs from the Vineyard Register area, hence the difference in totals between the planted area of 1,884-ha and the area given for the grape variety totals of 1,503-ha.

The ability to grow and ripen classic 'noble' varieties such as Chardonnay and Pinot noir and craft with them some world-class – in some instances even world-beating – bottle-fermented sparkling wines has also had some interesting consequences. Previously, a wine retailer or sommelier might have to say, when asked what an English wine was like: 'well it's made from Müller-Thurgau and Schönburger with a touch of Reichensteiner and its tastes a bit like German wine or maybe a wine from Alsace' and in doing so lose the customer's attention and interest before the second umlaut. Today, when faced with the same question about a bottle of English Sparkling

| Vine varieties in the UK 1984 and 2013 | | | | |
|---|---|---|---|---|
| Variety | 1984 Hectares | Variety | 2013 Hectares |
| Müller-Thurgau | 149 | Chardonnay | 327 |
| Reichensteiner | 47 | Pinot noir | 305 |
| Seyval blanc | 46 | Bacchus | 131 |
| Madeleine x Angevine 7672 | 26 | Seyval blanc | 92 |
| Huxelrebe | 23 | Reichensteiner | 80 |
| Schönburger | 16 | Meunier | 69 |
| Pinot noir | 11 | Müller-Thurgau | 56 |
| Bacchus | 10 | Rondo | 47 |
| Others | 102 | Madeleine x Angevine 7672 | 46 |
| | | Schönburger | 35 |
| | | Ortega | 35 |
| | | Pinot blanc | 25 |
| | | Regent | 24 |
| | | Phoenix | 24 |
| | | Pinot noir Précoce | 20 |
| | | Others | 187 |
| Total Ha | 430 | Total Ha | 1,503 |

Source: Wine Standards Branch of the Food Standards Agency

**Note**: The vine variety data runs a year behind Vineyard Register data, hence the difference between the total UK vineyard area of 1,884-ha and the area given above.

Wine, the same retailer or sommelier might say: 'well it's made from Chardonnay and Pinot noir and is just like Champagne' and, in doing so, convey a message that every wine drinker understands. This change I believe has made a huge difference to the industry and has given the wine trade in all its many guises the confidence to get behind, to support and to sell the home-grown product.

In still wines, the practice by UK wine producers of varietal naming has somewhat diminished and many still wines are now sold under brand names, thus getting round the 'umlaut' problem. The exception to this rule are wines made from Bacchus which have actually increased in popularity (in line with the planted area) and are now seen as something of an English speciality. The name is so non-German and so redolent of all things vinous, that most consumers have no idea that it's a vine variety (at least not until they read the back label) and even many wine-trade people think it some sort of UK-derived brand name. Let's thank Peter Morio and Bernhard Husfeld, its breeders, for not giving it a name like *Dionysüs-reben*.

*Sir Guy and Lady Hilda Salisbury-Jones standing outside the front door at Hambledon in 1953*

Other still wines, made from international varieties such as Pinot blanc, Pinot gris and Pinot noir will certainly benefit from having recognisable names and the days of trying to persuade the public to like wines made from Müller-Thurgau, Reichensteiner and Huxelrebe are mostly behind us. Seyval blanc, always the odd one out, is often used for sparkling wine production (where varietal labelling has never been as common as for still wines) and the variety is sufficiently peculiar to the UK (at least in a European context) and has enough supporters (Oz Clarke consistently rates it highly) that I am sure it will survive, indeed flourish, especially given that it can produce fruit and ripen that fruit even in poor years (although its performance in 2013 sadly let this reputation down) and requires little or no chemical treatments to keep it free of disease.

However, climate change and the consumer acceptance of our wines haven't changed the basic facts of viticultural life in the UK. We have a marginal climate for commercial grapegrowing. Climate change has not made the task of finding a suitable site for a vineyard any easier and it is no easier to plant and establish a vineyard that

will produce the quantity and quality of grapes required to create a viable, self-supporting, sustainable[10] enterprise.

---

1 The history of almost 2,000 years of grape growing in the British Isles can be found in the opening chapter of my *UK Vineyards Guide*, as well as in books by Edward Hyams, Ray Brock, George Ordish and Hugh Barty-King. See bibliography for a full list.

2 MAFF, the Ministry of Agriculture Fisheries and Food, was the forerunner of today's DEFRA, the Department for Environment, Food and Rural Affairs. Until 1989, all MAFF vineyard surveys were voluntary and therefore certainly inaccurate. In 1988 the total planted area was recorded by the last voluntary survey as being 546-ha (1,349-acres). The first compulsory survey a year later (1989) recorded a total of 876-ha (2,165-acres).

3 The Wine Standards Branch of the Food Standards Agency is the body responsible for implementing and policing the rules and regulations to do with wine marketing (of all wines – home grown or foreign) and wine making in the UK. It also collects vineyard data for the Vineyard Register and collects production data for the annual wine production statistics. http://food.gov.uk/business-industry/winestandards.

4 In 2012 the WSB's Vineyard Register recorded the planted area of vines in the UK as 1,438-ha (3,553-acres). However, with the release of the 2013 production totals in May 2014, the total area had dramatically increased by 446-ha (1,102-acres) to 1,884-ha (4,655-acres) planted and 1,571-ha (3,882-acres) in production. Exactly where this massive increase came from is anyone's guess, but I suspect that the WSB has at long last done a bit of chasing up of all the new vineyards planted in the last five years.

5 International Wine and Spirit Competition.

6 I remember visiting the Paget brothers at Chilsdown Vineyard (in Singleton, West Sussex) at harvest-time in 1981 and seeing their small patch of Chardonnay, the grapes of which were bright green and still as hard as bullets and joking that they would be good cannon-fodder to fire at the birds then starting to attack their Müller-Thurgau and Reichensteiner.

7 There is no single temperature at which photosynthesis starts as it is a progressive process which increases as temperatures rise. It is also affected by other factors – water availability, light intensity and wavelength – and is a hugely complex process. However, the warmer it is (within reason) the sooner it starts.

8 United Kingdom Vineyards Association

9 When I won my first Gore-Browne Trophy in 1981 (I won two more subsequently) the then Chairman of the English Vineyards Association – Colin Gillespie – said to me (I suspect only half-joking): 'Stephen, you cheated really, you were trained'. What he meant of course was that I had spent some time in Germany and spent some time at Geisenheim whereas almost all the other growers and winemakers in the UK at the time were self-taught.

10 The word 'sustainable' is being used in its true sense i.e. to keep going as a commercial enterprise. UK vineyards, if they are to survive into the future, have to learn to become self-supporting businesses, not reliant on the benevolence of their founders. Only once they have learnt to become sustainable in this sense can they get to grips with other matters lumped under the banner of 'sustainability'.

# Chapter 2
# Why plant a vineyard in the UK?

## Why plant a vineyard in the UK?

When I visit new potential growers – vineyard virgins as I call them – for the first time, I often ask the question: 'why do you want to plant a vineyard in the UK?' The answer I get is often along the lines of: 'we thought it would be fun' or 'well, we've got this field that's not doing very much and it's very sheltered'. Seldom is it: 'I have researched the subject and I believe it can give me a good return over the next thirty years' or 'I really like English wine and would love the chance to be involved with its production and marketing'. It's a pity because if there were a few more of the latter and a few less of the former, the UK grapegrowing industry would be in a better position than it currently is.

However, having said the above, I will own up straightaway to being in the first camp myself. I have often been asked: 'what made you want to start a vineyard in England' and I usually make some comments about being interested in wine (just about true); having seen some local vineyards (true, although I didn't like many of their wines); and having a father-in-law who was (a) a farmer and (b) keen to support his daughter and son-in-law in what he saw as an interesting enterprise (thankfully, very true) – none of which really answer the question in anything but a roundabout way. Many prospective vineyard owners in the UK have little idea of what their total outlay will be or how long it will take them to get to the point where the vineyard is self-supporting; and what sort of return on capital they are likely to see. In short, many have very little idea of what they are letting themselves in for!

There are several reasons for this. The first is that they often appear not to care. They believe they know roughly what it is going to cost to plant and establish a vineyard; they know that it takes approximately four to five years to get vines to crop; and they live in hope that it will 'be alright on the night'. They also take the view that 'if others are doing it, then I can do it' and plough on hopefully, forgetting (or perhaps ignoring) the fact that other people's pockets are sometimes both broader and deeper and other people's approach to a return on capital is not their bank manager's. I have often been told by those contemplating

spending hundreds of thousands of pounds, even several millions, on vineyards, a winery, stock and a workforce, that: 'return on capital is not important. I've made the money and might as well spend it. Land isn't being made any more and it's a sound investment. If I create a viable business which I can sell at some stage, then it will all have been worth it'.

The truth is that to make money out of growing grapes, making wine and selling that wine for a profit is a hard task in ANY country, let alone in a country where the forces of nature are ranged against you. When I say 'hard', I don't mean that its physically demanding (which it is) or that it takes a lot of perseverance (which it does). What I mean is that it is difficult to know, in advance, before a single sod has been turned, before a single vine planted or grape harvested or bottle of wine made, what the following will be:

- The yield from your vineyard
- The quality of your grapes
- The quality of your wine
- The price of your grapes and/or wine.

Without knowing these factors, who can say what the returns will be?

## The economics of grapegrowing in the UK

**Note**: References to a 'bottle' of wine refer to a 75 cl bottle unless otherwise stated. References to a 'case' refer to a nine litre case of wine, i.e. twelve x 75 cl bottles, even though many wines, especially sparkling wines, are packed in six bottle cases.

Vineyard economics worldwide are bedevilled by inconsistencies and finding the true cost of production of a tonne of grapes or a bottle of wine is almost an impossible task. Over what time period do you write off the investment in vines and trellising which could last forty or more years? Do you look at expenditure on land in the same way as expenditure on other assets? Many do not. A winery consists of equipment, much of which is static, made of stainless steel which, with care and upkeep, will last for decades, even centuries. How does one put a true cost on this? Investment in stock is often regarded as money in the bank, and therefore not really part of the overall capital expenditure. When you consider however, that someone making sparkling wine, which will only sell when it has been on the lees for between two and four (or five, or six, or even more years), might have to spend three to four times as much on stock as on the vineyard itself, then surely this has to be factored into the equation?

What follows is therefore an attempt to lay out, for the novice, the facts of life behind an investment in a wine producing enterprise in Great Britain.

## Land prices

The Smiths Gore survey of sales of UK farmland over 20-ha (50-acres) for October 2013 to March 2014 shows that in East Anglia, the South East, South Central and South West of the UK, the average price paid for 'bare arable' land was £19,753-ha (£7,994-acre), of 'bare pasture', £14,950-ha (£6,050-acre) and of 'equipped land', £24,710-ha (£10,000-acre).[1] These prices are based upon around 30 separate sales covering 1,943-ha (4,800-acres) and, as with all averages, the highs and lows tend to be disguised. It is well known that in 2009 a certain large West Sussex-based vineyard spent £40,000-ha (£16,000-acre) for around 30-ha of prime chalk 'bare' farmland near Stockbridge and whilst this might seem excessive, similar land near Canterbury was on offer for £25,000-ha (£10,000-acre) in 2012 and in Gloucestershire for £37,500-ha (£15,000-acre) in 2013. The right land, in the right location, and especially land with (a) neighbouring farmers who really want the extra land and (b) someone who is desperate to buy the land come what may, can fetch prices much above 'average' prices. Smaller farms, especially in good situations, with desirable houses and plenty of convertible stables, oast houses and other farm buildings, will always command a significant premium. Smiths Gore estimate that all land prices will continue to rise by 5-7 per cent with 'bare land' (the type many vineyard owners wish to buy) rising slightly faster. Since 2012, the price of all-UK 'bare land' has risen by 8.5 per cent.

Someone wanting to set up a vineyard on a reasonable amount of land to plant an initial swathe of vines – say 5-ha (12.5-acres), plus room for expansion – say another 20-ha (50-acres), plus some amenity land – say another 20-ha (50-acres), together with a modest house and some farm buildings and maybe a small cottage for agricultural staff, could be looking at an investment of £2-£3 million and possibly more. Add in the requirements specific for a successful vineyard enterprise (well-drained, south facing land, below 100 m above sea level, with buildings suitable for a winery and farm-shop, plus the requirement for it to be situated on or near an accessible road) and the 'vineyard premium' (as I have heard several land agents call it) could add significantly to the bill.

Whether land is (or should be) included in the calculation of the cost of grape production is an interesting question. Many will take the view that as land is one of the soundest long-term investments one can make, that land prices in the grape-growing regions of the UK have, and are likely to continue to, increase in value in the future and that there are inheritance tax advantages in holding land as an asset, then the cost of the land should be excluded from grape production. It is a view with which I have some sympathy.

There is also of course the question of what happens to the value of land after it has been planted with vines. Around twenty years ago I used to get calls from estate agents saying: 'I am selling a house with a vineyard and wonder what additional value it might have'. To which I would usually respond: 'minus £1,000 an acre since this is the cost of taking the vineyard out and reinstating the land to good grazing or arable land'. Whilst this might have been a slight exaggeration, the fact was that very few people wanted vineyards and they were usually only of value to the people who planted them. Today, the situation is somewhat different. Whilst it would be wrong to suggest that every vineyard is worth more than its bare land value, there have been a small number of sales of mature vineyards over the last few years where good prices have been achieved. My view is that a well-sited and well-established vineyard, planted with a spread of decent varieties, ought to fetch at least £60,000 per hectare (£24,282 per acre) and it wouldn't take many additional features to get a premium over that price.

*Nyetimber's 'Netherlands' vineyard*

In October 2012, the 4.17-ha (10.3-acre) Halnaker vineyard near Chichester, planted in 2006 with Champagne varieties, with a patchy, but not hopeless, cropping record over four vintages, was sold to Shellproof PLC (majority owned by Lord Ashcroft and now owners of Gusbourne Estate) for a total of £360,000. If you factor out the 1.13-ha (2.8-acres) of unplanted land at a value of £20,000-ha (£8,000-acre) and another £4,500 for some machinery and equipment, the price paid for the planted land was £79,912-ha (£32,340-acre). This was despite the vineyard requiring quite a lot of remedial work on the trelliswork – many of the end-posts and intermediates needed replacing – and being situated on a busy road with a difficult access. Although the site was viticulturally sound, it was certainly not a good location to establish a road-side sales outlet or a winery and this price included a large premium for scarcity value. Had this vineyard had more additional land to plant, a house and perhaps buildings to turn into a winery and sales outlet, one wonders what the price might have been. When the same company bought Gusbourne Estate in September 2013, the total purchase price was £7 million for the property, business, stocks and goodwill. The property element of the purchase price was £5.287 million which was for 20.5-ha (50.7-acres) of established vineyards, plus around 100-ha (250-acres) of arable land, woodland and farm buildings. The offer documents do not assign a value to the planted land, but by making some educated deductions, the price paid for the vineyards appears to be around £86,000-ha (£35,000-acre). Given that the value of grapes from these vineyards, net of costs, would appear to be around £11,000-ha (£4,450-acre) per year, this represents a multiple of eight times yield which is not unreasonable.

Some UK vineyards have been established on leased land and this may be an option if a site to buy cannot be found or if the capital is not available and it is certainly going to cost less than buying land. The length of the lease would need to be at least thirty years in order to recover the cost of the vineyard establishment and to get the best years of the cropping life of the vines. As for rents, they can either be straightforward annual amounts tied into some escalator like the Retail Prices Index (in one of its many different variants) or a combination of rent plus a percentage of crop value. Either way, I would not expect the rental to exceed £650-ha (£250-acre).

I have helped several growers negotiate leases for land for vineyards and whilst such things as the lease period, the rental and the basic tenure terms can be agreed, the question of what happens when the lease ends is always a tricky one. If the vineyard establishes well and you harvest good crops of grapes which produce award-winning wines, you as the tenant may feel that your thirty years or more of effort and energy ought to be recognised when you surrender the lease and leave the landlord with a mature, well managed vineyard. How this is to be calculated is tough, especially if your wine brand bears the name of the farm or estate where the land is as this doesn't allow you to re-create the wine on a different site. Most landlords are unwilling to agree to any terms that might commit them to pay out substantial sums when they cannot see what the UK winegrowing scene might be in a generation's time. How would you have worked out the future brand value of Nyetimber when it was planted in 1988? In March 2006, when the current owner bought it, the brand value element of the £7.4 million purchase price was around £2 million. Had the 16-ha (40-acres) of vineyards been leased, how much of that brand value would have been the landlord's? This aspect of a lease is often left 'to be negotiated'. Of course, if the vineyard, or the enterprise based upon it, fails and the tenant wants to hand the land back (or becomes insolvent and the landlord claims it back) the landlord may well want compensation to turn the land back into an arable field. Given the cost of taking out anchors, posts and wires, grubbing the vines and returning

it to arable will be around £1500-ha (£600-acre), the landlord may well want this written into the lease. Either way, leasing land for a vineyard is never straightforward.

## Establishing a vineyard

The cost of setting up a vineyard can vary hugely. My standard costings, based upon the spacings and equipment set out below, show that it costs a minimum of £21,000-ha (£8,500-acre) to prepare, plant, trellis and nurture 1-ha of vines for the first two years and quite easily up to £30,000-ha (£12,000-acre). The cost will depend upon the size of the vineyard, the types of material used, and whether contractors and contract labour are used for the work, or whether it is done by employed staff. The conversion rate of the £ to the € will also affect prices as vines and some of the materials will come from the Eurozone. The prices above are for a reasonably sized vineyard – say 4-ha (10-acres) – planted at 2.00 m row width x 1.20 m inter-vine distance (4,167 vines-ha or 1,686 vines-acre), GPS machine planted, steel end and intermediate posts and using contractors for the trellising, i.e. a top of the range, long-life, vineyard.

To my price must be added extras such as access roads, water to the site, serious land preparation, partial or complete land drainage and rabbit and deer fencing which could add several thousands to the bill. The price of planting and trellising depends very much on vine density which can vary between 7,000 and 2,700 vines-ha[2] (2,833 and 1,093 vines-acre) and row width: a 1.75 m row width gives you 5,714 running metres per hectare; a 2.50 m row width gives you 4,000 running metres per hectare. The establishment cost will also vary according to who does the work. Newcomers to the vineyard business might well feel safer employing a vineyard consultant (a wise decision) and getting much of the work done using contractors who have experience in planting and installing vineyard trelliswork. This will of course be a more expensive way to establish a vineyard than say if you manage much of the work yourself and use farm staff or directly employed local labour. If you were prepared to plant at a lower density, plant by hand, use less durable posts and do much of the work yourself, this price could be substantially reduced.

## Equipment for the vineyard

A professionally run vineyard requires a basic level of agricultural equipment in order to farm it efficiently.[3] A suitable tractor, a mower, a sprayer and (usually) some weed control equipment are an absolute minimum. Other items such as prunings pulverisers, shoot-trimmers, and deleafers can be either done without (i.e. much of the work can be done by hand or with other machinery) or can be hired. The bill for the minimum equipment outlined above (bought new) would be unlikely to be less than £40,000-£50,000 and quite possibly several thousand more. For the smaller grower and for equipment that is only used occasionally, the second-hand market is well worth investigating and for specialist vineyard (and winery) equipment, the French website *Agriaffaires* is a good place to start looking. See www.agriaffaires.co.uk.

## Running costs of a vineyard

The annual costs of running a vineyard (excluding picking) will depend upon unchangeable factors such as vine density – 7,000 vines per ha takes a lot longer to prune than 3,500 vines per ha – and row width – the narrower the rows, the more running metres there are in a hectare of vines. It will also depend – hugely – on who does the work. An owner-operator, who does much of the pruning, weed-control, pest and disease spraying and mowing him or herself, will cost a lot less per hectare than someone running a large vineyard and winery who uses farm staff, contractors and/or casual labour to do much – often all – of the manual and tractor work. One person might, with some additional contract and casual labour to help with canopy management, be able to look after 5-ha (12-acres) of vines, but any more would probably be too much for one person to prune on their own. However, if contractors and casuals were used for all the pruning, pulling out and tying down, plus the annual vine work and canopy management, then one tractor driver could probably spray and mow around 15-ha (37-acres) in a season.

*Vineyard at Painshill Park, Cobham, Surrey, re-planted in 1992 on the same site as a vineyard originally established between 1738 and 1773*

The annual materials used in a vineyard consist of fuel for tractors, chemicals used in controlling weeds and pests and diseases[4], annual replacements to vines and posts and small items such as vine ties. The cost of chemicals will vary according to several factors – a vineyard planted with Seyval blanc would cost a lot less to look after (in this respect) than one planted with say Chardonnay – but in most vineyards the annual chemical bill will be significant. £900-ha (£364-acre) would be a minimum and in many vineyards it would be nearer £1,250-ha (£506-acre). In total therefore, a reasonably sized vineyard, planted with a

2.00 m row width and with a vine density of 4,167 vines-ha (2.00 m x 1.20 m), will cost at least £7,000-ha (£2,833-acre) to run and quite possibly nearer £8,000-ha (£3,238-acre). There will also be maintenance costs for tractors and the other equipment, plus depreciation of equipment, vines and trelliswork. Additions to the vineyard in the way of fertiliser, compost and manure should also be allowed for but as vineyards vary hugely in this respect, the cost of these items is hard to estimate. A vineyard might spend £500-ha (£200-acre) every two to three years on fertiliser, but this is very much a ball-park figure. See *Appendix V* for additional information on vineyard running costs.

## Picking costs

Picking costs are not normally included in the annual cost of running the vineyard as they tend to be directly crop-size related, i.e. picking 10 tonnes of grapes costs one price and picking 20 tonnes costs twice that price – all other things being equal. They are therefore seen as a deduction from crop value and not an addition to cost of production. Picking costs will, like almost all costs in a vineyard and winery enterprise, vary according to several factors, not all of which are the same each year and not all of which are the same for all growers. Apart from such obvious factors such as vine density and row width, plus whether you are using friends and family, permanent staff or contract labour, one of the most important factors is level of yield. In a heavy yielding year where vines might be cropping at between 12 tonnes and 25 tonnes-ha (5 tonnes and 10 tonnes-acre), the per-tonne picking costs will be significantly lower than where a crop is small to very small and where pickers have to (a) hunt for the bunches and (b) select them for quality and (c) trim them of any diseased or rotten sections. The colour of the grapes will also make a difference – red grapes are easier to see than white (green) grapes – and some varieties are easier to pick than others – there are certain varieties that have a habit of tangling themselves up in the wires, making prising the grapes away from the vine that much harder.

The work done in the vineyard prior to harvest will also affect picking costs. A well maintained vineyard, where pests and diseases have been controlled, weeds have been kept down, the grass mown and, most importantly, the vines have been deleafed in the 3-4 weeks prior to harvest will be significantly easier (and therefore cheaper) to pick than a badly maintained vineyard. The method of picking – into small boxes or trays or into 350-kg bulk bins – and how the non-picking staff organise the distribution of empty picking boxes and bins and the collection and assembling of full picking boxes and bins, will all contribute towards speed of picking and therefore the cost per tonne. However, in a well-managed vineyard with an average yield of say 8-10 tonnes-ha (3.24-4.05 tonnes-acre), a motivated picker ought to be able to pick 300-500 kg in an eight hour day, giving you a per tonne cost of around £150-200-tonne. However, in low-yielding years, with a poorly managed vineyard and poor organisation, the cost might well be much more than that. If the vineyard site is remote from the winery, then haulage would be an additional cost and if selling grapes, then haulage to the purchaser would usually (although not always) have to be paid by the seller. There is more on picking in *Chapter 12: Management – cropping years* in the section on *Picking*.

## Yields

Ignoring such peripheral income streams as vineyard tours and rent-a-vine schemes in the calculation of vineyard returns (although I would certainly not ignore them in the overall picture of total enterprise income), the two central factors in a vineyard's income are yield and value. Yields in all agricultural and horticultural crops vary from year to year, but in vines, the yield variation is much greater than in most other crops. In regions with ideal growing conditions, it has been shown that annual yields in vineyards can vary by over 30 per cent and in regions with less than ideal growing conditions, into which the UK has to fall, factors such as spring frosts, poor flowering and difficult ripening and harvesting conditions can contribute to very significant variations in yield. In 1997, one night's frost in May reduced the average annual UK yield to 8.17 hectolitre per hectare (hl-ha); in 2012 exceptionally poor flowering weather lowered the annual yield to 5.98 hl-ha (around 0.8 tonnes-ha or 0.35 tonnes-acre) which was the lowest national average yield ever recorded[5]. These two yields (1997 and 2012) are between 25 per cent and 35 per cent of the UK long-term average yields. In 2013, a very late spring and a cool and wet October, led to the latest harvest on record. Many grapes were harvested at very high acid levels and very low sugar levels and some growers left grapes unpicked as they were judged to be too low in quality.

Low yields are by no means a new problem and Jack Ward, the first Chairman of the English Vineyards Association (EVA[6]), in his 1984 book *Vine Growing in the British Isles*, wrote: 'the survival of English viticulture will depend almost entirely on the ability to maintain an adequate yield per acre' and that 'the average [yield] at present achieved is scarcely sufficient, if the cultivation of vines is to be regarded as a profitable undertaking'. Some thirty vintages later, Ward's words are as true as ever.

The major problem in the UK is that the heat and light levels required for more consistent yields are right on the edge. Take some average to good years like 2006, 2009, 2010 and 2013 and no problem (or at least, less of a problem). The average annual yield for those four years was 27.00 hl-ha. However, take four less-good years like 2007, 2008, 2011 and 2012, and you can see the results of indifferent weather. The average annual yield for those four years was only 13 hl-ha, a touch over 50 per cent less. In all of these years, the variety spectrum has been very similar. The yield aspect of UK viticulture is dealt with in more detail in *Chapter 3: Site selection*.

Another factor in the yield figures in the last paragraph is vine varieties. The 2006-13 figures quoted above are from vineyards where Chardonnay and Pinots represented between 21 per cent and 48 per cent of the planted area. These are varieties which are more affected by poor weather conditions than the German varieties and French-American hybrids that they replaced. To illustrate this, take the eight years between 1989 and 1996, when the top seven vine varieties (accounting for 81 per cent of the planted area) were Müller-Thurgau, Seyval blanc, Reichensteiner, Bacchus, Schönburger, Madeleine x Angevine 7672 and Huxelrebe (WSB 1990) and the average annual yields were 26.86 hl-ha.[7] Take the seven years between 2007 and 2013, when the top two varieties were Chardonnay and Pinot noir, accounting for an average of 41 per cent of the total planted area, and the next five – Bacchus, Seyval blanc, Reichensteiner, Müller-Thurgau and Meunier – accounted for another 29 per cent (in total 70 per cent of the planted area) and the average annual yield was 18.00 hl-ha, which is 8.86 hl-ha or 33 per cent less.

In yield terms, this is the difference between picking say 9.0 tonnes-ha (3.64 tonnes-acre) and 6 tonnes-ha (2.43 tonnes-acre) – the difference in my view between a vineyard that is making something towards a return on its

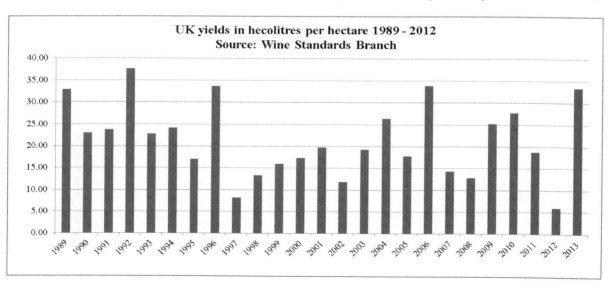

investment and one that is barely viable.

| Area and production totals in UK vineyards 1989 - 2013 | | | | | | | |
|---|---|---|---|---|---|---|---|
| Year | Total ha | Ha. in production | Ha. not in production | % of total not in production | Total yield in Hl. | Yield per Ha. | No. of Vineyards | No. of Wineries |
| 1989 | 876 | 652 | 224 | 25.6% | 21,447 | 32.89 | 442 | 147 |
| 1990 | 929 | 629 | 300 | 32.3% | 14,442 | 22.96 | 445 | 147 |
| 1991 | 992 | 650 | 342 | 34.5% | 15,429 | 23.74 | 454 | 150 |
| 1992 | 1054 | 701 | 353 | 33.5% | 26,428 | 37.70 | 457 | 157 |
| 1993 | 1065 | 767 | 298 | 28.0% | 17,504 | 22.82 | 479 | 148 |
| 1994 | 1035 | 733 | 302 | 29.2% | 17,693 | 24.14 | 435 | 123 |
| 1995 | 984 | 745 | 239 | 24.3% | 12,651 | 16.98 | 413 | 115 |
| 1996 | 965 | 775 | 190 | 19.7% | 26,080 | 33.65 | 408 | 123 |
| 1997 | 949 | 791 | 158 | 16.6% | 6,460 | 8.17 | 386 | 114 |
| 1998 | 901 | 842 | 59 | 6.5% | 11,202 | 13.30 | 382 | 108 |
| 1999 | 872 | 835 | 37 | 4.3% | 13,272 | 15.90 | 373 | 106 |
| 2000 | 857 | 822 | 35 | 4.1% | 14,215 | 17.29 | 363 | 106 |
| 2001 | 836 | 801 | 35 | 4.2% | 15,817 | 19.75 | 350 | 105 |
| 2002 | 812 | 789 | 23 | 2.8% | 9,385 | 11.89 | 333 | 114 |
| 2003 | 773 | 756 | 18 | 2.3% | 14,503 | 19.20 | 333 | 109 |
| 2004 | 761 | 722 | 39 | 5.1% | 19,071 | 26.41 | 339 | 106 |
| 2005 | 793 | 722 | 71 | 9.0% | 12,806 | 17.74 | 353 | 90 |
| 2006 | 923 | 747 | 176 | 19.1% | 25,267 | 33.82 | 362 | 102 |
| 2007 | 992 | 697 | 295 | 29.7% | 9,948 | 14.27 | 383 | 98 |
| 2008 | 1,106 | 785 | 321 | 29.0% | 10,087 | 12.85 | 416 | 116 |
| 2009 | 1,215 | 946 | 269 | 22.1% | 23,835 | 25.20 | 381 | 109 |
| 2010 | 1,324 | 1,095 | 229 | 17.3% | 30,346 | 27.71 | 404 | 114 |
| 2011 | 1,384 | 1,208 | 176 | 12.7% | 22,659 | 18.76 | 419 | 124 |
| 2012 | 1,438 | 1297 | 141 | 9.8% | 7,751 | 5.98 | 432 | 128 |
| 2013 | 1,884 | 1,571 | 313 | 16.61% | 33,385 | 21.25 | 448 | 131 |

Source: Wine Standards Board of the Food Standards Agency

Had the difference in the varietal make-up been more pronounced – which it will be as newer plantings of the Champagne varieties increase and as the older plantings of the German varieties, plus Seyval blanc decrease – I believe that the differences in yields would have been even greater. These yield differences show, with some emphasis, just how marginal the Champagne varieties are in our climate and how close many vineyards must be to make or break. The disaster that was 2012, when national yields fell to 5.98 hl-ha, and the biggest, best-funded, highest-profile vineyard, Nyetimber, didn't process a single grape, may well prove something of a turning point in our varietal selections and prove that the UK is not just about planting the Champagne varieties.

The yields that I would typically use in my costings for a new vineyard, that is to say a vineyard planted on land which has no track record of vines, will always err on the safe side. If the vineyard is planted with sparkling wine varieties, 7.5 tonnes-ha (3.0 tonnes-acre) would be a fair average to aim for; if planted with a selection of varieties including higher cropping ones such as Reichensteiner and Seyval blanc, then the average yield might creep up to nearer 10 tonnes-ha (4.0 tonnes-acre). It would be unrealistic to predict higher yields and I know of no reasonably sized and well managed vineyard that has exceeded an average yield over a reasonable length of time, say over ten vintages, of 10 tonnes per hectare (4.0 tonnes-acre) per year, although some come close.

## Grape prices

So, if yields are unpredictable, what about the value of those yields? Once again – it depends. Firstly let me deal with prices achievable under long-term grape purchase (or grape supply) contracts.

The price of grapes has always fluctuated according to variety, sugar and acid level and of course, supply and demand. In the 1980s, when Lamberhurst was under the ownership of Kenneth McAlpine and run by Karl-Heinz Johner (1976-88) and myself (1988-91), grape purchase contracts were given to growers with prices based upon a combination of the then retail price of English wine, the variety being grown and the sugar and acid levels of those grapes. Grape prices were always tied to the Retail Prices Index (RPI) so that they increased with inflation.[8] Thus really ripe Schönburger and Huxelrebe grapes, the basis of Lamberhurst's two highest priced wines, were valued more highly than mid-range Müller-Thurgau and significantly more highly than high-yielding, low sugar Seyval blanc. In the big harvest of 1989 I recall the price of Seyval blanc grapes was around £350-tonne. These were always delivered prices, in Lamberhurst's bins, with growers bearing the costs of both bin and grape delivery (although not bin hire). Since those days, things have changed quite significantly.

Whilst the main driver of grape prices remains the price that winemakers can command for their wines, there are a lot of factors which get in the way of a straight equation between these two. In 2000, Lamberhurst came under the influence of Chapel Down who took on most of its long-term grape purchase contracts. Chapel Down was then still operating under its original model, that of being a grape buyer, winemaker and wine-seller and not really a grower of its own grapes – that is apart from the 8.33-ha (20.6-acres) of vineyards around its winery at Tenterden. It had decided that it needed to secure supplies of grapes, especially of Champagne varieties, as it wanted to build up its production of sparkling wine and continued to hand out grape purchase contracts. The prices in these contracts, as they had been under the Lamberhurst model, varied according to variety and sugar level, with deductions for excess acidity and poor quality (as defined by percentage of rot or frost damage) and were tied to the RPIX. Therefore in harvest 2013, the price of good quality Chardonnay lay between £1,122-tonne for the minimum sugar level of 60°OE (7.7 per cent potential alcohol) up to £1,923-tonne at 85°OE (11.6 per cent). Sugar levels higher than that did not achieve a higher price. Likewise Pinot noir: at 60°OE the price was £1,026-tonne and at 85°OE it was also £1,923-tonne, the same as Chardonnay. These are delivered prices using Chapel Down's bins, but with all haulage paid by the grower. Pinot blanc and Meunier were similarly priced. However, in recent years, with some lower than average yields and high demand for wine, prices for Champagne varieties have improved and £2,000 per tonne is being achieved and even £2,500 in some contracts. Deductions for rot or frost are very seldom invoked, but deductions for acidity are certainly made. Most contracts have a maximum acidity above which a deduction of 5 per cent of the price for each 0.5 g/l is taken and the maximum acid level is usually set between 13.5 g/l and 15.5 g/l, depending on vine variety. Thus in high acid years such as 2011, 2012 and 2013, grapes picked with acids of 15.5 g/l, when the maximum level in the contract was 14.5 g/l, would suffer a 10 per cent price reduction.

Until quite recently, Bacchus was priced significantly lower than for Champagne varieties, typically at around 60 per cent of their prices. Thus when £1,500-tonne might be achievable for mid-quality Champagne varieties, Bacchus would seldom achieve more than £900. In recent years however, demand for wines made from Bacchus has risen, largely because of producers such as Chapel Down and Camel Valley who have been making excellent award-winning wines with the variety and introducing it to a wider audience. Therefore for good quality, moderately ripe Bacchus, I would advise a grower to expect at least £1,500 per tonne and more for proven quality.

Prices of grapes in grape purchase contracts will always be negotiated directly between buyer and seller and there is quite a wide range of prices known to me. Contract prices will always vary according to demand and supply, not on an annual basis, as contracts are typically on eight year rolling contracts with three year break clauses. Some contracts are not as reliant on sugar levels as Chapel Down's are (or at least used to be) which is sensible given that sugar level is not such a quality-decider in sparkling wines as it is in still wines. Wineries that are some way distant from their grape sources, say a winery in Cornwall buying grapes from Suffolk (if such a thing could possibly exist!), might have to contribute towards haulage costs. For some growers, especially if they are known for the quality of their fruit and can grow varieties such as Pinot noir suitable for still wine, it would not surprise me if prices rose to £3,000-tonne or more. In other countries, wineries pay considerably more for top-quality fruit for still wines. In Champagne, the price of grapes is around €5-€6 a kilo (or £4,000 -£5,000-tonne)[9].

Whether you can make money as a grower with these prices is open to question. A grapegrower who knew his or her sites well, who had the experience to manage their vineyards through seasons both good and not so good and who had the scale to get growing costs down to a minimum, might well make considerably more money from vines than wheat. A crop of 7.50 tonnes-ha (3.00 tonnes-acre) at £1,500 per tonne would yield a gross £11,250, from which growing costs of say £7,000-ha (£2,833 per acre), plus picking and haulage costs of say £250 per tonne (a total of £8,875) would leave a balance of income over direct costs of £2,375-ha (£961-acre) to pay the interest and capital repayments on the vineyard establishment (I am ignoring the cost of the land) of say £25,000-ha (£10,000-acre) and the investment in the machinery of say £40,000 spread over 5 hectares, i.e. another £8,000-ha (£3,200-acre).

Is £2,375 enough to service a loan of £33,000 and give something over for 'profit'? If we write the cost of the vineyard off over thirty years and the equipment over fifteen years, then according to the AMC (Agricultural Mortgage Corporation) you need a total of £2,033-year to service (capital and interest repayments) a loan of this amount. This leaves you with just £342-ha (£138-acre) – barely a king's ransom.

How might these figures be improved?  You could, by

| | Low yield and low grape price | | | High yield and high grape price | | |
|---|---|---|---|---|---|---|
| | Yield t/ha | Price per tonne | Income per ha | Yield t/ha | Price per tonne | Income per ha |
| Gross returns | 7.5 | £        1,500 | £      11,250 | 10 | £        1,750 | £      17,500 |
| Less growing costs | | | £       7,000 | | | £       7,000 |
| Less picking costs | 7.5 | £          250 | £       1,875 | 10 | £          250 | £       2,500 |
| Sub-total | | | £       2,375 | | | £       8,000 |
| Capital charges | | | £       2,033 | | | £       2,033 |
| Net return per ha | | | £         342 | | | £       5,967 |

using less durable materials and by doing some of the work yourself, cut the cost of establishment by a few thousand per hectare, although given that you are writing the vineyard off over thirty years, this makes little difference to the annual cost. You might, by doing some of the annual work yourself, reduce the cost of growing the crop, but again, this would only improve things very marginally and given that you would be doing some of the work, this cost is best left unchanged. However, the two factors that would definitely improve the returns are on the income side: yields and the grape prices. The above figures are based upon 7.50 tonnes-ha (3.00 tonnes-acre) which, as I pointed out above, is a 'safe' average yield for Champagne varieties. By planting at a higher density, by planting some higher-yielding varieties and by spending a bit more on canopy management, the average might be brought up to nearer 10.00 tonnes-ha (4.00 tonnes-acre) which would improve the income figures by a significant factor. The price of £1,500 per tonne is a realistic one taking sugar levels over the past ten years into account, but with luck one might be able to move this northwards to say £1,750 per tonne. Your income would then rise to £17,500, less your growing costs of £7,000 and picking costs of £2,500 (higher costs for picking more tonnes), leaving you a balance of £8,000-ha (£3,238-acre). After you have deducted your £2,033-ha for interest and capital repayments on the establishment costs, the 'profit' at £5,967-ha (£2,415-acre) starts to look more attractive.

A 4.00-ha (10-acre) vineyard, which might cost you a total of £265,000 to set up on bare land purchased at around £25,000-ha (£10,000-acre) might be returning you £23,868 a year. In reality, these enhanced figures are at the higher end of expectations and the truth is somewhere between the two, i.e. a return of around £3,500-ha (£1,416-acre).

*Results from one of the UK's best yielding vineyards. Planted in 2002 with Champagne varieties, between 2004 and 2013 it averaged 9.54 tonnes-ha (3.86 tonnes-acre)*

Having said all of the above, it must be pointed out that there are many UK vineyards which have not achieved anything approaching these yield figures. Choose the wrong site, plant the wrong varieties and/or rootstocks and fail to get the vines evenly and quickly established and

one's prospects of getting decent returns start to fade. Mismanage the weed control, falter with the pest and disease control and lo and behold, the crops are not going to be there. Growing vines and getting them to establish and crop over the long term is not always an easy task.

The above figures have all been based upon grape prices achieved when selling grapes to wineries via long-term grape purchase contracts. What then of other ways of selling grapes?

The spot market price for grapes in the UK, i.e. the annual price for grapes which wineries are prepared to pay, is notoriously fickle and unpredictable. In recent years, the price for high quality sparkling wine varieties has never been much less than £2,000-tonne, often £2,500-tonne and in exceptional circumstances (2012 when there were of course almost no grapes to sell) nearer to – and in some cases possibly even over – £4,000-tonne. Again, these are for grapes delivered to the winery door. These seemingly high prices – high at least when compared to the £1,500 - £1,800-tonne paid under long-term grape purchase contracts – have been fuelled by several factors. As has already been said, given that the price of grapes in Champagne is currently around €5-€6 a kilo (or £4,000 to £5,000-tonne) and given that English Sparkling Wines and many Champagnes sell for the same prices, why shouldn't the base cost of the product, i.e. the grapes, be broadly the same?

Since around 2005 there have been several new players who have come into the market for grapes which have helped keep prices firm. Some of these have been existing producers wanting to top up their tanks, but others have been non-vineyard owners creating brands, vineyard owners with vineyards either too young to be cropping fully, or just producers with poorly performing vineyards who need more grapes. The high level of demand for English Sparkling Wine in the last few years, helped by events such as the Royal Wedding, the Jubilee and the Olympics and favourable press comments and general publicity surrounding the product, has also helped increase the demand for grapes, as have the lower yields in 2011 and 2012 (after high yields in 2009 and 2010). Producers who typically sell their sparkling wines with two to three years of bottle age, have seen their sales increasing leading to diminishing stock levels, which they have not been able to top up fast enough from their own vineyards, hence the need to go out into the marketplace. All this has helped push up spot prices of grapes. But, before growers think that selling grapes on to the spot-market is a way of increasing returns, a word of caution.

The area under vine in the UK has grown by almost two and a half times in ten years (2004 to 2013) from 761-ha to 1,884-ha, with around 80 per cent of these additional plantings being of sparkling wine varieties. If you accept that a newly planted vineyard takes at least four years to come into full production and that UK-grown sparkling wines need at least two years (and often more like four years) of lees-ageing before they can be marketed, then one can see that many of the vineyards planted since 2004 have yet to fully impact upon the market. Just how big the market for UK-grown sparkling wines is, is a topic much debated amongst producers. As ever, there are too many 'what-ifs' in the equation to arrive at anything approaching a certain answer, but it is generally agreed that the amount of UK-grown sparkling wine available for sale will increase from the current total of around 1.7 million bottles a year to perhaps 4 million by 2018 and possibly 6 million by 2023. Of course, repeated harvests like 2012, when national yields were the lowest ever recorded, might well cut these forecasts, although over the next 5-8 years the amounts available for sale must double at the very least.

What impact this doubling (and possibly trebling) of supply will have upon wine prices and therefore grape prices is again, open to conjecture. There are some (myself included) who believe that there is sufficient capacity in the UK wine market, let-alone the prospects afforded by exports, to soak up the increased production and leave prices where they are – hovering around the £20 - £25 a bottle mark. Much will depend on maintaining (and hopefully even raising) the quality of the product and keeping the message in front of both the wine buying public and the wine trade alike, that English Sparkling Wine is as good as Champagne. However, anyone planting a vineyard today and hoping to crop it over the next thirty to forty years might well take the view that wine prices are bound to soften over the next five to ten years, leading to a reduction in grape prices. A fixed price contract, tied to the RPIX, remains – as long as the winery issuing the contract remains solvent – a more certain predictor of income from grape sales than selling them from year to year on the open market.

All of the above costings and predictions have been based upon selling grapes as grapes and thus succeeding or failing on the twin horns of yield and price. There is of course a second way of selling grapes: in the form of wine. If you thought that deciding what a tonne of grapes cost to produce and what a tonne of grapes was worth was problematic, stand by for an even knottier problem: what does it cost to produce, store and market a bottle of wine?

**Note:** the question of overproduction of UK-grown sparkling wine is dealt with more fully in *Chapter 4: Vine varieties, clones and rootstocks* in the section on *Oversupply of English and Welsh sparkling wine?*

## The cost of producing wine

Surprising as it might sound, I doubt that there are many people in the world of wine production who can tell you accurately what it really costs to produce a bottle of wine. The reasons are that wineries are often put together over many years, even decades and often generations, with much of the equipment made from stainless steel which lasts indefinitely and which wears out very slowly. In addition, many of the overhead costs of running a winery – heat, light and power, finance costs and essential staff, which together probably account for a high percentage of the cost of production – are fixed and therefore the amount attributed to each bottle produced fluctuates according to the annual throughput. Say, for instance, that your fixed costs of running a winery are £100,000 and one year you have a throughput of 500 tonnes and the next year only

250 tonnes. Do you increase the price of your wine to take account of this? No – of course not – you have to take the longer view. In any event, the price of one's wine is a function of many factors: its market position, the overall demand for the type of wine you are producing, the demand for your wines in particular, the depth of your wallet to overcome cash-flow issues (if you decide to keep your prices higher than your buyers really want to pay) and the willingness of your competitors to lower their prices when offered a marketing opportunity that you are not able, or prepared, to take up. These will all play a part in how you price your wine.

Some of the cost of a bottle of wine, of course, is predictable and relatively simple to arrive at. The value of the grapes in the bottle is either known because that is what you paid for them, or can be implied by the costs of running your own vineyards, divided by average yields. The costs of materials used in the production of the wine – sugar and yeasts, fining materials, barrels (if used), bottles, labels, capsules and other packaging – can be costed and a total arrived at. They will vary of course, depending on the style of wine and the type and quality of your overall package. The materials used for a quick-turnaround, still wine with a lightweight screw-cap bottle, a simple label and the minimum of packaging, might cost a quarter the cost of materials for a bottle-fermented sparkling wine in a fancy sparkling wine bottle, with a three part label, a printed capsule, a printed muzzle cap, a six-bottle printed sparkling wine case with fibre dividers and even a single-bottle printed box.

Owning and operating a winery, especially in a climate like the UK's, where yields and qualities fluctuate and are very unpredictable, is very much an act of faith in the long-term future of the enterprise. Most UK wineries have started out small and grown as the business has grown, increasing capacity and upgrading equipment as they progress from one vintage to another. Some wineries start out by doing elements of the processing themselves, the pressing, fermentation and filtering are the most typical, then have the bottling, and in the case of sparkling wine, the post-storage operations – riddling, disgorging and *dosage* – carried out by another winery. Therefore actually arriving at a true cost-per-bottle is often extremely difficult.

*Hush Heath winery, Kent*

Another way to look at production costs is to see what a contract winery might charge you to produce a bottle of wine. At the moment in the UK, there are around twenty-five wineries that undertake 'contract crushing' as it is known and will take in your grapes and produce a bottle of wine to an agreed specification. Prices will (naturally) vary according to a number of factors. A winery would tend to give a better price to a grower sending in a larger tonnage and prices will vary according to the style of wine and type of packaging, as outlined above. As a guide though, a bottle of still wine would cost around £3.50 to produce; a bottle of sparkling wine around £6.00. In addition to these costs would be such things as label design and labels, which might come to several thousands of pounds for the design and between 20 p and £1.00 for the labels.

There is also the cost of storage which has to be taken into account. Even if you have your wine processed by another winery, they will usually be unwilling to provide storage for more than a few weeks after bottling (or, if they do, it will be at a punitive storage rate) and therefore most producers making wine to sell themselves will need to find suitable storage space. Still wines are typically placed in bulk bins after bottling and are generally unlabelled. The reasons for this are that some corks will weep in storage, labels will deteriorate making them unfit for sale and bottles inevitably get dusty and dirty. Better to store them as 'cleanskins' and then wash, capsule and label them as required. Washing, labelling and packaging is therefore an additional cost to the above costs of production. In the case of sparkling wines, after bottling and closing with crown caps, the wines have to go through the secondary fermentation and, once that is finished, are put away for the next two to five years whilst they undergo *sur latte* ageing. It is only after this process is finished that sparkling wines can be riddled, disgorged, have their *dosage* added and then finally be made ready for sale by corking, muzzling, labelling and packaging. Some larger wineries will have the equipment for these post-ageing operations; smaller wineries may well send their wines to another winery to have this work done under contract.

Whether you have your own winery or have your wine made under contract, there is also the matter of cost of stock to be discussed. If you are producing still wines and your wines are bottled in the spring following the harvest, unless they are the type of wines that require ageing (not generally produced in the UK, but quite possible in the future if good quality still wines are to be made for Chardonnay and Pinot noir), then you will probably be carrying around two to three year's stock. Assuming yields of 7.5 tonnes-ha (3 tonnes-acre) and an output of still wine of around 7,125 bottles per ha (based upon 712.5 litres-tonne) and production costs of £3.50 per bottle, then the cost of stock, ignoring the costs of producing the grapes, will amount to £24,938-ha (£10,092-acre) for each year of production, i.e. for two years, £49,876-ha (£20,185-acre), for three years, £74,814-ha (£30,277-acre).

For sparkling wines, however, the sums are considerably higher. Let us assume that yields are the same – 7.5 tonnes-ha (3 tonnes-acre) – giving an output of around 5,625 x bottles per ha (based upon a lower juice output for sparkling wines of 562.5 litres-tonne) and that production costs up to and including secondary fermentation (but not riddling, disgorging, *dosage* etc) are £5 per bottle. In this case the cost of stock will amount to £28,125-ha (£11,382-acre) for each year of full production, ignoring a small crop in the first cropping year (year three or four). The number of year's stock of sparkling wine carried will be a function of two things: how long you age your wine *sur latte* and how quickly you sell the wine once you start disgorging it and offering it for sale. Ageing times depend on the quality of the vintage, the acidity at bottling, the style of the wine, and the level of dosage you favour (the drier the wine, the longer the ageing tends to be). Once you start selling your wine, your rate of sale will depend upon a myriad of factors, but you are highly unlikely to sell out 100 per cent of the vintage you are offering within twelve months of starting to sell it, meaning that you will probably be selling it over two, three, four and even more years. One UK producer I know well and who has been selling sparkling wine for more than fifteen years, takes on average six years to go from the point where he starts to sell a new vintage, to the point where he is down to a few hundred bottles of 'library stock'. So, taking a modest ageing time of three years, plus a modest sales time of another three years, you might well be carrying stock equal to six year's production of sparkling wine. Therefore, taking the production costs above, the cost of your stock for the six years will be £168,750-ha (£68,292-acre) which at 5 per cent adds exactly £1.50 per bottle to the cost of production for sparkling wines up to this point – almost the same as the value of the grapes!. Of course, you will have income to set against this stock cost, but, somewhere along the line, the stock has to be financed. Chapel Down, a PLC whose accounts are available for all to see, in the twelve months to 31 December 2013, held stocks 'valued at cost' of £3,391,591 and had sales of £5,033,361. Their costs of course are based upon running their own winery and are therefore much less than the costs of having your wine made by a contract winemaker, and their sales and stocks are a mix of non-wine items, entry-level and mid-range still wines, plus both non-vintage and vintage sparkling wines. Even so, stock levels running at almost sixty-four per cent of sales are an expense that has to be financed and built in to your cost of production. Gusbourne Estate, also a PLC, in their accounts to the year ending 31 March 2013, had wine stocks valued at £558,000 against sales of £219,000.

## Returns from wine sales

The returns from sales of wine will depend very much on where the wine is sold and by whom. Assuming you are VAT registered (the pros and cons of the Agricultural Flat Rate Scheme[10] are dealt with in *Appendix IV*), the income from all sales, apart from duty-free sales[11], will have both VAT and Excise Duty deducted. Wine sales direct to the public will bring you 100 per cent of the bottle price, although selling wine direct is certainly not a cost-free sale. If you want to sell direct to the public then you have to be available when the public want to buy, not when you feel like selling. If you propose to sell a reasonable quantity to the public, then you will have to have some sort of shop, somewhere the public can taste your wines, somewhere they can park without getting their cars stuck in the mud, and of course, lavatories. Your premises must also be licensed for sales of alcohol and at least one of the people running the business will require a personal licence to sell alcohol. In addition, unless you propose to stand behind the counter yourself for eight hours a day, you will have to employ staff. However, selling from the farm-gate engenders loyalty from your customers, they become part of your wine 'family' and a satisfied customer will be your best ambassador. Although individual customers may not visit you every week or every month, they may well visit you once or twice a year, taste your new wines and buy a case or two. Almost all of the successful vineyards and wineries in the UK (and indeed those in many other parts of the world) see direct sales as a very valuable part of their sales mix and a very valuable part of their overall PR and marketing exercise. In my opinion, it would be a very brave UK wine producer who decided not to open up to the public, although I accept that there might be circumstances where public access is impossible or undesirable.

Selling direct to the public away from the farm-gate at places such as farmer's markets, country shows, fairs and other sales 'opportunities' are often less rewarding than on the face of it they might appear. You have all the costs of getting to the venue with your stock, setting up a stall, and staffing it and usually the organisers of the event will want you to pay for the privilege of attending. You also have the licencing issues to deal with. You will usually have no control over which other vendors will be attending (you are unlikely to be the only seller of wine and/or other alcoholic drinks), will be expected to give away endless samples and many events will be very weather-dependent. In short, such events are not always a very cost-effective way of selling high volumes of wine, although there may be circumstances where you get valuable publicity or exposure for being there. There are also sales over the internet and if you start to win prizes and can get mentions in your local and national press, these sales will build up.

*Chapel Down in Kent now sells around 50,000 bottles of wine a year directly to visitors*

Exports have been mentioned by some as the way to sell quantities of English and Welsh wine and Ridgeview are already quoting that '20 per cent of their sales' are exported. The larger, more established and better known sparkling wine producers are already making forays abroad and the appearance of several major producers, under the umbrella of English Wine Producers (EWP)[12], at Dusseldorf's *Prowein* wine show in April 2013 and 2014, was a definite attempt to sell more overseas.[13] For smaller producers though, I am not so sure that exports are the way ahead. With around 30 million wine drinkers resident in the UK, plus visitors from abroad, and with the additional costs of finding and servicing export markets, why would you want to go abroad to sell your wines? However, if you are not proposing to sell all your wines to the public yourself, and in reality this is only an option for smaller growers, then you will have to put yourself in the hands of someone who can: the wine trade.

The UK wine trade is split into several sections, all of whom have their own peculiarities, requirements and pricing mechanisms. There is a broad division between 'on' and 'off' trade, on-trade being those that are licensed to sell alcohol for consumption 'on the premises', i.e. public houses, wine bars, restaurants and hotels and off-trade being those that sell alcohol for consumption 'off the premises', i.e. retail shops, wine warehouses and other sales where the public is not permitted to open the bottle and pour the wine into a glass. There are also trade resellers who might loosely be termed 'wholesalers'. These might be traders who sell to the whole range of both the on and off-trade, as well as to the public, or they might be traders who target specific sectors of the trade, say just hotels and restaurants. There are also sectors such as the catering trade, airlines and cruise ships – all of them large buyers of wines – who have their own peculiarities and timetables which as an outsider you will find difficult to penetrate. Whichever section of the trade you end up selling to, you will find that they are, in one respect, all the same: they will require a discount.

*Even some of the UK's best wines get discounted from time to time*

My experience of the trade has been forged over my thirty-plus years of being involved with growing, making and selling wine, both as a producer, a consultant and, for four years, as the wine-buyer and manager of a retail wine shop in Putney. The first time I sold any wine was on 21 June 1980 (I can remember it because it was my father's birthday) when our first two wines, Spots Farm Dry and Spots Farm Medium-dry, from the 1979 vintage, were ready for sale. Those sales were made direct to the public – friends and family – who had gathered to taste the fruits of our years of research, study and labour that had gone into establishing what became Tenterden Vineyards (and is today Chapel Down). Those first sales were all full-price sales – £3.00 and £3.75 a bottle – and the question of discounts didn't arise. However, it wasn't long before one of the local off-licences wanted to stock our wines and wanted to know a price. I remember distinctly being torn between the pleasures of selling wine myself at full-price and my reluctance to give anyone a discount. What was fair? 10 per cent, 20 per cent? Surely not more? I forget what we eventually agreed, but I do remember that having agreed a price, based upon our retail price, the off-licence immediately marked it up by another 50p or so, thus giving them even more profit!

Since those early days, I have come to realise that everyone has to take a slice from producer to consumer and the more attractive you make your product to the

wholesaler, the retailer or the restaurateur, the more likely they are to want to sell it. A typical specialist wine shop, i.e. excluding the thousands of licensed corner shops and small grocery stores that typically sell branded wines and own-label wines bought from a cash-and-carry, will have at least 500 wines, maybe even double that, and one thing is certain, they cannot afford to carry a product that doesn't contribute to their overheads and to their profit. You must also understand that a retailer will work, not on a mark-up, but on a margin. A mark-up of say 33.3 per cent (as an example) will see a bottle of wine a retailer buys for say £5, become £7.99 on the shelf: £5 + 33.3 per cent (£1.67) = £6.67 + 20 per cent VAT = £8.00 less 1p to make the price look attractive. But, the £1.67 only represents a 25 per cent of the takings – the gross profit or the 'margin'. Thus, at the end of the day when the retailer has taken £1,200, he or she wants to know how much of that is gross profit, i.e. profit before expenses. If 20 per cent is deducted for the VAT, leaving £1,000, what is left? The answer, in the case of the wine above and the day's takings, is £250.[14] If that same bottle is to sell at £7.99 and the retailer wants his 33.3 per cent margin, then he or she will only want to pay £4.45 per bottle 'DPD' (duty paid delivered). Remember too that retailers will also probably have to give a discount for quantity sales – 5 per cent for six bottles is common and 10 per cent for twelve bottles is not unknown – and will also perhaps have 1-2 per cent of the retail price (inc. VAT) taken by credit-card costs. Merchants with multiple outlets may also need to build into their pricing structure an amount to cover head-office and internal distribution costs. Therefore to the producer, who has after all done ALL the work, margins of between 25 per cent and 40 per cent may seem huge and out of all proportion. But, to the retailer, who has rent, rates, heat and light, staff and – I almost forgot – profit to pay for, this level of margin is needed in order to be viable and remain in business.

Most on and off-trade buyers will be buying wines duty-paid, so the duty will be part of the price and it is up to you, as the producer, to pay that over to HM Revenue & Customs (HMR&C). This may seem unfair as it means that their margin represents an even larger percentage of your net income from the sale. But, right or wrong, you need to get used to this, as this is how the UK trade works. Some larger buyers may want you to ship the wine directly from your duty-free premises to a 'bonded warehouse' – either their own or one belonging to a storage company – in which case they will want an 'IBD' (in bond delivered) price, even though they will most probably still calculate their margin on the DPD price.

The level of margin you are likely to meet will depend on exactly who you are selling to and it is difficult to be prescriptive about levels. However, as a guide, you could expect the on-trade (pubs, wine bars, hotels and restaurants) to want a margin of 10-15 per cent, multiples 25-40 per cent, independents and small-chain retailers 30-35 per cent and wholesalers 50 per cent or even higher, given that they will be selling the wine on to on-trade and retailers at a discounted price. Wholesalers may also want you to consider promotional sales or additional discounts in order to get your wines noticed by their customers. Such things as lowering the retail price for a certain period of time, offering 'stock' as an incentive, i.e. they pay for five bottles but get six, and offering staff incentives for sales are all part of the game that has to be played if you want your wine noticed. These inducements to buy will all be at your expense and the wholesaler will still expect to make their margin.

The chart at the bottom of this page has been calculated at a 35 per cent margin for still wines and a 30 per cent margin for sparkling wines as these are higher in price and therefore, on a cash basis, more profitable for the retailer to sell. The chart illustrates the importance of pitching the price of the wine as high as you can, justifying this on quality grounds, on the grounds of exclusivity and rarity value and, above all, making the product look the price. If you are wanting the retailer or the sommelier to persuade his or her customers that your wine is worth paying for, then before it gets anywhere near their lips (that's the consumer's lips – one has to assume that its already passed the retailer's or the sommelier's taste-test) the product has to look professional: scuffed labels, poor quality printing, low-grade capsules, bottles, corks, muzzles and other packaging materials just will not do. You cannot, except in exceptional circumstances, get away with the story: 'we are only small, we only produce a few thousand bottles a year, and we don't have very good equipment'. The difference in net income between say a bottle of sparkling wine selling at £24, compared to £22, taking the above illustration, is £1.17. Let's say you have a 10 ha vineyard and sell 25,000 bottles a year, that's an extra £29,250! To get the higher price of course you have to work at it: grow good grapes, make good wine, enter competitions, win awards and publicise your successes.

In reality of course, you are likely to be selling a proportion of your output directly to the public in one way or another and a proportion through the trade in all its many guises. Exactly what the proportions will be will depend upon many factors, size probably being the most important. Chapel Down, which has been selling wine from the farm-gate for thirty-plus years, sells around 50,000 bottles a year direct to the public, but probably sells six times that amount through the trade. One well-established, medium sized vineyard I know well, sells around 40 per cent by volume to the public at full prices and 60 per cent via the trade at discounted prices and this would be fairly typical for this size of producer.

## Value of promotion in selling wine

Producers should also not underestimate the value of promotion in both selling their wines and of obtaining higher prices. Over time, producers can create a real demand for their wines by a combination of winning medals and awards, local (and even national) publicity and just good, old-fashioned self-promotion. I remember very well when, in 1981 we won the Gore-Browne Trophy with our 1980 Spots Farm Seyval blanc (very unexpectedly, as it was only our second vintage), the Sunday Times sent down their new wine correspondent, a pre-MW Jancis Robinson and a top photographer, Denis Waugh. The result of this was three full-colour pages in the Sunday Times Magazine which really helped us get on the English wine map and sell our wines. That wine, which pre-Gore-Browne had been retailing at £3.75 a bottle, immediately went up to £4.75 in order to (a) slow down sales (it didn't) and (b) increase our income (it did). If I were to single out one UK vineyard which has created a solid market for its still wines by a combination of producing good wines, winning awards and medals and lots and lots of promotion, it would be Camel Valley. There, the Lindo family – Bob, Annie and Sam – have together got the message and proved that you can sell still wines at £12-15, a price that is undoubtedly profitable and which many other producers can only dream about. Of course it goes without saying that their wines are good, amongst the best in the UK, but the edge they get by good, solid promotion lifts them above other producers with similar quality wines. Of course, not everyone enjoys self-promotion like this and many find it difficult. If you are amongst this number, then perhaps a wine producer's life is not for you?

## Buying a vineyard as a going concern

Over the past 35 years, I have been involved one way or another with several instances of buying and selling existing vineyards, including selling, in 1986, what was then my own Tenterden Vineyards and is today Chapel Down. What we sold then was the complete works: a 150-acre farm, 20-

| Still wines | Rate | Bottle price | Bottle price | Bottle price | Bottle price |
|---|---|---|---|---|---|
| | | £8.00 | £10.00 | £12.00 | £14.00 |
| VAT | 20% | £1.33 | £1.67 | £2.00 | £2.33 |
| Sub-total | | £6.67 | £8.33 | £10.00 | £11.67 |
| Less Margin | 35% | £2.33 | £2.92 | £3.50 | £4.08 |
| Price to retailer | | £4.33 | £5.42 | £6.50 | £7.58 |
| Excise Duty - Still Wine | £2.05 | £2.05 | £2.05 | £2.05 | £2.05 |
| Net to producer | | £2.28 | £3.37 | £4.45 | £5.53 |
| | | | | | |
| Sparkling wines | Rate | Bottle price | Bottle price | Bottle price | Bottle price |
| | | £18.00 | £20.00 | £22.00 | £24.00 |
| VAT | 20% | £3.00 | £3.33 | £3.67 | £4.00 |
| Sub-total | | £15.00 | £16.67 | £18.33 | £20.00 |
| Less Margin | 30% | £4.50 | £5.00 | £5.50 | £6.00 |
| Price to retailer | | £10.50 | £11.67 | £12.83 | £14.00 |
| Excise Duty - Sparkling Wine | £2.63 | £2.63 | £2.63 | £2.63 | £2.63 |
| Net to producer | | £7.87 | £9.04 | £10.20 | £11.37 |
| Note: 2014 Excise Duty rates | | | | | |

acres of vineyards, a winery, a farm-gate sales and visitor business, the stock, all the equipment and our house. It was a complex and at times, long-winded process, given that it all had to take place in secrecy as we were determined not to let any of our staff or the public know that we had sold until contracts had been signed and (at least some of) the money was in the bank. Looking back on it I am glad that we did keep it hush-hush as it stopped the purchasers asking around too much!

Today, my advice to anyone wanting to buy an existing vineyard would be: tread carefully. Of course each sale will be different. Is it just a bare vineyard, is there a business to be bought, and is there property involved? All of these will play their part in arriving at a value and a price. However, the central issues in all sales will be: what is the quality of the vineyard, what is its productive capacity and what are the quality of the grapes and wine like? Always ask to see the official WSB December 15 production returns that every grower is required to make annually and, if they are selling wine, ask to see copies of their monthly HMR&C Excise Duty returns. They are required by law to make both these returns and, as they form part of their accounts, ought to be kept for at least six years. Try and get them for as far back as they are available. If these documents are not forthcoming, then assume that whatever they tell you about the level of yields and sales is suspect.

*Sam Lindo from Camel Valley with another shelf full of silverware*

## Why plant a vineyard? A summary

So – after all of the above advice, are you any the wiser? There is no doubt that owning a vineyard in the UK is not a quick or sure way to untold riches. But, given a good site and good management, money can be made. Whilst over the past four decades I have seen many vineyards disappear, I know some that have produced good wines, sold them well and prospered and in some cases these successful vineyards are in third-generation hands and expanding. Yes, they are in the minority, but they do exist and I am ever hopeful that the numbers will grow, given the enthusiasm shown for good UK-grown wines.

Prospective vineyard owners should realise that site selection is crucial, attention to detail is taken for granted and that creating a valuable wine brand is a slow, steady process, even more so when the wine is bottle-aged

sparkling wine. Of course, the 'whether it is worth it' question is only one that you can answer. Different people have different views about the value and cost of their capital and the return they expect from it. Different people also place different values upon creating something from nothing and being part of a trade they find enjoyable.

Now is the point of no return and the remainder of this book is about the A-Z of planning, planting, establishing and running a vineyard in the UK.

---

1 The Smiths Gore survey covers all publicly marketed farmland over 50 acres in England, excluding land where the residential value of the property exceeds 50 per cent of the total sale. It thus excludes 'trophy estates' and other estates with high-value houses and properties on them. 'Equipped land' is land with houses and farm buildings. www.smithsgore.co.uk

2 This is for cane pruned vines. Trellising systems such as GDC or wide-rowed Sylvoz might lower the density even further. For GDC at 3.66 m x 2.44 m you could get down to 1,120 vines-ha or 453 vines-acre (although I wouldn't recommend this system).

3 I am excluding what I would call 'hobby' vineyards where much of the work can be done by hand and/or with garden tractors. These would typically be less than 0.2-ha (0.5-acres). A vineyard above this size, which would hopefully produce at least 1 tonne of grapes, would be too big to mow and spray with garden equipment.

4 The pros and cons of using chemicals to control weeds and pests and diseases, plus the alternatives, are dealt with in *Chapter 1:4 Weed control*.

5 The annual yield data collected by the WSB is based upon the Annual Production Returns which every vineyard is required by law to return by December 15. Whilst the 'total' area, the area 'in production' and the area 'not in production' can probably be relied upon, the 'yield per hectare' figures are to be treated with caution. Given that ALL vineyards are included, young and old, well managed and almost abandoned, and you are required to submit a return even if only a handful of grapes are harvested, then there is bound to be some interpretation required in the results. The yield per hectare has never been higher than 37.7 hl/ha (1992) which is about 5.2 t/ha (2.1 t/acre), a figure that almost all growers would consider unsustainable. My rule of thumb has been to double or treble the average yield per hectare figures to arrive at what I would consider achievable in well sited and well managed vineyards planted with a selection of suitable varieties. Thus the current five year yield average of 19.78 hl-hl, which includes the exceptionally poor 2012 vintage, shows yields of around 2.73 tonnes-ha (1.10 tonnes-acre) which, when subjected to my multiplier, become 5.5 to 8.2 tonnes-ha (2.2 to 3.3 tonnes-acre). Hardly a king's ransom, but at least covering basic costs.

6 The EVA was founded in 1965 and was the national vineyard association for the UK. It was wound up and its assets transferred to the UKVA in 1996.

7 To convert hectolitres per hectare to tonnes per hectare or per acre is not a straightforward equation as different presses and different winemaking techniques and styles will produce different volumes of wine from one tonne of grapes. As a rule of thumb, for typical still wines, white, red or rosé, I take a press-out of 725 litres of wine per tonne. Thus 28.02 hl/ha becomes 3.86 tonnes per hectare or 1.56 tonnes per acre. For sparkling wines, the equation is more problematic, as some producers will only use the *cuvée* juice, which under CIVC (the official Champagne regulatory body) is limited to 512.50 litres per tonne, whilst others will also use the *taille* juice. What remains is known as the *rebêche* and is usually sent for distillation. This is why yields in Champagne are always expressed as kilos per hectare and not hectolitres per hectare as they are in other regions.

8 Prices are now tied to the RPIX, the Retail Prices Index excluding mortgage interest payments.

9 Growers in Champagne will soon tell you why. A hectare of vineyard in Champagne might set you back around €1 million (£835,000) which makes the £50,000 a hectare (£20,000 per acre) it might cost in the UK look decidedly cheap. Having said that, growers in Champagne can expect to harvest between 10 and 20 tonnes per hectare (4 to 8 tonnes per acre) of grapes.

10 See HM Revenue & Customs Notice 700/46 Agricultural Flat Rate Scheme.

11 Duty-free sales would be where wine is sold into a tax warehouse ('duty-free bond') in the UK where someone else will be paying the duty, or to an exporter where the wine is immediately exported or to a purchaser such as a cruise line, the Government for overseas use in embassies or to the Ministry of Defense for use on an overseas armed-forces base.

12 English Wine Producers (EWP) is the marketing arm of the UKVA. Funding is provided by those (generally larger) producers who are its members and does not come from UKVA funds.

13 In 2013 and 2014, several UK wine producers took a stand at Prowein under the EWP umbrella. The stand, travelling and subsistence costs for each participant were around £7,500. The cost of salaries was an additional expense.

14 For a fuller explanation see: en.wikipedia.org/wiki/Gross_margin

# Chapter 3
# Site selection

## Where to plant?

Now that you have decided to go ahead and plant a vineyard in the UK, the first big question arises: where? Where in the UK will produce the best grapes and therefore – all other things being equal – the best wine? The question of course is not a simple one and there will be many factors to be taken into account: what areas and regions suit you most; are there family matters, work, schools, and relatives that have to be considered? But the one thing you do know is that the better the site, the better the wine. Get this wrong and it will affect all aspects of your enterprise – for all time.

The question of where the best grapes can be grown can only really be answered by looking at the problems facing UK vineyards and seeing whether there are some regions that might help address these problems and some regions where these problems might be made worse.

## Sunshine, light and heat

The main problem in the UK is not getting vines to grow: there are plenty of places where this can happen. It is not even really getting vines to fruit and getting that fruit to ripen: again, there are enough places in the UK for this to happen, especially if you select the right vine varieties. The main problem is to find a site where the vineyard can produce a high enough yield – in monetary value whether via grape sales or wine sales – of grapes of the right quality to turn into good wine. It is only on this basis that the substantial investment required will be repaid and the enterprise will become self-supporting and 'sustainable' over the long-term.

There will be those who will be able to fund vineyards from their back pockets – the wine world is littered with such vanity enterprises – but I have seen too many vineyards in the UK like this and they tend not to make the best wine. Yield of course is a moveable feast and the monetary value of a crop will be different to someone selling it as grapes at £2,000 a tonne, still wine at £8 a bottle or sparkling wine at £25 a bottle. However, one thing you do know is that the larger the crop, the more there is to sell whether it be as grapes, still wine or sparkling wine. Yield, therefore, has to be a very important factor in the viability, the sustainability if you want to use that word, of a vineyard, a winery and/or a wine sales enterprise. And it is because of low yields that the track record of many, many vineyards is poor and the main reason why so many vineyards have disappeared over the years.

In my 1989 book *The Vineyards of England*, I listed 338 vineyards. By the time I came to write *The Wines of Britain and Ireland* in 2001 only 118 of those still existed. Today, only sixty-two of those original 338 vineyards remain, a loss of 276 vineyards covering 562-ha. Some of these were substantial vineyards, even by today's standards: Barnsgate Manor 20.0-ha, Barkham Manor 13.7-ha, Chapel Farm 8.0-ha, Chiddingstone 11.33-ha, Highwayman's 9.71-ha, Honeybee 11.37-ha, Horton Estate 3.6-ha, Isle of Wight 17.4-ha, Leeford 14.06-ha, Mapperton 9.8-ha, Meon Valley 6.4-ha, Pilton Manor 7.74-ha, St. George's 8-ha, Wellow 32.38-ha (and this is just a few of the larger ones – my database of grubbed vineyards runs to almost five hundred different vineyards). Where are they now? All gone or at least very much reduced. Many grubbed vineyards produced good wines including the following Gore-Browne Trophy winners: Adgestone, Barton Manor, Brede, Chiltern Valley, Kelsale, Lamberhurst, Pilton Manor, Pulham, Valley, Wootton – all gone or much reduced. If yields had been higher, might these vineyards have survived, been taken over by another generation or been sold on as going concerns?

And what drives yields? Sunshine, light and heat and the UK often has too little of all three. As has been shown in the previous chapter, the tantalising thing is that yes, in some years we can get by. The vines get enough heat and the buds on the cane are filled with viable inflorescences (flower clusters) which in the following spring and early summer, given enough decent weather, will flower and produce a reasonable crop. But in years when we have too little, the potential is not even there in the buds and, given perhaps a cool spring and poor flowering weather, the yields are light or, as we saw in many vineyards in 2012, non-existent.

Many regions are categorised by the number of 'Growing Degree Days' (GDD). Originally a system developed for Californian growing regions by Amerine and Winkler in 1944, it is now sometimes accepted as a guide to how warm (or cool) any region is for viticulture. The figure of GDD is arrived at by taking the mean temperature on each day during April to October (in the northern hemisphere – October to April in the southern), deducting 10°C from the figure, and arriving at a total. Thus if the mean temperature on 1 April is 12°C, then this is 2 degree days, if on 2 April it is 13°C, then this is 3 degree days and so on until the end of October. In practice, the mean temperature of the month is often taken, 10°C deducted and the answer multiplied by the number of days in the month. This gives you a slightly different figure, but not massively so. In the UK, being a maritime climate, our GDD vary between mid-700s in really cool years to the heady heights of 1,000+ in warm years. Champagne in comparison varies between 900 and 1,050, Chablis averages around 950 and the upper Loire 975. However, in my experience GDD is not actually of any use to UK growers in deciding where to plant as other factors (such as shelter and exposure) have to be taken into account.

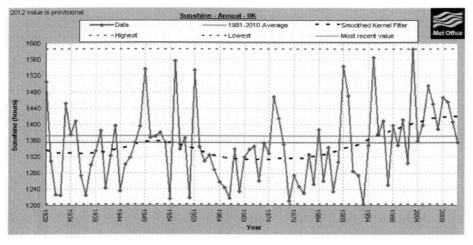

*Met Office chart showing variability in UK sunshine levels*

The effect of sunshine, light and heat is different for different vine varieties and one of the issues facing UK vinegrowers is that because of the warming of our climate, much of the area under vines has changed from using true cool-climate varieties such as Müller-Thurgau, Reichensteiner and Seyval blanc – varieties that had stood the test of time and which in some places, even in 2012, produced viable yields – to more marginal varieties such as the Champagne varieties: Chardonnay, Pinot noir and Meunier. These varieties are far more sensitive to both cool growing conditions in the preceding year, as well as poor conditions leading up to and during flowering in the cropping year. In 2012 this was very visibly demonstrated where I saw a block of Chardonnay with almost no harvestable crop right next door to a block of Seyval blanc with a 5.0 tonnes-ha crop. Same site, same soil, same management, but different yield outcomes. The reason? Chardonnay requires more heat and light than we had at the critical times in 2011 and 2012 for producing viable flowers and for pollination. Study after study has shown that poor light and low temperature levels, both in the

period when the bud-bearing cane is being produced and in the period up to and during flowering, i.e. late-May to mid-July, influence the production of cytokinins which are stored in the roots. Low levels of these hormones are one of the principal causes of low yields.[1]

In *The Grapevine*[2] (p. 68), the authors state that: 'maximal initiation [of inflorescences] for most varieties occurs at around 30-35°C. A pulse of only 4 hours in 24 hours of high temperatures, e.g. 30°C, during the critical period --- is sufficient to induce maximal initiation'. Given that in the UK we seldom see days when the temperature rises to 30°C even in high summer (July-August) let alone in late May and June when initiation is occurring, it is not surprising that we suffer from low yields.

Having said the above, many UK grape growers have wondered why the 2013 crop was relatively heavy, given that the weather during the spring and early summer in 2012 was so poor. Although the weather during flowering in 2013 was excellent, really hot and dry, the spring was one of the coldest on record and bud-burst and flowering consequently very late. It may be that at the critical time, the temperature and light levels were high enough to promote the production of cytokinins leading to good inflorescence formation. This is really an area that requires more research in respect of UK growing conditions.

Another factor in low yields in the UK is the lateness of our harvest and the strain it places upon the vines. In warmer climates, the harvest is often over well before leaf-fall, giving the vine a chance for a period of recuperation and reserve-building prior to the winter. Indeed in many regions, vines are irrigated straight after harvest so that fresh shoots and leaves can grow and as many carbohydrates as possible are put back into the woody parts of the vine – the canes, trunks and roots – before winter. In the UK, with harvest taking place as late as the last week of October and even into early November and often with harvest-time frosts to contend with, the vines seldom have time for any fresh shoot and leaf growth after harvest and before dormancy. Add to that the propensity of many young leaves to succumb to Downy Mildew in the period between when spraying has to stop and harvest, and many vines will be entering dormancy under-provided with nutrients. In the following spring, if weather conditions around budburst are also poor – cool and wet – then the vine will struggle to produce good shoots in the spring added to which bud development, i.e. the propensity to produce inflorescences on those shoots, will be impaired. A 2013 study[3] carried out in Tasmania, which has a climate which, although better than the UK's for grape growing, could still be described as 'marginal', showed that: 'both reproductive development and shoot growth in the following season can be influenced by the amount of reserves stored over winter' and that 'cane starch was shown to be a significant predictor for inflorescence count and cane size was positively correlated with the mean number of inflorescences per node'.

I accept that yield is not everything, and that there may be wine styles and there may be times, where yield has to be restricted, but these are relatively rare styles and rare times. And, even if yields are restricted, the grapes need to be ripe. In my experience, the conditions that give you large crops (large in a UK context, not large when compared to say the Champagne region or New Zealand) will also very often give you the conditions to ripen those large crops. In years when the levels of flower initiation are low and when the pre-flowering and flowering weather is poor, the weather is often not suitable to ripen even small crops. Only if I was trying to produce say red wine from Pinot noir, where quality and colour really are yield related, would I be worried about over-cropping and think about reducing the crop after flowering (and probably after *véraison*[4]). Or, if I was trying to ripen a high-acid variety for still wine, Chardonnay perhaps or Pinot blanc or Pinot gris, might I consider crop reduction to around 5 tonnes-ha (2 tonnes-acre) to aid ripening. I accept that for still wine, a relationship between yield and quality is more likely, but I doubt the difference between say 7.5 tonnes-ha (3.0 tonnes-acre) and 10 tonnes-ha (4.0 tonnes-acre) is noticeable to most consumers in terms of quality in the glass for varieties such as Bacchus, Reichensteiner and Seyval blanc, although it certainly would be noticeable on the profit and loss account. At these yield levels, the degree of ripeness will be the deciding factor in quality and this is often a function of the quality of the summer and autumn, not the yield level.

For sparkling wine, there is very little evidence in a UK context that high yields are detrimental to final wine quality. There are so many stages in the production of a sparkling wine, from the *assemblage* of the base wines, via the *sur latte* ageing process, to the addition of *dosage* and post-corking ageing – all of which contribute in part to the style and quality of the final wine – that absolute grape quality at harvest time is less important and certain imperfections can be overcome in the cellar. This is one of the reasons why yields in Champagne are so high and that the vast majority of Champagne is a multi-site, multi-variety and multi-vintage wine.

The figures in the tables below are from an established vineyard in Kent, with 0.8 ha (1.98-acres) of both Chardonnay and Pinot noir (1.6 ha – 3.95-acres in total) planted on the same rootstocks (two for each variety) and on the same site. Over the three years, 2005, 2006 and 2007, for Chardonnay, the yields varied by a factor of four – from 6 tonnes-ha to 24 tonnes-ha (2.45 – 9.78 tonnes-acre) but sugar levels were much the same – between 9.4 per cent and 9.8 per cent potential alcohol – although acidities did vary some 5 g/l (expressed as grammes per litre of tartaric) but with the highest acidity being for the lowest yield, something common-sense would tell you ought to be the other way round. It just so happened that the ripening conditions in 2005 and 2006 were better than in 2007, although picking dates were within a day or two of each other.

| Chardonnay | | | | | |
|---|---|---|---|---|---|
| Picking Date | Sugar °OE | Sugar % alc | Acid g/l | Tonnes per ha | Tonnes per acre |
| 24.10.05 | 74.00 | 9.80 | 10.50 | 11.11 | 4.50 |
| 23.10.06 | 72.00 | 9.50 | 10.30 | 24.17 | 9.78 |
| 22.10.07 | 71.00 | 9.40 | 15.50 | 6.04 | 2.45 |

For the Pinot noir the story was similar. Yields also varied by about a factor of four between around 16 tonnes-ha (6.5 tonnes-acre) in 2005 and 2006, and only 4 tonnes-ha (1.66 tonnes-acre) in 2007. But potential alcohol levels were almost the same – 8.3 per cent to 8.6 per cent potential alcohol – picking dates within a week of each other and acid levels not too far apart.

| Pinot Noir | | | | | |
|---|---|---|---|---|---|
| Picking Date | Sugar °OE | Sugar % alc | Acid g/l | Tonnes per ha | Tonnes per acre |
| 10.10.05 | 66.00 | 8.60 | 13.00 | 15.88 | 6.43 |
| 16.10.06 | 64.00 | 8.30 | 11.30 | 16.03 | 6.49 |
| 15.10.07 | 66.00 | 8.60 | 12.80 | 4.10 | 1.66 |

Looking at the above sugar and acid figures in isolation, it would be difficult to make any assumptions about yields and wine quality. It is far from the case that the higher sugars or the lower acids were in the lower yielding years, which is what you might expect. As for wine quality, the 2005 was clearly the best, doing very well in tastings. The 2006 wine was of lesser quality and in terms of medals and awards didn't win as many as the 2005, yet sold for the same price. The lowest quality wine was quite certainly the 2007, the wine from the lowest yielding year!

## Site quality

So, back to the question of site selection. What we need for a site in the UK is one that gives us the most sunshine hours, the highest light levels and the highest temperatures which will enable high-quality vine varieties to be grown, producing viable yields of adequately ripe grapes.

## Location in the UK

In cool climates – and in mainland European terms this means much of Germany, the Loire from its source to its mouth, Champagne, Chablis, most of Burgundy and Bordeaux – the best sites are those which are the warmest and which will produce the ripest grapes, all other things being equal. This means sites that are well sheltered, not too high above sea level and typically on a south-facing slope. The reasons for this are well known and shouldn't come as a shock to anyone reading this book: sheltered, south facing slopes under 100 m above sea level warm up more quickly, prompting the vines growing on them to come into leaf earlier than later sites, giving them longer to ripen their grapes to a higher degree of natural ripeness, with lower acid levels, riper fruit flavours, higher levels of dry extract and more body, substance, length and concentration. Different soil types may help or hinder this process, but **site quality** is by far-and-away the most important determinant of fruit quality, all other things being equal. This is why traditional European winegrowing regions, especially cooler ones, put so much emphasis on *terroir*. Because, whatever else you may do to a site, you can never move it, change its altitude, its slope or its basic topography. And, along with better fruit quality, brought about because the vines are growing in a better environment, comes the likelihood of better (and more) fruit in the following year as the vine is laying down its fruit-buds for the year to come in the weeks leading up to flowering which, in the UK, would be late April, May and June.

The warmest regions in the UK are naturally in the south of the country and if you look at where the orchards for the best dessert apples are (or were) and where hops are (or most definitely, were) grown, you can see that they are: the counties of Suffolk, Essex and part of Hertfordshire, Kent, East Sussex, West Sussex, parts of Surrey, Hampshire and the Isle of Wight, the south coastal fringes of Dorset, Devon and Cornwall, the parts of Somerset, Gloucestershire, Wiltshire and South Wales that are influenced by the Severn, and up into Herefordshire and Worcestershire. This is a large area and of course not every hectare is suitable for vines. My personal choice would be Kent, followed by the more coastal areas of East and West Sussex and Hampshire. Climatically the Isle of Wight might also be considered, but perhaps not from a pure business location point of view. I am probably biased towards Kent because I have spent forty-plus years in and around the region, but it is uncanny how many gold medals have come out of this county.

If you look at where UK vineyards are today, the South East (Kent, East and West Sussex and Surrey) is by far the most widely planted region with over forty-three per cent of all vineyards. The next region, Wessex (Hampshire, the Isle of Wight, Dorset and Wiltshire) which is actually slightly larger in total physical area, has less than half of the planted area of vineyards. One could argue

that the proximity of London and the populous and wealthy Home Counties makes the South East a better place to have a vineyard offering wine for sale, although this hasn't helped East Anglia or the Thames and Chilterns regions, both of which have the same proximity and if anything, even wealthier populations. The fact is that climatically, the South East is the most favourable place to grow a sun-loving plant like the grapevine.

| Region | No of vineyards | Ha of vineyards | Percentage |
|---|---|---|---|
| South East | 161 | 707.2 | 43.4% |
| Wessex inc. Channel Isles | 98 | 332.1 | 20.4% |
| South West inc. Ireland | 168 | 230.4 | 14.2% |
| East Anglia | 69 | 197.5 | 12.1% |
| Mercian inc. Scotland | 98 | 100.7 | 6.2% |
| Thames and Chilterns | 36 | 51.7 | 3.2% |
| London | 11 | 8.1 | 0.5% |
| **Totals** | **641** | **1627.7** | **100.0%** |
| Source: UK Vineyards Guide | | | |

I would also consider the influence of rainfall when selecting an area to establish a vineyard, as vines naturally prefer dry conditions over wet, not least because when it is raining the sun is usually not shining! However, although the east of the UK is quite a bit drier than the west in general terms, in my experience rainfall on a given spot tends to be quite variable and subject to influence by local factors. One has often heard of sites that are drier than sites only a few miles away, usually because there is an intervening hill which deflects rainfall-containing clouds. How easy it is to select a site based upon this level of micro-weather knowledge is another matter.

It should also be remembered that the Lizard in Cornwall, the UK's most southerly mainland point, is actually slightly further south than Geisenheim which is in the middle of the Rheingau, Germany's best winegrowing region and Camel Valley is on the same latitude as Germany's Ahr winegrowing region, famous for its Pinot noir wines. Norwich however, is some 300 km (187 miles) to the north of the Lizard and is almost on the same latitude as Hanover and there are not many vines there. People tend to forget that the UK tilts to the west!

As to the question of how far north to grow vines, all I can say is: *caveat emptor*. As I have pointed out above, growing vines is not the issue, you can probably do that in the Shetland Isles (given enough protection from the wind).[5] The problem is (a) growing vine varieties that give high quality wine (b) getting them to fruit (c) fruit at the right level of yield to make it worthwhile and (d) getting that fruit to ripen. Whilst I applaud the efforts of those growers who have planted vines north of Birmingham, I cannot say I would recommend it.

In early October 2013 I made a pilgrimage north to visit all of the major Yorkshire vineyards – Holmfirth, Leventhorpe, Ryedale, Summerhouse and Yorkshire Heart – plus Somerby and Three Sisters in Lincolnshire and was pleasantly pleased to see in most of them (sadly not all) good crops of grapes, in some cases ripe and already being picked, in sharp contrast to some vineyards in Kent and Sussex, which were still waiting for their grapes to ripen! The vine varieties that appeared to be doing the best were Madeleine x Angevine 7672, Rondo, Seyval blanc and Solaris – some of which I would not rate in the first division of wine quality – but still, grapes are grapes and I wish these producers all the best in producing award-winning wines. Varieties such as Bacchus, Ortega, Phoenix, Pinot noir and Siegerrebe were faring less well. However, it does prove it is possible to grow grapes in some unlikely parts of these islands!

The proof of the pudding of course, is in the eating (or in this case, the drinking), but I would point out that if you chart the location of trophies and gold and silver medals that have been awarded to wines entered into the UKVA's national competition, they get thinner the further north you travel. Yorkshire's main producing vineyards have to date between them amassed a few bronze medals and highly commendeds, but nothing better: no trophies, golds or silvers[6]. It may not be much evidence, but it's some. Of course, you can probably survive and maybe even prosper if you are a tourist-magnet, can charge high prices, sell lots of tours and teas and can purchase extra grapes when your own harvest is lacking, but that is not really the point of this book.

## Altitude

The altitude of the site is important for two reasons: the higher a site is above sea level, the cooler it is and the more exposed it will be to the prevailing winds (which in the south of the UK are typically from the south-west). Both of these factors will make the site cooler. It is an often quoted fact that for each 90 m that land rises above sea level, the average annual temperature drops by 0.5°C and the growing season is shortened by two days – one in the spring and one in the autumn[7]. I would therefore start getting concerned about sites where the land was above 100 m, get very concerned about land over 125 m and would not consider land over 150 m. Of course, on a sloping site, some of the land is bound to be lower and some higher, so a site that had 50 per cent of the land below 100 m and the rest above, especially if the site had excellent shelter with rising land behind it and good cover to the south-west, might be better than one with all the land below 100 m but on the top of a hill with views for two counties. An additional factor might also be soil type (dealt with more fully later in this chapter) and one might be more forgiving about altitude on a site with a dry, stony, lean soil which retained heat compared to a fertile, loamy, damper soil which would be cooler.

## Aspect

The next most important requirement for a top vineyard site is that it should slope towards the south, the south-west or the south-east. Vineyards facing east of south will probably dry out faster in the morning and those facing west of south will get the benefit of evening heat. Any generally south facing site will be warmer and will

therefore give you a better quality and quantity of grapes than a flat site, or one facing north which would be around 1°C cooler. However, having said that, I would be prepared to sacrifice a slope facing due south if one facing south-east or south-west was better sheltered from the prevailing wind or was at a lower altitude. At Breaky Bottom vineyard, a site I have known for 35 years, a small block of Chardonnay on a north-facing slope, but a block very well sheltered by a large hedge and rising ground, is always earlier, and crops better than the Chardonnay growing on the south-facing slope in the valley bottom which is exposed to winds that blow up the valley off the sea. This, however, is the exception that proves the rule: vines like shelter.

A sloping site will also always help with air-drainage which will allow frost to drain away, so long as there is lower land for the frost to drain to. On all accounts, avoid what is known as a 'frost pocket'. Sites lucky enough to be near a body of water – a large lake or river – will also be less prone to frost damage as the water will both hold heat and help create air circulation which will keep frost moving. Frost pockets and the problems of frost and how to avoid and/or overcome them are dealt with fully in *Chapter 13: Frost protection.*

Whilst gently sloping sites are ideal for vines, steep sites, whilst they can also be very good, can also be problematical. Unless terraced, something that has never really been done on anything other than a very small scale in the UK, steep sites can only really be planted directly up and down the slope and will require more powerful four-wheel drive tractors in order to get up the slope towing and powering sprayers and mowers. In addition, turning at the top and bottom of the rows on a steeply sloping site, unless there is a flat area that has been created specifically to turn on, has its dangers and tractor drivers will have to take extra care if they are to avoid tipping over. However, steep slopes will be typically warmer than gently sloping sites and drainage will often (but not always) better. As to how steep is too steep, this depends entirely on the equipment used. In many European regions, sites with slopes as steep as 45° are successfully planted with vines.

## Shelter

A major factor in site quality is shelter and this cannot be emphasised enough. A sheltered site is one which has rising ground, or perhaps a block of woodland, or failing those two, some shelter belts and/or windbreaks planted on the windward side in order to slow down the prevailing wind, stop it moving the leaves and stop it cooling the site. Forget all about having a breezy site to blow away diseases – I have never known a site for vines in the UK that didn't have some degree of wind blowing through it – you are after a site with as little breeze as possible. The windier the site, the cooler it will be: the more a vine's leaves are moving, the less they will photosynthesize; the less they photosynthesize, the lower will be the sugars in the grapes, the reserves of carbohydrates in the trunk and the roots and the fruiting ability for the vine in the coming year. Shelter belts and windbreaks (which are dealt with in *Chapter 6: Site planning and preparation* in the section on

*Windbreaks*) whilst these can be very valuable to a site, are never as effective as a naturally well-sheltered site. This also means that sites within the influence of sea breezes should be treated with caution, even though they may well be less troubled by frosts. I am very familiar with sites such as Adgestone on the Isle of Wight, 2.1-km from the coast, and Breaky Bottom near Lewes in East Sussex, 3.9-km from the coast, where grapes grow happily and good wines have been made over 35+ years, but I know that they are sometimes negatively influenced by the cooling effect from their proximity to the sea. My advice therefore would be to think carefully before attempting to establish a vineyard within 5-km of the coast, especially the south coast which catches the full brunt of the prevailing wind travelling up the Channel.[8]

*A windy site will never make the best vineyard. This photograph was taken at a vineyard in the Channel Isles.*

I suspect that one of the reasons why many vineyards in Cambridgeshire, Norfolk, Suffolk and the less sheltered parts of Essex have not proved successful, is the cold east winds that hit this part of the UK. When I look back to the 'East Anglia' section in my 1989 book *The Vineyards of England*, the roll-call of grubbed vineyards is alarming: Boyton, Brightlingsea, Broadwater, Bruisyard, Cavendish Manor, Clees Hall, Coton, Deben Valley, Elmham Park, Essex Crown, Felsted, Finn Valley, Fenlandia, Fyfield, Gamlingay, Greens, Harling, Helions, Haywood, Highwayman, Isle of Ely, Ilsington Lodge, Langham, Lexham Hall, Nevards, Oak Hill, Priory, Roding Valley, Pulham, Sotterley Farms, Swafield House, Uggeshall, West Hanningfield, Willow Grange, Writtle. It would have been easier to list those that have survived: Chilford, Giffords, Mersea, New Hall, St. Mary Magdalene, and Wyken. Of the 117-ha (290-acres) listed in my 1989 book, only 48-ha (119-acres) survives of which 35-ha (87-acres) is at New Hall, situated in the southern, coastal part of Essex.

Location, altitude, aspect and shelter are for me the key elements to a good site in the UK for growing vines. Get these wrong and the enterprise is already starting with a handicap. I am not alone in this view. Peter Hayes, the WineSkills[9] Viticulture Mentor, wrote in his first report, dated March 2010, following visits to twelve different vineyard operations, several with multiple sites:

*'Site selection and site amelioration*
*Some evidently superior sites were observed in the course of these visits. These were characterised by:*

• *Relatively low elevations (30-100 m)*
• *Southerly aspects with considerable slope for sun exposure and soil drainage*
• *Protection from, in particular, S-W winds*
*Several other high potential sites at greater elevations appeared to have adequate wind protection either in place or planned and some had clearly inadequate arrangements for moderating impacts of wind. Wind can severely inhibit vine function and vineyard establishment and beyond the establishment phase may also severely suppress vineyard performance. For example, wind speed greater than 3m/sec are reported as suppressing stomatal conductance and photosynthesis with effects potentially lasting days depending on variety.'*

## Business considerations

The next consideration is the location of the site in relation to the type of business enterprise you are proposing to create. Are you growing grapes to sell to another winery? Or are you hoping to make wine and sell it? If so, then the proximity of your site to your market and its suitability for establishing a wine production and wine sales enterprise will be critical. You might have found the best site in the UK, but if it is miles from anywhere, only accessible down a farm track and impossible to get to except with a four-by-four, then think twice. Fine if it's just for growing a crop and the only visitors will be you and the farm staff – but even then you will have to think about getting the crop out – but it will be no good if you want to build a winery, a farm-shop and a visitor enterprise.

Remember also that by planting a vineyard, you are signing up to a thirty to forty year investment and whilst you might hate the idea of dealing with the public and having visitors crawling all over your property, one day you might well want to sell up and move on. The potential buyers of your well-established, high production and therefore high-value vineyard might have other ideas. They may well want to get involved in farm-gate sales, vineyard tours and teas, rent-a-vine visitors – the full wine experience – and if there is nowhere to put the car park, the shop, the winery, the lavatories and all the other add-ons that come with the territory, then you might lose out. In addition, they might also want somewhere to live, so having nearby property or a suitable site where a house could be built might be a huge advantage.

Therefore, if you are looking for a site for a vineyard and are thinking about the prospect of having a winery and/or selling wine from it, remember such things as sight-lines for access for the public in their cars, visitors in coaches and lorries collecting or delivering grapes and/or wine; whether there is three-phase electricity somewhere nearby (and preferably on site); and whether there are any buildings that might be converted into a winery and wine store or added on to.

Although, under 'Permitted Development Rights', wineries up to a certain size and subject to certain other requirements do not generally require planning permission to make wine from fruit grown on the site where the winery is situated, it is so much easier to start with an existing building.[10] There is more about planning permission in *Chapter 19: Getting started.*

*Electricity cables over a vineyard offer a great vantage point for birds to congregate as the grapes ripen*

## Soil

I am very sure that some people will be thinking that the question of soil ought to have come first in this long list of site requirements and whilst I have sympathy with this view, I do not agree with it. Soil is an extremely important factor in a vineyard and countless studies on the influence it has on wine style and quality have been written and absorbed by generations of viticulturalists and winemakers. Soil is, after all, the basis for the theory of *terroir.* It is where the vine has its roots and from where it draws almost all its water and nutrients. Soil comprises not only the physical material from which it is made – clay, silt, sand and stones – it also contains chemical elements, both major and minor, plant material which we generally call 'humus' and an unimaginable range of organisms – yeasts, moulds, fungi, mycorrhizae[11], bacteria, protozoa[12], algae and worms – all of which play a part in the ecology of the soil and which in all probability influence the way in which the vine grows and fruits. Soil therefore certainly influences a vine and the grapes it bears. Recent studies at Stellenbosch University[13] have hypothesised that variations in tanks of wine made from grapes harvested from a vineyard which was in all respects identical, i.e. same variety, clone, rootstock, age and vineyard management, may be due to differences in the yeast composition within the vineyard. The authors state in their abstract: 'Importantly, yeast species distribution is subject to significant intra-vineyard spatial fluctuations and the frequently reported heterogeneity of tank samples of grapes harvested from single vineyards at the same stage of ripeness might therefore, at least in part, be due to the differing microbiota in different sections of the vineyard.' Whether soil actually 'flavours' a wine though, is a different matter.

Despite everything you read about soil and its relationship to the style and character of a wine (usually on back-labels or in publicity material) there appears to be no scientific proof that any substance, any element or any chemical in the soil can jump the divide between the soil and the root, travel up the roots, trunk and cane and lodge itself in the grape, thus flavouring the wine. Dr Jamie Goode in *Wine Science* states:

*'Do chalk, flint or slate soils impart chalky, flinty or slate-like characters to wine? As a scientist who has a working knowledge of plant physiology, I find this notion, which I call the 'literalist' theory of terroir, implausible.'*

Goode also quotes Dr Richard Smart who was asked what he thought of popular notions of *terroir* which propose direct translocation of flavour molecules from the soil to the grapes, and hence the wine. Smart said, with his typical Antipodean honesty: "This is an absolute nonsense".

Professor Jean-Claude Davidian of the *Ecole Nationale Supérieure Agronomique* in Montpellier echoes these sentiments: 'Nobody has been objectively able to show any links between the soil mineral composition and the flavour or fragrance of the wines. Those who claim to have shown these links are not scientifically reliable'.[14] David Farmer, a geologist and graduate of the University of Tasmania, in a posting on the website glug.com makes the quite interesting point that even if soils vary greatly from one site to another and trace element levels also vary: 'why would a vine take up more than was required of any element just because it was more abundant? If say the trace element selenium varies from region to region why would vines take up more than needed, assuming of course that these trace elements are playing some active rôle and are not just sucked up and have no real end use?' Farmer continues to question why a vine would: 'want to concentrate more of an element than it normally needed just because more was available?'

Professor Alex Maltman from Aberystwyth University's Institute of Geography and Earth Sciences, who has made a study of the 'influence of vineyard geology on wine' called *Minerality in wine: a geographical perspective*[15], points out that most soils which produce wines said to have 'minerality' are in fact those soils which are poorer and less nutrient-rich, whilst the soils which produce wines which tend towards the soft and fruit-driven, are likely to be higher in nutrients and minerals – the exact opposite of what pro-mineralists believe. In his 'Discussion and conclusion' Maltman states:

*'In fact, it may turn out with further research that the nutrient minerals of geological origin in vines and wines – miniscule in concentration and flavourless though they maybe themselves – are pivotal in determining wine character and flavour. However, this would have to take place in complex and circuitous ways. Thus perceiving minerality in wine would not involve tasting minerals but permutations of complex organic compounds whose production has been influenced by inorganic cations. Future research will no doubt evaluate this speculation. In any event, for all the reasons explained here, minerality in wine – whatever that perception is – cannot be in any literal, direct way, the flavour of minerals derived from vineyard rocks and soils.'*

The fallacy about chalk soils somehow contributing to the 'mineral' character of a wine is a prime example of 'mineralist' thinking. Why do growers of Chardonnay in Champagne prefer chalky soils? Not because the chalk gets into the wine and causes 'steely', 'flinty', 'mineral' (or even 'chalky') characteristics. They prefer it because deep down, chalk soils retain moisture, even in drought years, and their vines, which can root deeply in these soils, have access to water, thus keeping their foliage green and sustaining high yields and keeping acidities higher than on less chalk-rich soils. I sometimes wonder if those UK growers who have actively sought out (and paid high prices for) chalk land to grow their vines on, have actually taken on board the reasons why Chardonnay growers in Champagne like chalk. After all, in the UK, we have no requirement to retain acidity in our grapes (or at least not in most years).

*Soil profile showing three distinct layers*

However, origin – which includes the influence of soil – does have an effect upon the character, style, flavour and quality of wine, a fact which partially enables wine tasters to distinguish one wine from another. (The other factor in the party trick of wine identification is, of course, the memory of flavours and tastes.)

What certain soils do is to cause the vine to grow in a certain way, perhaps promoting high yields, perhaps promoting low yields. Some soils will cause the vine to be vigorous, leading to a crowded canopy and shaded grapes and this will make the grapes taste different to ones grown on a soil which is low in vigour, causing a vine's canopy to be very open and airy which would tend to produce riper, lower acid grapes. Much of this is due to the way in which a soil receives, stores and releases water, whether rainfall or via irrigation. The way a vine deals with water is at the heart of how a vine grows, the quality of its canopy and the degree of air and light that the grapes are exposed to. Some soils are able to store water; others not. The porosity and permeability of a soil and how the vine's roots access the water falling on it, passing through it and stored in it are at the heart of how a vine grows. The soil in a vineyard must, therefore, not be taken lightly.

The question therefore, of what type of soil is best for a UK vineyard, a soil that will enable us to produce viable yields of good grapes, is another matter.

The UK is in a different situation to almost all other established European winegrowing regions. There are an estimated 3,530,000-ha of vines in Europe (OIV 2012[16]) and if you go to France, Germany, Spain, Portugal or Italy, where they have been growing vines on the same sites for hundreds and in some cases, thousands, of years, they have been able, by experimentation and by measuring the results, to determine which section of which hillside or river valley or estuary or escarpment produces which quality of grapes and in doing so, have built up a picture of where the best sites and soils are for certain types of wine. Would that it was like this in the UK: but it is not. Firstly, we have only been growing vines commercially for wine production in the modern era for around sixty years and for over half of those sixty years the area under vine was (a) extremely small and (b) growing a selection of varieties that have, if not now totally gone, then greatly diminished and (c) our vineyards are spread over an extremely wide area with distinct differences between the east and west of the country in terms of rainfall and exposure to prevailing winds. The major varieties that we now grow, Chardonnay and Pinot noir, plus Meunier, have in reality only been producing wine in the UK since the early 1990s and the area under vine of these varieties is only 701-ha (1,732-acres) (WSB 2013). Compare this to Champagne where there are 34,000-ha (84,041-acres) of these three varieties and where they have been growing them for more than 150 years. Couple that to the fact that all vinegrowing in Champagne is entirely controlled and regulated by the CIVC, the *Comité Interprofessionnel du Vin de Champagne*, who carry out endless research and experimentation in all aspects of both viticulture and winemaking, and you can see that UK vineyard owners are currently at a distinct disadvantage.

The truth is that in the UK, as far as viticulture is concerned, we have almost no data to work with. Much of what people believe about different sites for vines in the UK is circumstantial and not based upon evidence. Additionally, many UK wine producers (especially the larger ones) either have sites in several different locations, sometimes many miles apart and on completely different soils, or are buying in grapes either under contract or on the open market, again from sites in many different locations, so that trying to associate soil type with wine style is impossible. However, that is not to say we know nothing and we must use such knowledge as we do have, to find the best places to grow good grapes.

**Note:** For general information about soil types see National Soil Resources Institute *Soilscapes* website: www.landis.org.uk

## Drainage

For the same reasons that we know the best fruit growing soils are well drained, we know that vines like well-drained soils. Good drainage can be natural drainage and of course that is the cheapest form of drainage. But, for generations, growers on heavier soils, clay soils and the like, have produced good crops of top-fruit – apples, pears, cherries and plums – on soils which have been so-called 'tile drained'. These days, the half-round clay drains, their tile covers and their straw covering may have disappeared and been replaced by efficient plastic piping and 300 mm of 'beach' over-fill, but the reasons for field drainage have not changed. A well-drained soil will warm up more quickly (because wet soils require more heat to dry them out before they warm up) and will provide better conditions for access by tractors and machinery at both ends of the season leading to less compaction, rutting and damage to the structure of the soil. A drier soil will also create less humid conditions and lessen the pressure of disease. A vine growing in a well-drained soil will tend to have both a deeper and more extensive rooting system than one growing in soil where the top soil is wetter (sometimes a problem in vineyards with poorly designed irrigation systems). Then, when the soil dries out in the upper reaches in the summer, especially post-*véraison*, the vine will have the ability to draw water from lower down. Claude Bourguignon, who, together with his wife Lydia, runs probably the viticultural world's the best known soil analysis laboratory (LAMS[17]), and is a self-confessed soil 'nut', believes fervently that for vines, depth of rooting is a very significant quality marker and that effectively, the deeper the roots, the better the wine. Whether this is totally true is another matter. Given that the deeper you go, the less nutrients there are in the soil, one might think that a deeper rooting vine would pick up less in the way of minerals, which runs counter to the *terroir* argument. However, it may be that because there are less minerals the deeper you go, a vine has to develop a much larger root system, which gives it two advantages: the larger root system is able to store more carbohydrates; and the deeper roots are able to access a steady supply of water less influenced by rainfall. The question of drainage is further addressed in *Chapter 6: Site planning and preparation* in the section on *Drainage*.

## Soil type

The question of what type of soil suits vines growing in the UK is another open question and I would say that as long as the site conforms to the criteria laid down above – somewhere in the traditional fruit and hop growing regions of the south of England (or possibly Wales), below 100-125 m above sea level, well sheltered from the south-west, sloping to the south, the south-west or the south-east, well drained, or capable of being drained, and preferably well-sited for the establishment of a winery and farm-shop, then I would say, in all honesty, forget the type of soil you are presented with and learn to live with it. Drain it if it needs draining, lime it if it needs liming, add humus if it needs humus (it will), subsoil it (always), plant your vines at the right density and on the right rootstock, treat it with respect and almost any soil type can be made to work. I know vineyards on heavy clay (New Hall, Hush Heath), on light sandy soils (Gusbourne, Tenterden), on brick earth (Nyetimber's original vineyards), on high-pH, chalk-rich soils (Squerryes, Leckford) and they all produce good to very good grapes. I have also known vineyards on the same soils which have failed. It is NOT the soil type that ultimately makes the difference.

In a hundred years' time, when perhaps the area under vine has risen from today's bare 1,500-ha (3,706-acres) to perhaps 20,000-ha (49,420-acres) and the whole of the M25 valley is planted with vines and all the available land between Pulborough and Petworth is planted with vines, and someone has bothered to do the research, then we might know a bit more about which soil types produce the best grapes in the UK. But, until that happens, don't worry about it.

My attitude towards the soil of a vineyard does not mean however, that I don't think it important – far from it. I was brought up in the countryside, was a member of my school's farming club, a member of my local Young Farmer's Club and started working for my father-in-law, a large-scale arable and dairy farmer, in 1971. I started my studies into UK vineyards in 1973-4 and spent almost two years in Germany, working in a vineyard, studying at Geisenheim, visiting vineyards belonging to friends and fellow students and since 1977 have been very actively involved with growing vines, producing grapes and/or making wine since then. My final paper for the Master of Wine Theory examination, which helped me win the Mondavi Award for the highest marks in this section of the exam, was eight handwritten pages titled: 'The Secrets of Soil'. In short, I have been involved with, and thinking about, soil for a long while.

Soil is, after all, the medium into which the vine places its roots; it is the medium from which it almost entirely draws its moisture and its nutrients; and it is the factory-floor which has to take the traffic of our feet when we work in the vineyard and of our machinery when we tend the vines. How could it not be important? But, what effect does the type of soil (note: the type of soil not the condition of the soil – that is a different matter) have upon our vine and our crop?

The type of soil is important because it has an effect upon the way the vine grows. The water-holding capacity of the soil will dictate how much water the vine has access to and will affect the vigour of the vine, how much shoot and leaf growth there is and how crowded the canopy will be. A vine growing in a soil that drains well in its top layers, but holds on to its water lower down, is likely to retain its foliage longer, grow longer shoots and more leaves and keep a fuller canopy than a vine in soil that is the opposite. Whether this is good for growing vines in the UK is the question and even if you have a soil which does promote growth, by having a high vine density, growing the vines on a deep rooting, devigorating root-stock, using an appropriate pruning system, carrying out the correct canopy management and growing something in between the rows of vines (grass, weeds, green manure etc) that uses up the moisture, you will almost certainly be able to counteract the effect of a soil with a higher water-holding capacity.

The humus content of the soil is a second major factor in a soil's qualities. Humus is a vital source of nutrients for the multitude of different organisms that are crucial to a healthy soil. The worm population of a soil is a very good indicator of its overall health and there can be as many as 4 million worms per hectare which together would weigh over 1,000 tonnes. Each worm will produce around 4.5 kg of casts – earth, grit and vegetable matter – per year which will help improve the soil. Worms will be active in many soils down to 2 m and will both take down vegetable matter from the surface as well as provide channels for water to drain into the soil and for carbon dioxide to escape. Appreciating what is happening beneath a vineyard's surface is key to understanding your *terroir*.

Plant a vine in a soil too low in humus and it will struggle to establish as it tries to grow new roots and settle into its environment. If it is also faced with other hazards, water and/or nutrient shortage, competition from weeds, damage from pests and diseases, then it may fail altogether. Roots cannot of themselves take up moisture and nutrients, but require mycorrhizal fungi to act as intermediaries between the tip of the fine root hairs and the water and nutrients.[18] Much of the root activity in a vineyard in a region well supplied with summer rainfall (such as the UK) or in vineyards which are irrigated, takes place in the top 500 mm of soil.[19] Vines that are staked and trellised as soon as they are planted do not require their roots to act as anchors and roots will spread sideways, as well as down, taking the easy path to find water and nutrients. Once the roots have colonised the upper reaches of the soil, only then will they start diving deeper. Although typically in the UK we allow the vineyard alleyways to grass down after planting (and I much prefer to allow this to happen naturally from self-sown grass and weed seeds, rather than actually sowing grass seed), in Europe and in drier, un-irrigated regions, vineyard alleyways are often cultivated, at least for the first few years, if not for the entirety of the vineyard's life. The reason for this is that if any roots do grow near the surface they will be disturbed by the cultivations, thus forcing the vine to root deeper.

The humus in a soil before planting a vineyard is a combination of what has been left behind from previous crops plus what has been added. Even if the straw from an arable crop is baled and taken away, some will be left behind and this will be incorporated into the soil after harvest. If the farmer has no use for the straw, then all of the crop's straw will be left behind – especially now that straw burning has disappeared. Grassland used for grazing is generally rich in humus as the animals who graze it return much of the humus element of the pasture that they eat in the form of manure. Grassland which is used to make silage or hay, a so-called permanent pasture, will be less humus-rich, as large quantities of plant material are actually removed from the land each time the grass is cut, although a good farmer will rotate crops so that perhaps after five years, a grass field is put into cereals for a few years to restore fertility before it is planted with grass again.

Land that has been used for fruit crops, especially hardwood fruits where little in the way of vegetation, apart from leaves and prunings, is left behind after harvest, is often in danger of being poor in humus content which makes the grass alleyways between trees (or vines) especially important providers of this element. Vineyards are usually better in terms of their humus content as the grassed area covered by the alleyways is typically 65-70 per cent of the surface area of the vineyard, with the rest, i.e. the area under the vines, being kept free of vegetation. The weight of leaves, shoots and prunings, which are generally left behind in the vineyard, is high compared to the weight of crop taken out. A yield from an apple orchard might be as high as 50 tonnes-ha (20 tonnes-acre) compared to say 8.5 tonnes-ha (3.44 tonnes-acre) in a UK vineyard and the area of the alleyways might be as low as 30 per cent of the area of the orchard. This is because an apple tree has a much wider spread than a vine.[20]

In almost all situations, before planting a permanent crop such as vines, the land will benefit from an addition of humus and any addition is better than none. If there is time before planting, then a 'green manure' crop can be planted and either grazed off or ploughed in and incorporated into the soil. Otherwise additions of farm yard manure (FYM) will always help vines establish, although if not well rotted, may aggravate the weed situation. FYM will also provide some nitrogen and other fertilisers and trace elements and help improve the overall soil fertility. Otherwise, compost such as commercial green waste (BSI PAS 100[21]) or spent mushroom compost are useful sources of humus, although the latter will not improve the nutrient status that much. Green manuring is discussed in *Chapter 7: Vineyard Nutrition*.

The third aspect of a soil is its physical character, i.e. how deep is the top soil, how deep is the subsoil and what is the soil made of?

A deep top-soil, such as is often found in UK vineyards, is good for getting vines established and will usually be rich in humus, nutrients and soil organisms that promote healthy root growth. Soils such as this will often promote vegetative growth and therefore vine density and the choice of rootstock will be important. These soils will typically have a fairly neutral pH – 6.5 to 7.0 – and will require little in the way of adjustment at the pre-planting stage. Drainage in these soils may also be an issue and need addressing. Sites with leaner top-soils, those with visible stones, flints and gravel for instance, will certainly make fine vineyards, but will require good soil preparation, subsoiling and deep ploughing and may well require some additions of humus both pre-planting and at times throughout the life of the vineyard. Natural drainage on these soils may well be good, but there can always be areas and sections of any site (where there is a spring perhaps or compaction) where drainage should be installed. Sites with very shallow top soils are probably best avoided and those with subsoil constraints certainly are. If possible, it is always best to dig some soil pits of at least 1 m deep (and probably nearer 2 m deep) to see what's down there using a mechanical digger of some type. How many pits and to what depth will depend upon the size of the site and the uniformity (or lack of it) of the soil. The MAFF publication *Bulletin 105: Soils and Manures for Fruit* (dated 1975 and now out-of-print, but still obtainable second-hand) has some very good advice about soil types and the digging of soil pits.

Soils with noticeable stones, flints and gravel may help retain heat in the vineyard into the early evening when the sun has gone down, thus keeping the vines dry for as long as possible and aiding ripening, although with vines in the UK typically having their fruiting wires at least 700 mm from ground level and with the breezes that usually blow through UK vineyards, this benefit may be more in the imagination than in reality. Soils with a high stone content may also prove problematic when installing posts and anchors, but this is usually a one-off problem and can be lived with. Also, if mechanical methods of either weed control or alleyway management are used on stony soils they will be more difficult and more costly.

The pH of a soil, which is dealt with more fully under the section on rootstocks in *Chapter 4: Vine varieties, clones and rootstocks*, should not be a determining factor in whether a site is suitable for vines or not. With the correct lime additions (to an acid soil) or with the correct rootstock (in an alkaline soil), most soils can be planted with vines. Having said that, soils below pH 5.0 and above pH 8.5 are best avoided unless they have some exceptionally positive attributes in their favour.[22]

## Previous land use

Land that has been previously cropped with arable crops, or grazed by animals will probably pose no problem when it comes to establishing a vineyard. However, land that has previously been planted with fruit trees or fruit bushes or was previously woodland – either managed or scrubland that has run to rough woodland – may pose a problem. On old fruit land, vines may suffer from something similar to Replant Disease which affects several species, especially apples and pears. Whilst this classically only occurs when plants are replanted on a site that was previously planted with the same species, I have known situations where vines following apples have failed to establish in certain small patches of the vineyard, possibly due to the presence of old roots which are rotting below the surface. On land that was previously woodland there may be traces of *Armillaria* (honey fungus) which might give rise to problems with establishing vines as it does in California. If you are concerned about the land use prior to planting vines, the best thing to do is to make sure that as many as possible of the old roots of the previous species are removed and burnt off-site, make sure the site is well subsoiled and cultivated, plus, allow a crop (or two) of a cleansing green manure such as mustard[23] to grow and be incorporated back into the soil. Follow that with a good application of FYM or compost and also consider the use of dips based upon mycorrhizal and/or a *Trichoderma* fungi dip on the vines at planting. See *Chapter 8: Planting your vineyard* for more discussion on these dips.

**Note:** The best book on the subject of vineyard soils that I have found is: *Understanding Vineyard Soils* by Robert E. White.

## Other factors

Footpaths can often be a big problem when they are near, within or even run across sites for vineyards. Footpath users are very territorial about 'their' paths, which will probably have been in use for centuries, and seem to dislike new owners planting what they see as ugly vineyards. If a footpath actually crosses the land you propose to plant, then the only practical way you can accommodate it is to align your rows with the footpath (assuming it runs in a straight line) and you must allow at least 1.50 m of clear space for the footpath. Whilst footpaths can in theory be re-routed or diverted, in practice it can be a long and often unfruitful battle to get them moved. In addition, footpath users will almost certainly complain about any weed spraying or pesticide spraying taking place and in addition, under the buffer zone rules (which have not yet been formulated) you may have to keep your sprayer a considerable distance from any public access areas.[24] The DEFRA (Department for Environment, Food & Rural Affairs) website has detailed information on Public Rights of Way.

The residents of houses close to vineyards can often prove problematical, especially with regards to such things as early morning, late night and weekend vineyard and winery operations, spraying and noise made by bird scarers. See *Chapter 16: Pest and disease* control in the section on *Bird damage* for more information on audible bird scarers. Apart from the legal aspects surrounding both spraying and audible bird scarers, disgruntled neighbours can make life unpleasant for vineyard owners. There have been many cases of vineyard vandalism – anchor wires cut, vines cut off at ground level, and vines sprayed with weedkillers – and it pays to make friends with any neighbouring owners, telling them of your plans, especially if you intend to welcome visitors, have farm-gate sales, start a winery etc. Disaffected neighbours can easily disrupt planning and licensing applications.

I would also guard against selecting a site near a pheasant shoot and especially near a pheasant release pen. How near is debatable, but in my experience a site within 1.6-km (1-mile) of a well-stocked pheasant shoot is to be avoided. Although the case law established under *Rylands vs Fletcher* in 1868 gives landowners protection against damage done by livestock that escapes from neighbouring land, the 1971 Animals Act specifically exempts 'pheasants, partridge and grouse' from this provision and when they escape (or are released) they instantly become 'wild' birds. It is also very difficult to prove that the birds actually eating your grapes have come from a particular source. I have been involved as an expert witness on two substantial claims for pheasant damage (one of which was successful, the other is still pending) and in these instances the shoots were established after the vineyard was planted, so it was not a case of poor site selection.

If the site you have chosen for your vineyard is right next door to an arable farm, a golf course or horse paddocks, you should also be aware of the possibility of herbicide damage. Vines are easily damaged by hormone weedkillers which can vaporise in warm weather and then drift to adjoining fields. The chief culprits in this respect are farmers with grass fields spraying off nettles and thistles and other broad-leaved weeds early in the season, prior to cutting the field for hay, and golf course greenkeepers who are very keen on keeping their fairways and greens free of weeds.

There is also the possibility of spray-drift contaminating your grapes with a substance which might show up in the final wine. Whilst this is probably a more remote possibility, it is something to be borne in mind should drift occur. If in doubt, test for it.

Of course, if your vines are damaged by drift from a neighbouring farm, you are entitled to compensation for any damage caused, but proving it and getting their insurers to pay is another matter. It is best to keep on good terms with your neighbours (farming or otherwise) and tell them of your plans and remind them about their legal obligations not to let sprays drift. (If you do suffer weedkiller damage, you will need to collect evidence straightaway and notify your neighbours, their insurance company and call in the loss adjusters.)

Sites with telegraph poles, electricity pylons and other obstacles are best avoided if possible, not only because they give somewhere for birds to perch as they size up the ripening grapes, but also because they make laying out and planting a vineyard more difficult. However, if the site is perfect in every other respect then such obstacles can be accommodated. Sites which are long and thin which can only be planted with the rows in the short direction are of course plantable, but will result in higher establishment costs (more end-posts and anchors), higher working costs as tractors will spend more time turning round than driving in a straight line and more land will be lost to headlands.

## Site selection – a summary

Choosing the right site for growing vines in the UK is without doubt one of the most difficult tasks facing a potential vineyard owner, yet is probably the most important. Ignoring the factors of availability and affordability, finding a site that fits all the major criteria – location, altitude, aspect and shelter – and is then in the right place for the business model that fits your plans, has a soil that is suitable and isn't blighted by any of the other considerations that need to be taken into account, is a major, major problem. Many of the pioneers of course, selected their sites on the 'because it was there' principal, planting vines in the field 'I can see from my front door' or in the field empty 'because my daughter has got fed up with her pony' or – and probably the worst reason I have yet come across – 'because it was the only land on the farm that wouldn't grow sugar-beet'. All of those reasons were actually given to me as the criteria for site selection. Much as one might envy those pioneers the ease with which they chose their sites, all of the above examples are now ex-vineyards. Inevitably compromises have to be made when selecting a site, but my advice is not to compromise on the ability of the site to grow good grapes.

---

1 There are many sources of information on this subject. The paper *Grape bud fruitfulness – what causes a bud to produce a bunch or not* by Devin Carroll can be found at www.englishwine.com/wgigb.htm

2 *The Grapevine – from the science to the practice of growing vines for wine* by Iland, Dry, Proffitt, and Tyerman

3 *A statistical model to estimate bud fruitfulness in Pinot noir* by Joanna E. Jones, Greg Lee and Stephen J. Wilson. AJEV.2013.12086.

4 *Véraison* is the stage of growth when grapes start softening, start turning red (in red varieties) and sugars start to accumulate and acids decrease.

---

*Véraison* takes place at different times on different bunches and is a good guide to the order in which those bunches flowered.

5 You can certainly grow raspberries and blackcurrants on the east coast of Scotland in the open (although they are mostly grown under plastic tunnels these days) but I would not advise growing vines. Despite plenty of light, there is just not enough heat to ripen grapes.

6 In the 2014 UKVA Competition, Somerby Vineyard in Lincolnshire won a Gold with their *2013 Solaris* and Rydale Vineyard in Yorkshire won a Bronze for their *2013 Wolds View White*. Another northern vineyard, Renishaw, just south of Sheffield, also won two Silvers and a Bronze. Obviously my visit had nothing to do with these successes!

7 Lockhart and Wiseman's Crop Husbandry, eighth edition 2002, p. 79.

8 For this reason (amongst others), I will follow with interest the fortunes of the Rathfinny Estate which is 4.2-km from the coast at Seaford, East Sussex and has started to plant what will become by 2020 (according to their website) a 160 ha (395 acre) estate.

9 WineSkills is the Plumpton College based training scheme which is partly DEFRA funded.

10 See *Planning Policy Guidance No. 7* at www.englishwine.com/wgigb.htm

11 This is the RHS (Royal Horticultural Society) website description: 'Mycorrhizae are beneficial fungi growing in association with plant roots, and exist by taking sugars from plants 'in exchange' for moisture and nutrients gathered from the soil by the fungal strands. The mycorrhizae greatly increase the absorptive area of a plant, acting as extensions to the root system.'

12 Protozoa are microscopic single-celled organisms that live in the soil. They are vital to the break-down of plant matter in the soil.

13 *The Vineyard Yeast Microbiome, a Mixed Model Microbial Map* by Mathabatha Evodia Setati, Daniel Jacobson, Ursula-Claire Andong and Florian Bauer. December 2012.

14 For a fuller discussion on this, see Dr. Jamie Goode's paper on The Mechanisms of Terroir: www.wineanorak.com/mechanisms_terroir1.htm and in his: *Wine Science – the application of science in winemaking* in Chapter 2. *Terroir: how do soils and climate shape wine?*

15 *Minerality in wine: a geographical perspective*, Professor Alex Maltman, Journal of Wine Research, Volume 24, Issue 3, 2013. Available at www.englishwine.com/wgigb.htm

16 OIV – International Organisation of Vine and Wine.

17 Laboratoire Analyses Microbiologiques Sols www.lams-21.com

18 *Understanding Vineyard Soils*, Robert E. White, p. 60-1.

19 Although you will often read about vine's roots growing down to five, ten, even twenty metres below the vineyard surface, very few of the writers who state this know this for a fact and it is highly unlikely that any more than a small percentage of a vine's roots in the UK's well-watered vineyards ever get below 1 m deep.

20 Some modern systems of growing apples – the tall spindle system for instance – where the trees are trained and trellised much more like vines, are better in this respect, but the alleyway to non-alleyway area is still typically only 50 per cent of the total orchard area.

21 This specification, plus much other useful information about compost for use in agriculture, is available from www.wrap.org.uk.

22 For a more complete discussion about vineyard soils, see *Chapter 5: Soils for vineyards* (p. 41-7) in my book: *Viticulture – an introduction to commercial grape growing for wine production* should also be consulted.

23 Mustard, when allowed to grow and then incorporated into the soil, releases compounds called isothiocyanates which act as a biofumigant and suppress certain pests and pathogens.

24 See *Chapter 16: Pest and disease control* for buffer zone details.

# Chapter 4
# Vine varieties, clones and rootstocks

## Vine varieties – the legal situation

**Note:** The WSB's vine variety data lags behind that of the production data, hence the difference between the total UK planted area in 2013 of 1,884-ha (4,655-acres) and the total of 1,503-ha (3,714-acres) in the vine variety tables.

Until the UK reached a total of 500-ha (1,235-acres) of planted vines, MAFF was reluctant to get involved with the vine varieties growers had in their vineyards, although in theory growers were only meant to plant those varieties on the 'Recommended' and 'Authorised' lists. These lists, which had been drawn up prior to the UK's entry into the Common Market in 1973, were subsequently updated by the 'Vine Varieties Classification Committee' and brought into line with the varieties actually in the ground. Once a planted area of 500-ha was reached, a fact MAFF reluctantly discovered in the 1987 voluntary vineyard census, growers in the UK were restricted to planting varieties on the lists, but all the while the UK's wine production was under 5,000 hl in any one year, there was no restriction on the area that could be planted and there would be no planting ban, something that existed in all other EU member states with sizeable vineyard areas. But as the area under vine in the UK increased and with it, volumes produced, the limit on wine production before a planting ban would be introduced was upped to 25,000 hl average annual production over 5 years and then again to a 50,000 hl average annual production over 5 years, the figure it stands at in 2013. The current 5 year average annual production (2009-13) is 23,585 hl.

The UK vine planting situation in 2013 is that except for six old American and/or hybrid varieties – Clinton, Herbemont, Isabella, Jacquez, Noah, and Othello, which are not permitted to be planted anywhere in the EU – there are now no restrictions on the vine varieties one may plant and any variety may be used for winemaking and the variety name may be used on the label. This is of course subject to the usual winemaking and labelling regulations which dictate how wines may be labelled

## Categories of wine that may be produced in England and Wales

Following changes to the basic EU wine legislation in 2011, there are now four distinct categories of wine which can be produced in the UK: wines with 'Protected Designation of Origin' (PDO), also called Quality Wines; wines with 'Protected Geographical Indication' (PGI), also called 'Regional Wines', which are Table Wines with some additional quality parameters; 'Varietal Wines' which are Table Wines which have gone through a 'Certification' process; and wines which are none of the above which I have termed 'UK Wines' and which may not bear a vintage or the names of any vine varieties.

Until these changes took place in 2011, the only Quality Wines in the UK were still wines. To gain Quality Wine status wines had to be made from *vinifera* varieties, i.e. no hybrids, had to be made to certain quality parameters and all wines had to be tested and tasted. This system is still current. Somewhat confusingly, sparkling wines made to certain standards could (and still can) be called Quality Sparkling Wines even though they can be made from any variety including hybrids. This is because the term 'Quality' in 'Quality Sparkling Wine' refers to the method of sparkling, not the base wine from which the *cuvée* is made. After the 2011 changes, the UK gained the right to make PDO Quality Sparkling Wines which are the sparkling equivalent of the UK's still Quality Wines. The most important difference between PDO Quality Sparkling Wines and non-PDO Quality Sparkling Wines is that the PDO wines can (in theory) only be made from certain varieties. Therefore the categories of wine are:

**PDO Still Wines**
English Quality Wine, Welsh Quality Wine
**PDO Sparkling Wines**
English Quality Sparkling Wine, Welsh Quality Sparkling Wine

**PGI Still Wines**
English Regional Wine, Welsh Regional Wine
**PGI Sparkling Wines**
English Regional Quality Sparkling Wine, Welsh Regional Quality Sparkling Wine

**Non-PDO/PGI Still Wines**
Varietal Wine – allowed to state origin e.g. Kent, but may not state 'English' or 'Welsh'. May bear vintage and variety name(s).
UK Wine – allowed to state origin e.g. Kent, but may not state 'English' or 'Welsh'. May not bear vintage or variety name(s).

**Non-PDO/PGI Sparkling Wines**
Quality Sparkling Wine – allowed to state origin e.g. Kent, but may not state 'English' or 'Welsh'. May not bear vintage or variety name(s).

English and Welsh still Quality Wines (PDO) may not be made from hybrids and the following seven are currently shown on the WSB's lists as being planted in the UK: Cascade (Seibel 13-053), Chambourcin, Gagarin Blue, Léon Millot, Maréchal Foch, Seyval blanc, and Triomphe. English and Welsh still Quality Wines (PDO) can, however, be made from newer hybrids, known as interspecific crosses (ISC), which have been legally classified as *vinifera* varieties. Orion, Phoenix, Regent and Rondo are definitely classified as *viniferas* and the following nine varieties are on the current (2011) DEFRA list as being eligible for PDO still wines, although WSB are not sure if they have been legally classified as *viniferas* for UK use: Bolero, Cabernet blanc, Felicia, Johanniter, Merzling, Monarch, Sirius, Solaris, and Villaris. Cabernet Dorsa and Manzoni Bianco, both *viniferas*, and Muscaris, an ISC variety, are on the WSB's list, but NOT on the DEFRA list of eligible varieties and Cascade, Gagarin Blue and Zalagyöngye, all of which are hybrids and therefore in theory ineligible for PDO status, are however on the DEFRA PDO list. If you are a grower of any of these last six varieties and want to get a wine made from them through the PDO system, I suggest you try and see what happens!

English and Welsh Quality (PDO) Sparkling Wines (which are not the same as non-PDO Quality Sparkling Wines which can be made from any vine variety planted in a UK vineyard) may only be made (in theory) from the following six varieties: Chardonnay, Meunier, Pinot blanc, Pinot gris (Ruländer), Pinot noir and Pinot noir Précoce (Blauer Früburgunder)[1]. However, there are currently at least two sparkling wines which have been granted PDO status which contain wine from other varieties and it would appear that this regulation is being poorly policed! English and Welsh Regional (PGI) still wine and English and Welsh Regional Quality Sparkling Wine (PGI) can be made from any variety, as can both 'Varietal Wines' and 'UK Wines', i.e. wines without classification.

All PDO and PGI wines have to be tested and tasted before they may be so labelled. Varietal Wines have to be 'Certified' by providing certain information, before they may be so labelled. The benefits of Varietal Wine are that the labels may bear varietal and vintage information, something the final category of wine, wines that are not PDO, PGI or Varietal Wines, may not.

A list of all varieties in UK vineyards and their status for different wine categories can be found in *Appendix II*.

## Planting ban?

As has been outlined in the previous paragraph, at the present level of production, the EU has exempted the UK (as well as the other small EU wine producing Member States) from a planting ban and until the 50,000 hl 5 year average annual production level is reached (or more likely increased once again), or until 31 December 2018 when the 'transitional' arrangements end and come up for review, there is little prospect of a planting ban being introduced to the UK. However, given that there is a planting ban in the other major EU wine producing member states and, despite talk of it being abandoned, there appears to be a great reluctance on the part of those member states to allow their winegrowers to plant what they want, there is nothing in the regulations preventing Brussels imposing a planting ban in the UK.

Whether this would actually happen is questionable. DEFRA takes the view that competition should be encouraged whenever possible and is against artificial barriers to the production of any crop or foodstuff. They have stated on several occasions that they are against a vine planting ban and have stated that: 'we will continue to fight for - - - there being no restrictions to planting [vines] anywhere in the EU'.

Of course, DEFRA has bigger fish to fry than a few vines. I can well envisage a situation where the UK's area under vine has doubled once again, where our annual production is nudging 50,000 hl and Brussels is offering the UK a great deal on wheat or milk or sheep or fish, i.e. a sector of much more importance to UK farmers than a few hundred winegrowers. If this were to happen, then DEFRA might agree to a limited planting ban being introduced. This could, for instance, restrict existing growers from planting more vines unless they could show they were producing only (or a good proportion of) Quality (PDO) Wines and only allow new entrants to plant on sites that could be shown to be capable of producing PDO wines and with varieties that had a track record of PDO wine production and limit the area they could initially plant. All things are possible in the corridors of the EU. What impact this would have upon UK wine production is debatable, but I would suspect that existing growers would be secretly quite pleased, as it would, place a limit on the rate of expansion of production and therefore their market share; make their vineyards more valuable; and for existing growers wishing to grub up and retire, the prospect that their planting rights would probably be tradeable (as they are in other EU winegrowing regions) and therefore have a value.

## What varieties to plant

After you have chosen your site, the next major decision is: what varieties to plant? The answer, strangely, is actually quite easy: it should be the ones that (a) suit your site and (b) make the style of wine you will be able to sell! Of course, this is far easier said than done. Given that on a site with no previous history of growing vines – a common situation for many UK winegrowers – prior knowledge of what varieties 'suit' your site is of course difficult, but not impossible. And again, the question of what style of wine 'you will be able to sell' maybe something you have not considered and is therefore also quite difficult to answer.

But, by asking these two questions it brings to the fore two essential points: the quality of your site will dictate the best varieties for you to establish on it; and you need to have a vision of the wine you would like to produce and how and where you propose to sell it before you plant. Do not fall into the trap of growing a variety that your site will not support or attempting to make a wine for which there is a limited market. I often ask potential growers at my first meeting 'what English wines have you enjoyed recently' or 'tell me what styles and types of English wines you like' and it always amazes me how many look rather blank, shuffle around a bit and then mention one or two wines that they vaguely recall having tasted. In order to have a successful vineyard, especially if you are proposing to make and sell the wine, it is imperative that you should know and enjoy the product. The other major question of course is still or sparkling and this is dealt with at length later in this chapter.

The range of varieties available to plant is huge and, to the uninitiated, the question of which to plant is either a problem to be run away from or an opportunity to experiment. There are advantages and disadvantages of both views. For those that see the selection of varieties as a problem, the answer is to stick to the varieties that have proved themselves in the UK and which suit your site and the style of wine you wish to make. Don't try and re-invent the wheel. If you were a grower in Chablis or Sancerre, Burgundy or Alsace would you be worried about what variety to plant? No. The *appellation* has already determined which varieties suit your region and whilst you may have the choice of clone – although even this is not certain – your task is to grow the best grapes you can.

The selection of the right varieties for your site, your financial position and your marketing plans is the most important decision you will have to take, apart from that of site selection itself. In taking this decision, the best advice I can give is to learn from others and to look backwards to what has been successful, rather than to look forwards and hope the obscure varieties you have chosen will produce award-winning wines. When looking backwards, I am guided by the collective wisdom of the 500-plus growers in the UK, by the membership of the UKVA and of the judges who judge the wines entered into the annual 'Wine of the Year' competition. If you just take the trophies and gold medals for both still and sparkling, and white, red and rosé wines, the list of successful varieties is very small (see table below). The only real criteria is to choose those varieties that have proved themselves capable of making high quality wines because it is only by making wines of high quality that your enterprise will be successful in the long run. I accept that looking back has its problems, as

growers can only make wines from the varieties they have in the ground and therefore, some of today's (and yesterday's) wines are made from varieties that, given a fresh start, many growers would never plant today and will certainly not plant again.

For those that see the selection of a variety (and more often, varieties) as an opportunity to experiment, let me issue a health warning straight away. Although we have seen considerable changes in the spectrum of varieties being grown in the UK since modern commercial vineyards started in the 1950s, the top eight varieties in 1984 (in order of area planted) were Müller-Thurgau, Reichensteiner, Seyval blanc, Madeleine x Angevine 7672, Huxelrebe, Schönburger, Pinot noir and Bacchus. With the exception of Huxelrebe, which has fallen to seventeenth in popularity, all of the others are still in the top ten, and Chardonnay, Meunier and Rondo have come from (almost) nowhere to complete the top ten line-up. My point is that despite the availability of countless varieties – the WSB currently lists sixty-three varieties as being grown in the UK in excess of 0.10-ha (0.25-acres), plus another 5.44-ha (13.4-acres) of 'miscellaneous' varieties – there have been very few new varieties which have proved themselves worth growing, over and above those already tried and tested. The three that have – Chardonnay, Meunier and Rondo – have done so on the back of climatic changes which have seen sparkling wines become the UK's major product and red wine production become more of a reality than it hitherto was. Newer varieties have been tried in the past and sadly found wanting. Finding the 'perfect' new variety for the UK is not an easy task, and although a few have moved up in the lists – Acolon, Orion, Phoenix, Regent, Rondo, and Solaris have all shown gains since 1990 – there are plenty of others that have come and gone. In 1999 there were 83.4-ha (206.1-acres) of Faberrebe, Kerner, Kernling, and Würzer. Today these four varieties cover 19.7-ha (48.7-acres) and the area looks set to reduce further with the passing of time. Finding a new variety for the UK covers not only its ability to thrive under UK climatic conditions and produce worthwhile quantities of grapes, but also the suitability of those grapes to be turned into good wine and that wine, with possibly an unknown varietal name, to be sold to the public. Many growers take the view that it is better to stick with the devil you know.

**Note:** See *Newer vine varieties* later on in this chapter.

| Number of Gold Medals awarded in EVA-UKVA 'Wine of the Year Compeition' 1974-2013 | | | |
|---|---|---|---|
| **Vine Variety** | **No. of Gold Medals** | **Vine Variety** | **No. of Gold Medals** |
| Pinot noir - still and sparkling | 35 | Cabernet Sauvignon and Merlot | 3 |
| Bacchus | 28 | Pinot blanc | 3 |
| Champagne blend | 26 | Madeleine x Angevine 7672 | 2 |
| Chardonnay - still and sparkling | 18 | Ortega | 2 |
| Müller-Thurgau | 12 | Siegerrebe | 2 |
| Seyval blanc and blends | 8 | Ehrenfelser | 1 |
| Ortega | 6 | Gutenborner | 1 |
| Reichensteiner | 5 | Huxelrebe | 1 |
| Schönburger | 4 | Meunier | 1 |
| Source: EVA and UKVA Wine of the Year Compeition results | | | |

## Varietal change

Although I have pointed out above that there have been only minor changes in the varieties being grown in the UK in the last few decades, what have changed of course, are the areas covered by the individual varieties. In 1990, seven varieties – Bacchus, Madeleine x Angevine 7672, Huxelrebe, Müller-Thurgau, Reichensteiner, Schönburger and Seyval blanc (listed in alphabetical order) – accounted for 72 per cent of the total planted area of 929-ha (2,296-acres) and Pinot noir only occupied 32-ha (79-acres) and Chardonnay 20-ha (49-acres), these two accounting for less than 6 per cent of the total. In 2013, Chardonnay, Pinot noir and Meunier account for 46.6 per cent of the Vine Variety area and Bacchus, Madeleine x Angevine 7672, Müller-Thurgau, Ortega, Reichensteiner, Rondo, Schönburger and Seyval blanc account for another 35 per cent. Together these eleven varieties account for 81 per cent of the total UK Vine Variety area of 1,503-ha (3,714-acres). See note at start of this chapter for reasons for discrepancy between total planted area of 1,884-ha.

| Vine varieties in the UK in 2013 | | |
|---|---|---|
| Variety | Ha 2013 | % of UK area |
| Chardonnay | 327 | 21.8 |
| Pinot noir | 305 | 20.3 |
| Bacchus | 131 | 8.7 |
| Seyval blanc | 92 | 6.1 |
| Reichensteiner | 80 | 5.4 |
| Meunier | 69 | 4.6 |
| Müller-Thurgau | 56 | 3.7 |
| Rondo | 47 | 3.2 |
| Madeleine x Angevine 7672 | 46 | 3.1 |
| Schönburger | 35 | 2.3 |
| Ortega | 35 | 2.3 |
| Pinot blanc | 25 | 1.7 |
| Regent | 24 | 1.6 |
| Phoenix | 24 | 1.6 |
| Pinot noir Précoce | 20 | 1.3 |
| Others | 187 | 12.4 |
| **Total Ha** | **1,503** | **100%** |
| Source: Wine Standards Branch of the Food Standards Agency | | |

Not only has the change in varieties affected the type and style of wines produced in the UK, with sparkling wine now probably accounting for 60 per cent of total production[2], but it has also changed consumers' perception of our wines. Again, as I said in my opening chapter, in earlier times, when a wine retailer or sommelier was asked what an English wine was like, he or she might have said: 'well it's made from Müller-Thurgau and Schönburger with a touch of Reichensteiner and its tastes a bit like German wine or maybe a wine from Alsace' and in doing so lose the customer's attention and interest before the second umlaut. Today, when faced with the same question about a bottle of English or Welsh Sparkling Wine, the same retailer or sommelier might say: 'well it's just like Champagne' and then perhaps as an afterthought, in order

to make sure the customer was completely at ease, add: 'and it's made from Chardonnay and Pinot noir'. In saying this, in such simple terms, a message which every wine drinker understands has been easily and simply conveyed. I believe this has made a huge difference to the industry and has given the wine trade in all its many guises the confidence to get behind, to support and to sell, the home-grown product.

Those vineyards planted with German varieties in the 1970s, '80s and '90s weren't defeated by poor quality wine, and they weren't necessarily defeated by poor yields. What defeated them was the problem of marketing their (mainly still) wines in the time-frame you have to sell still wine. Most new vineyards start cropping in their third or fourth year and if you are producing still wine, six months after picking, your wines are usually bottled and ready to sell. Initially, with a small maiden vintage, and with some local interest in your wines, they may sell quite quickly, but come October and another vintage, this time hopefully a full-sized one, is ready for picking and by the next May, you have another vintage for sale. The pressure is on.

Most buyers, especially trade buyers who perceive typical UK-grown still wines as being fresh, fruity, lively wines, at their best within twelve to eighteen months of picking, are not so interested in older vintages and would rather taste your more recent wines. If sales are not matching output, you cannot afford to store your wines in tank indefinitely – there is another harvest approaching – and the temptation (and the reality) is to cut your losses, lower the price and move the stock. In 1984, Kenneth McAlpine, then the owner of Lamberhurst Vineyards, the largest and (seemingly) most successful vineyard in the country,[3] found himself, after the larger than average crops in 1982 and 1983, with 1 million bottles in his cellars and sales lagging behind production. At the time, the vineyard's best-selling 'Lamberhurst White' sold for £2.99. Faced with the prospect of another large crop in 1984, McAlpine looked at the alternatives: take on more sales staff, advertise, promote, attend more shows and fairs and maintain the price; or slash the price and stimulate sales. He took the latter route, cut the price to £1.99 and within six months had cleared the excess stock. Short-term, the problem was cured; long-term, it set the benchmark price for entry-level English wine at a low – and probably unprofitable – point from which it would struggle to recover. Other large-scale producers, such as Carr Taylor (who would face bankruptcy a few years later), Barkham Manor, Penshurst, Three Choirs and Wellow all found it hard to lift their prices above those of their main competitor – Lamberhurst.[4] Sparkling wines, however, are different.

You cannot get into the (bottle-fermented) sparkling wine business without putting the wine into a bottle, putting that bottle into a store (usually in a storage or riddling crate) and stacking the crates in an insulated, secure, temperature-controlled store. Once the wine is in the store, all you can do is wait for it to mature. Therefore, why sell it (a) before the wine is ready and (b) until you can find someone willing to pay what you perceive to be the right price? With sparkling wines, bottle-age is seen as a plus: two years good, four years better, six years even better. This places the decision of when to sell firmly back in the producer's hands and although building up stocks creates havoc with the cash-flow, at least it means that the temptation to cut and run towards an easy sale at a low price is lessened. You can probably sell enough to keep the cash-flow positive, leaving you time to re-double your sales efforts, open that farm-gate outlet, build that website, visit more hotels and restaurants, send out more samples to merchants, attend more shows, investigate export opportunities – in short – find ways of getting your wine to market. I believe this difference between still and sparkling wines has helped the prices of UK-grown sparkling wines stay resiliently high even though both the number of different sparkling wines and the amount available for sale have risen in recent years.

statistics also do not include duty-free sales (sales into UK bonds or exports). However, if we assume that almost all of the Chardonnay and Meunier and probably the majority of the Pinot noir planted in vineyards ends up in sparkling wines, plus some of the other varieties (Seyval blanc, Müller-Thurgau, Reichensteiner, Pinot blanc, Pinot gris) then the split between sparkling and still is probably around 60:40. Add into this equation the fact that almost all vineyards up until the late '90s were planted with still wine varieties and these are the ones most likely to be grubbed on the retirement of their owners, and that many of the newer Champagne-variety vineyards are larger, better trellised and better managed than the older vineyards, and you have a scenario that is biased even more heavily towards sparkling wine in the decades to come.

| Hectares of Chardonnay, Pinot noir, Meunier and Pinot noir Précoce in UK vineyards 1990 - 2013 | | | | | | | | | | | | |
|---|---|---|---|---|---|---|---|---|---|---|---|---|
| Variety | 1990 | 1999 | 2004 | 2005 | 2006 | 2007 | 2008 | 2009 | 2010 | 2011 | 2012 | 2013 |
| Chardonnay | 20 | 34 | 36 | 49 | 91 | 120 | 180 | 202 | 249 | 285 | 304 | 327 |
| Pinot noir | 32 | 44 | 49 | 62 | 85 | 121 | 185 | 218 | 248 | 258 | 278 | 305 |
| Meunier | 6 | 8 | 10 | 14 | 23 | 27 | 32 | 49 | 53 | 56 | 58 | 69 |
| Pinot noir Précoce | 0 | 0 | 0 | 0 | 0 | 8 | 15 | 17 | 18 | 20 | 20 | 20 |
| Total of above | 57 | 87 | 95 | 126 | 198 | 277 | 412 | 486 | 568 | 619 | 660 | 721 |
| UK planted area ha | 929 | 872 | 761 | 793 | 923 | 992 | 1,106 | 1,215 | 1,324 | 1,384 | 1,437 | 1,503 |
| % of total area | 6% | 10% | 12% | 16% | 21% | 28% | 37% | 40% | 43% | 45% | 46% | 48% |
| Source: Wine Standards Branch of the FSA 2013 | | | | | | | | | | | | |

However, the sparkling wine business requires large amounts of capital to be tied up in stock. As I have already pointed out in *Chapter 2* in the section on *Costs of production*, many producers will be working with at least three and maybe six vintages in stock at a cost of around £28,125-ha (£11,382-acre) for each year of production, based upon a modest 7.5 tonnes-ha (3 tonnes-acre). Take four years as an average stock level and the total is a frightening £112,500-ha (£45,528-acre); six years stock and the bill is an astronomical £168,750-ha (£68,292-acre), which adds £1.50 a bottle to your production costs. Larger crops and longer-aged wines – Nyetimber has just started selling its 2009s and is still selling wines from 2003 – and the overall cost of stock will be even greater. Your selection of varieties and wine styles must therefore be taken not only from a marketing perspective, but also from a financial one.

## Still or sparkling?

Over the last 15-20 years the viticultural landscape in the UK has changed dramatically from one that was producing almost entirely still wines to one that produces predominantly sparkling wines. Although the WSB collects overall production statistics, they do not differentiate between still and sparkling wine. Likewise HMR&C, who publish statistics on the amount of duty paid on UK-produced wines, do not split the amount between still and sparkling wines. Why, I have no idea. It cannot be that difficult (and I have asked them). Their

The reasons for the switch from still to sparkling are not difficult to see. The quality of the best UK-grown sparkling wines is by any measure streets ahead of our still wines. They have elegance and finesse, plus lasting power and have proved themselves in tasting after tasting to be the equal of Champagne and other fine sparkling wines. In addition, as I have already pointed out, they are much easier to explain to the wine buying public and much easier to sell. The 'success' of brands such as Nyetimber, winners of major national and international awards with their first wines (from the 1992 and 1993 vintages) in 1997-8, and Ridgeview, whose first wine (a 1996) was released in 1999 and who won the Gore-Browne Trophy in 2000 and 2002, plus the high prices they achieved, gave credence to the idea that sparkling wine was the way forward. The idea that 'because they can do it, so can I', much in the way that the prominence of Lamberhurst Vineyards persuaded still winegrowers that they too could grow grapes, make wine and make money, persuaded many growers that sparkling wine was the product for the future. In addition, it wasn't very difficult to see that a £20-£25 bottle of Nyetimber or Ridgeview really was of an equivalent quality to a bottle of Moët, Lanson or Taittinger costing much the same, whereas a bottle of still wine from Three Choirs or Chapel Down at £7-10 was OK, but perhaps slightly (or even very) overpriced and therefore poor value for money. Couple this to the fact that bottle-fermented sparkling wine (aka Champagne) has the aura of prestige and quality about it and the average customer expects to pay more for it, and the appeal of sparkling wine to the producer is an obvious one.

Another factor to be considered in the switch from still to sparkling is the level of the return to the producer. In *Chapter 2* I showed how a bottle of still wine selling at £10 retail price and sold through a retailer returned £3.42 to the producer, whereas a bottle of sparkling wine selling through a retailer at £20 returned £9.11, a 'bonus' of £5.69. If you can get £24 for the sparkling, then the difference is over £8 a bottle. If you can sell the same wines directly to the consumer, then the returns are of course much better and show a difference of between £7.77 and £11.10 a bottle. The costs of buying land, setting up a vineyard, the running costs and the picking costs are exactly the same for both still and sparkling wines, and the only differences in production costs, assuming the same yields, are accounted for by the reduced output from a tonne of grapes for sparkling as against still wine (perhaps 550-600 litres-tonne for sparkling wines and 700-725 litres-tonne for still), the additional costs of the sparkling wine production process and the costs of the additional stock a sparkling wine producer needs to carry. These make the cost of producing a bottle of sparkling wine at least £2.50 a bottle more than still wine (and probably nearer £4) and therefore a premium of £5 just about covers this and one of £11 certainly does. As I have already pointed out, setting your retail price as high as possible must be the aim of every producer and the factors that affect this ought to be considered.

*This is the sort of newspaper article that helps sell English Sparkling Wine and persuades consumers that the 'high' price is worth paying*

The still wine sector in the UK is vast, over-supplied and hard-discounted and for whatever reason – there are several and it's not worth going into them here – still wines will always be heavily price-promoted. It is said that 75 per cent of all wines sold in the UK are 'on promotion'. The quality of cheap wines from overseas has also risen hugely over the past fifty years and such things as better viticultural techniques, refrigeration, stainless steel equipment, screwcaps and the conditions placed upon suppliers by supermarkets, has lifted the quality of all wines, but especially wines at the bottom end of the

market. The problem for UK-grown still wines trying to compete in this market is that they tend to be produced on a very small scale and when measured on a price-quality basis, are perceived as 'poor value'. Will consumers buy UK-grown still wines at a premium to wines from overseas? Yes, because it's part of a visitor experience; yes, because they have tasted it; and yes, because its local and they support local producers. But, none of these really apply when English and Welsh wines are exposed on a supermarket shelf alongside hundreds of other, cheaper offerings from overseas. You must also add into the equation the fact that UK-grown still wines have had a very chequered reputation over the last fifty-plus years and whilst there have been many honourable exceptions, there is no getting away from the fact that for many wine drinkers, UK-grown still wines have been (and often continue to be) a disappointment.

Having said all of the above about the benefits of sparkling wine over still wine, and having gone on record to say that still wines don't have much of a future, there are several scenarios where still wines can be successful and can make money. If you have a farm-gate or winery outlet where your wines can be tasted before purchase, then you have a head start over someone selling them via an outlet – shop, supermarket, hotel or restaurant – where they cannot normally be tasted before purchase and where there is no one 'hand selling' them. Once someone has tasted a wine and liked it, a high price becomes less of a handicap. In addition, buying wine direct from the farm-gate is part of a day out in the country and I will often buy a jar of honey from a roadside stall for £5-6, knowing full-well that I can buy a perfectly good jar of honey in my local supermarket for half that price. If you can build up a loyal following for still wines from your home base, then this will give you the confidence (and income) to pursue sales in other markets.

## Over-supply of English and Welsh sparkling wine?

Another factor that ought to be taken into account when considering planting a vineyard for the production of sparkling wine is the question of over-supply. And when I say 'over-supply' I am talking specifically about the market in the UK. I accept that there are export markets for UK-grown sparkling wines, but export markets are expensive to find, to service and to supply. For the bigger, better-known and/or better-funded producers, this may not be a problem, but for the majority of smaller producers and for those producers who have yet to make a name for themselves in the UK, I do not believe that exports are the easiest way of selling substantial quantities at a profit. There will always of course be exceptions – the person on the plane you sat next to who just happens to own a hotel, restaurant or wine shop in Bogota or the friend of a friend who is just dying to import your wine into Belgium – but these will be the exception rather than the rule. Of course I could be completely wrong, and UK-grown sparkling wines will be a hit in some surprising overseas markets, but I wouldn't personally bank on it in the short term.

In Champagne itself, production has risen inexorably, with slight deviations due to vintages and up-turns and down-turns in the world economy, ever since the Second World War. According to the CIVC, the area in production in Champagne in 1982 was 25,337-ha and in 2010 it was 33,344-ha, a 32 per cent increase. Not only has the area increased, but also the yields. The 30 year average prior to 2000 was 9,825 kg-ha (3,976 kg-acre); since 2000 it has been 14,980 kg-ha (6,062 kg-acre). Put these two together and the total amount harvested in the '80s was 250,000 tonnes; today it is almost double that. But, even despite this massive increase in production, the Champenois think that there will be shortages in years to come and are considering adding another 5,000-ha (12,355-acres) to the *appellation* and in addition, raising the permitted yields to 15,500 kg-ha (6,273 kg-acre). This is at least one indication that sales of sparkling wine (or at least of Champagne) are likely to increase substantially in the foreseeable future. However, let us now look at the market for all sparkling wines in the UK.

*Little West End Farm Vineyard which produces Meonhill. The only UK vineyard to date to be planted by a Champenoise. Now part of Hambledon Vineyard.*

There is no doubt that UK drinkers like sparkling wine. Between 2002 and 2012, HMR&C data showed that sales have risen by 53 per cent, a larger increase than for all other alcoholic drink sectors. The UK is the biggest export market for not only Champagne, but also Cava and Prosecco. HMR&C statistics show that for the twelve months between May 2013 and April 2014, UK importers and producers paid Excise duty on 960,599 hectolitres, the equivalent of  just over 128 million 75 cl bottles, of sparkling wine of all types: Champagne, Cava, Cremant, Sekt, Prosecco and other sparklers, plus of course sparkling wines of UK production. Around 31 million bottles of the 128 million were Champagne. In that period, sales of all sparkling wines were said to be up by 10 per cent for the year, but Champagne down by 4 per cent.

Most of the non-Champagne sparkling wine sold in the UK is priced at under £10 a bottle with the average price of Cava sitting at £5.68 a bottle and all sparkling wines at £6.24 a bottle (Harpers Wine and Spirit Weekly, April 2013). These are not price sectors UK producers want to, or can afford to, be in. Of the wines sold at £15 or above, most of it is cheap Champagne on special offer and when

supermarkets run a '20 per cent off everything week' (typically pre-Christmas).  Much of the Champagne that the UK imports is non-vintage and in 2012, according to the Champagne Bureau[5], 87 per cent was white non-vintage, 9 per cent rosé vintage and non-vintage, 2 per cent 'Brut Vintage' and 2 per cent 'Prestige Cuvée'. My researches suggest that around 75 per cent of the 31 million bottles of Champagne that the UK drinks, is sold at less than £20 a bottle, again, a price sector that UK producers probably, except in exceptional circumstances, do not want to be in. This leaves around 25 per cent of 31 million bottles, or under 8 million bottles a year that is sold at £20 or more, the sector that I suggest UK producers DO want to be in, and frankly, need to be in if they are to survive. The question therefore is: where do UK-grown sparkling wines fit into what is currently an 8 million bottle market? Will they steal sales from Champagne and other sparkling wines? Or will they expand the overall sparkling wine market by creating their own niche? To attempt to answer this, we need to look at what the production of UK sparkling wine is likely to be.

As has been shown in the table above, plantings of the three Champagne varieties, plus Pinot noir Précoce, have risen from 95-ha (235-acres) in 2004 to 721-ha (1,782-acres) in 2013, a rise of almost 850 per cent in ten years. As can also be seen, the percentage of the UK total vineyard area devoted to these varieties has risen to almost 50 per cent. Owing to the fact that sparkling wine production figures are not available and that it is up to producers both how much of their total crop they turn into still or sparkling wine and, having made sparkling wines, how long they keep them *sur latte* before they bring them on to the market, the amount of UK-grown sparkling wine available for sale at any moment in time can only be an estimate. However, lack of data and the flexibility of producer's production and marketing strategies should not stop us making some informed guesses of the amount of UK-grown sparkling wine that might be available at any one time. Therefore, by making some assumptions, one arrives at the figures in the table on the next page.

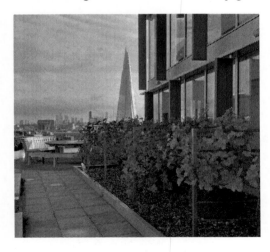

*One of the UK's least likely vineyards. Six vines planted on Decanter Magazine's terrace in Southwark with the Shard in the background.*

| Year | Ha planted | Ha. In production | Ha. Not in prod. | Hl-Ha | Total Yield in Hl. | No. 75 cl Bottles in millions of bottles | Sparkling x 60% of total in millions of bottles |
|---|---|---|---|---|---|---|---|
| 2004 | 761 | 722 | 39 | 26 | 19,071 | 2.54 | 1.53 |
| 2005 | 793 | 722 | 71 | 18 | 12,806 | 1.71 | 1.02 |
| 2006 | 923 | 747 | 176 | 34 | 25,267 | 3.37 | 2.02 |
| 2007 | 992 | 697 | 295 | 14 | 9,948 | 1.33 | 0.80 |
| 2008 | 1,106 | 785 | 321 | 13 | 10,087 | 1.34 | 0.81 |
| 2009 | 1,215 | 946 | 269 | 25 | 23,835 | 3.18 | 1.91 |
| 2010 | 1,324 | 1,095 | 229 | 28 | 30,346 | 4.05 | 2.43 |
| 2011 | 1,384 | 1,208 | 176 | 19 | 22,659 | 3.02 | 1.81 |
| 2012 | 1,437 | 1,297 | 140 | 6 | 7,751 | 1.03 | 0.62 |
| 2013 | 1,884 | 1,571 | 313 | 21 | 33,385 | 4.45 | 2.67 |
| 2014 | 2,072 | 1,762 | 311 | 25 | 44,039 | 5.87 | 3.52 |
| 2015 | 2,280 | 1,938 | 342 | 25 | 48,442 | 6.46 | 3.88 |
| 2016 | 2,508 | 2,131 | 376 | 25 | 53,287 | 7.10 | 4.26 |
| 2017 | 2,758 | 2,345 | 414 | 25 | 58,615 | 7.82 | 4.69 |
| 2018 | 3,034 | 2,579 | 455 | 25 | 64,477 | 8.60 | 5.16 |
| 2019 | 3,338 | 2,837 | 501 | 25 | 70,924 | 9.46 | 5.67 |
| 2020 | 3,671 | 3,121 | 551 | 25 | 78,017 | 10.40 | 6.24 |
| 2021 | 4,039 | 3,433 | 606 | 25 | 85,819 | 11.44 | 6.87 |
| 2022 | 4,442 | 3,776 | 666 | 25 | 94,400 | 12.59 | 7.55 |
| 2023 | 4,887 | 4,154 | 733 | 25 | 103,840 | 13.85 | 8.31 |
| 2024 | 5,375 | 4,569 | 806 | 25 | 114,225 | 15.23 | 9.14 |
| 2025 | 5,913 | 5,026 | 887 | 25 | 125,647 | 16.75 | 10.05 |

**Note:** The assumptions made in the above table are:

• Vineyard areas up to and including 2013 are actual WSB totals. From 2014 onwards they have been arrived at by increasing the area by 10 per cent per year which is slightly less than the 11 per cent increase seen since 2004. Whether this is realistic is questionable as the massive increase between 2012 and 2013 has very much thrown the averages into disarray. However, given that plantings will increase, it's as good a figure as any.

• From 2014, 85 per cent of the planted vineyards will be in production and 15 per cent not in production, figures that are broadly in line with what has happened in the past.

• From 2014, the UK average yield will be 25 hl-ha. Although this is a fairly low figure by any international standards, it is higher than the average yields for the ten years 2003-2013 of 20.29 hl-ha. As older vineyards get grubbed and newer ones come into production, yield levels ought to rise, but if the past is anything to go by, not by very much.

From the above table it can be seen that the level of production of UK sparkling wine (which runs ahead of the amount available for sale by around two to four years because of the lees-ageing time) will rise from the current level of around 2.0 million bottles a year (based upon 2010-13 production figures) to over 5 million by 2018 and over 8 million by 2023. Taking a lees-ageing time of two to four years, this makes the amounts of UK sparkling wine available for sale look something like this:

• 2014        1.7 million bottles
• 2018        4.0 million bottles
• 2023        6.0 million bottles

Of course, there are many factors that could blow these projections off-course either way:

• Plantings increase or decrease. The dramatic increase in the UK area under vine from 2012 to 2013 of 446-ha (1,102-acres) announced by the WSB in May 2014 has to be seen as something of an anomaly and may well have skewed the figures. An increase per year of 10 per cent is possibly slightly too high.

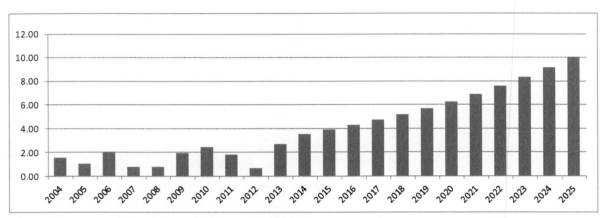

*Chart showing estimated production of sparkling wine in millions of 75 cl bottles from 2004-2012 and estimate of future growth from 2013*

• If the prices of grapes and/or wine start to decline, then in time this must have an impact upon future plantings, although probably not in the short term.

• Yields are lower than the 25 hl-ha suggested. Given that the ten year average (2004-13) is 20.40 hl-ha, then I accept that this is a possibility. However, given that it is not possible to make a return on anything much less than 35-40 hl-ha, I feel that the trend of the yield figure will be upward, rather than downward. If yields do fall lower than 25 hl-ha then many vineyards will become financially unsustainable and the overall levels of planted area and production might well fall.

• Producers might switch from sparkling wine to still wine with its more immediate returns and lower levels of stock. For some producers, this will always be an option, especially those with vine varieties that are either/or varieties. For growers wedded to Champagne varieties however, their options are more limited. In any event, sparkling wine production is like a large ship that takes a long time to turn round. By the time you realise your sales are suffering and your income is falling, you already have several vintages in stock maturing.

• Prices of sparkling wine might fall, prompting higher levels of sales. This might happen as larger volumes become available for sale and re-sellers are able to squeeze producers into accepting lower prices. This will probably happen to some producers, most likely producers who are new to the market and have not yet established relationships with merchants. Plus there are bound to be producers with cash-flow issues for whom the lure of higher sales at lower prices will be appealing.

• Producers facing slower sales or downward pressure on prices may well decide to concentrate their sales efforts in those markets which give them the highest returns – farm-gate, website and other direct-to-consumer sales – and accept a building-up of stocks and the consequent costs. In the short term (say 5 years) their sparkling wines are not going to deteriorate in store (in all probability they would improve) giving them breathing space to sell more via their highest margin outlets, find new outlets and methods of selling and perhaps cut back production over time. Immediate cash-flow problems could be helped by say selling some grapes at harvest time at a modest price rather than face the additional expense of making, bottling and storing the wine.

So, where does all the above leave UK-grown sparkling wines? I have shown that the current market for £20+ sparkling wines in the UK is around 9 million bottles a year and UK producers currently account for about 1.7 million bottles or 19 per cent of the total. Whilst of course one can expect the overall market for sparkling wines to increase, this is more likely to be with lower-priced wines (Prosecco for instance) than in the much smaller £20+ sector. Supplies of UK-grown sparkling will grow, more than trebling over the next ten years and would, if demand from other areas didn't materialise, have to account for nearer to two-thirds of the current UK market for sparkling wines of £20+. Whether this is a realistic scenario is open to debate. The big fear is that the increase in supply will force retail prices down.

We have seen (or in the case of some, are seeing) the creation of several major enterprises whose main – and in most cases, sole – product is English Sparkling Wine: Chapel Down, Coates & Seely, Gusbourne, Hambledon, Nyetimber, Rathfinny, and Ridgeview, between them have planted, or have plans to plant, around 650-ha (1,600-acres) of Chardonnay, Pinot noir and Meunier. These enterprises are all well-funded and have big plans for the future. If it comes to a price war, then the battle could be intense. At the 2013 International Sparkling Wine Symposium held at Denbies, Frazer Thompson, Chapel Down CEO, was quoted as saying: 'there isn't a market for five million bottles [of UK-grown] sparkling wine at between £20 and £25 a bottle'. Ian Kellett from Hambledon added: 'there will be a range of producers in the market and we must see products on the shelf priced at £12 to £14 a bottle'. Even high-flyers such as Nyetimber are not averse to a bit of price promotion. In December 2013 Majestic had a pre-Christmas offer of *2004 Nyetimber Classic Cuvée* at £23.98 a bottle (as long as two bottles were purchased), a significant reduction from the headline price of £35.99 and as I write this, news has reached me that for the remainder of 2014, this wine (but of a more recent vintage) will be on promotion at £23.99.

What is missing from the above is any discussion about the volumes of sparkling wines (and indeed of wines in general) that producers will sell themselves via the farm-gate, a website and other full-price (or at least at a minimal discount) direct-to-consumer sales. This is of course, a totally unknown (and unknowable) amount. I have always worked on a figure of 50 per cent of total production (of all wines) given the large number of small to very small vineyards, many of whom manage to sell, barter, or give away their wine without ever bothering the 'trade'. As some of the larger producers get even larger and as newer entrants to the business pick up speed and expand their production, I can see the percentage of total UK production sold direct to the public might well fall.

However, having said that, I can also see a slightly different scenario where UK-grown sparkling wines achieve something akin to a cult following and become the 'must-have' wine at smart weddings, parties, presentations and celebrations and it becomes quite chic to go down to the winery, taste what's on offer, and come away with more than just the odd bottle. Given a fair wind and with the influence of what I call 'generational change' which sees today's fifteen year olds who are just discovering alcohol become fully-fledged wine drinkers, and therefore wine buyers, in ten years' time, the amount of wine sold direct could escalate substantially. There are also the prospects afforded by exports, which have already been mentioned, which I feel will be important for some (mainly larger) producers, but may not have that much effect upon the total sold. In any event, because exports are duty-free sales, they do not appear on the HMR&C Excise Duty statistics, making them impossible to quantify other than by reference to producer's claims.

## Still or sparkling? – a summary

Therefore, to summarise the 'still or sparkling' question. There are some good reasons for planting varieties to produce still wines, but one needs to understand the production and marketing problems associated with UK-grown still wines before taking that decision. On balance, the tide has already turned against still wines and going forwards, the very much larger area of vines for sparkling wine already planted and known to be in the pipeline, confirms that sparkling wine will be the dominant UK product over the next decade or so and the one likely to garner most press and public attention. At the 2014 UKVA AGM, Mike Roberts from Ridgeview and Chairman of English Wine Producers suggested the split would become 90:10 in favour of sparkling wine by 2020. I am not sure I agree entirely with this split, but it shows the way some people are thinking.

However, this is not to say that still wine production in the UK is completely finished. If the climate continues to improve (although I hesitate to write 'improve' after the difficult 2011, 2012 and 2013 vintages), and the production of high quality still wines from Chardonnay, Pinot blanc, Pinot gris and even perhaps Pinot noir becomes a reality, then some of the grapes previously destined for sparkling wine could end up in still wine. However, in order to make this worthwhile, the wines produced must be of the equivalent quality of say a *Chablis Village* or *Bourgogne Rouge* and sell for a similar price – around £12-15.

In 2011, when ripeness levels were higher than average, some excellent still wines from Chardonnay and Pinot noir were produced which were selling for (what I thought were) quite extraordinary prices. The *Gusbourne Estate 2011 Guinevere Chardonnay*, which had a natural alcohol level of 13 per cent, sold for £19.99 (and sold out very quickly) and the *Chapel Down 2011 Kit's Coty Chardonnay*, still on sale from the winery at the same price, are both pointers to the future for UK-grown still wines. Find a great site, reduce the crop so that the grapes get extra ripeness and fruit concentration, throw some high quality oak and Burgundian winemaking at them and – hey presto – you have an award winning, profitable, still wine. The *Gusbourne 2011 Pinot noir*, which Berry Bros & Rudd have for sale at £17.45 – too cheap in my estimation! – and Armit Wines are selling for £22.99, is an amazing wine and by my reckoning THE best red wine produced in the UK to date and well worth the money. Even allowing for some extra expense in the vineyard and winery, wines at these prices will make any accountant smile. Still wines made from Bacchus are already achieving a good reputation and the best already sell for high prices. *Chapel Down Bacchus Reserve* and *Camel Valley Bacchus* – both admittedly wines from multi-award winning estates – sell for £14.99 and £12.95 respectively from the vineyard. (Berry Bros & Rudd list the *2011 Camel Valley* at £14.95 for a single bottle). The future for UK wine is not completely sparkling, but any still wines need to be of excellent quality and sell for good prices if they are to make money for the producers. Producers who are open to the public, give tastings and sell direct to the public will find it easier to sell still wines than producers who propose to sell them via the trade.

## Vine variety recommendations

**Note:** Please see separate section in this chapter on: *Clones of Chardonnay, Pinot noir and Meunier for sparkling wines*. See also vine variety recommendations in *Chapter 18: Organic and biodynamic viticulture*.

### Sparkling white wines

For white sparkling wines, the Champagne trio of Chardonnay, Pinot noir and Meunier, either singly or in blends, have proved themselves more than capable of producing world-class wines on good sites in the UK. *Blanc de blancs* made from 100 per cent Chardonnay have been particularly successful and are amongst the very best wines. However, they do not suit all sites and I would caution against planting these higher acid varieties (especially Chardonnay) on challenging sites and as we have seen in difficult and late years (2012 and 2013) acid levels can remain stubbornly high. Having praised the Champagne varieties, I wouldn't discount using other varieties such as Auxerrois, Pinot blanc, and Seyval blanc, especially if used in blends. Seyval blanc as a single (or dominant) variety certainly has its place in UK sparkling wines, although it is usually going to lag slightly behind the Champagne-variety based wines in terms of quality and retail price (although some producers – Breaky Bottom, Camel Valley, Denbies – are successful with it and their wines fetch good prices). However, the ease with which Seyval blanc can be grown and the level of yields it typically produces may well be more than adequate compensation for these shortcomings. Although there have been a few acceptable sparkling wines made from varieties such as Reichensteiner and Müller-Thurgau, usually in blends but occasionally as solo varietal wines, I do not believe anyone planting today would choose these varieties for this style of wine. As for others, I would avoid any of the aromatic varieties and world-wide, these seldom make classic sparkling wines (Riesling Sekt for instance).

**Sparkling rosé and sparkling red wines**

Rosé sparkling wines can either be: classic Champagne variety blends; Pinot noir as a single varietal; or Pinot noir and Meunier blends. All can be very successful. For the red element, I prefer wines where the colour has come from red-fermented Pinot noir or Meunier. I can understand why some growers use a small addition of wine made from Pinot noir Précoce, or one of the other red varieties such as Dornfelder, Regent and Rondo, although I don't think they are as good and would not advise it for a new vineyard. Other neutral sparkling wine varieties – Seyval blanc, Pinot blanc, Auxerrois – can be used for blending into rosé wines, but they are rarely as good. Rosé sparkling wines often have their colour tweaked at the time of disgorging and dosage and in my experience, red Pinot noir works best, although I have known wine from other high-colour varieties used successfully.

As for sparkling red wines, to date there have been very few that could be called 'red' – a few dark rosés perhaps. However, I personally quite enjoy semi-sweet sparkling reds – some of the Australian Syrah-based ones can be very good and I have also had a Nebbiolo-based red sparkling wine from Asti which was excellent – so I see no reason why Dornfelder, Rondo and Regent could not be used. I would prefer to see them in the *demi-sec* or even *doux* category as UK acids and tannins would normally be too high for dry red sparkling wine.

**Still white wines**

For still white wines, Bacchus has to be the top variety, especially if you have a site that really suits it and you know how to grow it. The trade and the public are beginning to recognise it and given its success in tastings and with a great marketing name, its future is secure – at least in the medium term. I have already discussed the use of Chardonnay for still wines and on good sites and in ripe vintages, it can be very good. It would be a brave grower though who set out with the intention of growing Chardonnay solely for the production of still wine, although I can see that growers with good sites who are currently making sparkling wine, will, in good years, be able to divert some of their grapes to still wines. Given the lower price profile of most other still white wines made from varieties such as Reichensteiner, Seyval blanc, Müller-Thurgau, Madeleine x Angevine 7672 (which with

Bacchus make up the top five still wine varieties) I cannot really suggest that anyone planting a new vineyard would choose these as their main varieties, unless they had good reason. In 2003 these four varieties accounted for just under 46 per cent of the planted area, but have fallen to today's figure of just over 18 per cent, a statistic which I believe shows which way growers are voting. Having said that, I believe that Reichensteiner and Seyval blanc, and maybe even Madeleine x Angevine 7672, still have a place in some UK vineyards and under certain conditions, I can envisage them being planted.

Whilst I can see merit in planting varieties such as Ortega and Schönburger (the next most widely planted of the still white wine varieties), even though they can both produce very good wines in a certain style, they are difficult varieties to sell through the trade and I would only recommend planting them if the vineyard proposed to sell these wines mainly from the farm-gate. The same advice goes for Optima and Siegerrebe. On a good site I can see that one might test the water with Pinot blanc, Pinot gris (Ruländer) and possibly Albariño (called Alvarinho in Portugal) and I have a soft spot for Auxerrois, Gutenborner and Regner, all varieties that have done well in the past and from which very good wines can be made. Except in certain circumstances (in an organic vineyard perhaps or in a vineyard in a less-favourable part of the UK) I cannot see much point of planting any of the newer varieties such as Orion, Phoenix, and Solaris, as I don't believe that their wine quality has yet been shown to be high enough.

As for other varieties, there are precious few that will make money. There are some growers who believe that Riesling and Sauvignon blanc can be grown in the UK – except in very exceptional vintages I disagree – and whilst there are plenty of new varieties coming along, none have yet shown themselves to be better than the varieties already mentioned. Varieties such as Faberrebe, Huxelrebe, Kerner, Kernling, Scheurebe, and Würzer have had their day and I cannot recommend that they be planted anymore.

**Still rosé wines**

For still rosé wines, which can be very successful in the UK and which I wish most growers currently striving to make red would make instead, Pinot noir (and maybe Pinot noir Précoce) is by far the best variety and has the advantage that in poorer years it can go into sparkling wine and in really ripe years you can attempt a red. Rosés made from other red varieties, or from blends of white and red varieties can also be successful, but none to my mind have the class to match Pinot noir. Again, as with red wines, varietal naming of rosés is not so important and a multi-variety rosé can work well.

I would avoid the bulk of the wine being made from aromatic varieties – Bacchus, Müller-Thurgau, Schönburger, Ortega, Siegerrebe – and go for a more neutral variety such as Seyval blanc, Reichensteiner, maybe even Madeleine x Angevine 7672, or Pinot blanc if your site will ripen it, and colour it with one (or more) of the better reds.

| Red vine varieties | 2013 Ha |
|---|---|
| Rondo | 47.4 |
| Regent | 24.3 |
| Pinot noir Précoce | 20.2 |
| Dornfelder | 19.2 |
| Triomphe | 14.7 |
| Acolon | 6.9 |
| Dunkelfelder | 2.8 |
| Léon Millot | 2.6 |
| Merlot | 2.1 |
| Zweigeltrebe | 1.7 |
| Cabernet Sauvignon | 1.5 |
| Gamay noir | 1.2 |
| Miscelaneous red varieties | 3.7 |
| Total Red varieties | 148.2 |
| Note: The above does not include Pinot noir or Meunier | |
| Source: Wine Standards Branch of the FSA 2013 | |

### Still red wines

For still red wines – if REAL quality is the aim – the choice is limited. I rarely taste a UK red wine that I like and very rarely taste one which can be said to be good value. In really ripe vintages, certain clones of Pinot noir can be ripened well and, if you ignore price, the wines from them can be recommended. Some of the large number of the UK's Pinot noir growers are learning about their sites and are learning that with crop reduction and good canopy management, really ripe Pinot noir can be harvested in some vintages and turned into good wines, but they are few and far between. My advice would be to treat this as a bonus in really ripe vintages and not base your whole business plan on producing red wine from Pinot noir. As for other red varieties, the next most widely planted four (ignoring Meunier) are Rondo, Regent, Pinot noir Précoce and Dornfelder which together in 2013 account for 7.4 per cent of the total planted area. Whether any of them are really worth planting for red wine is open to question. If you have a vineyard open to the public and intend to major on farm-gate sales, then a red wine made from a blend of Dornfelder, Regent and Rondo is probably about as good as it gets. Red wines are not quite so dependent on a variety name to sell them – there are plenty of wine drinkers wouldn't know which vine varieties went into Beaujolais, Chianti, Claret, or Rioja, – so a multi-variety red blend is not a problem in this respect. Of the other sixteen red varieties being grown in the UK (some in tunnels, so the list for outdoor vines is actually more like fourteen) I wouldn't advise planting any of them, again, unless your vineyard is organic or in a less-favourable part of the UK. The old hybrids Cascade, Léon Millot,

Maréchal Foch, and Triomphe have definitely had their day and I have never tasted a UK wine made from Acolon that I liked. Dunkelfelder might have its place if you wanted to add some colour to a blend, but not as a major variety. Of the other reds, I cannot see any that offer any advantages at the moment, although the new variety Cabernet Dorsa might surprise us all

## Vine varieties for less favourable sites

For growers determined to plant in less than favourable sites (sites I term 'challenging') which may be at altitudes over 150 m above sea level, with poor shelter to prevailing winds, or just in a less-proven and/or less favourable part of the UK, your choice of varieties must be made with these disadvantages in mind. There is no doubt that one of the reasons for the survival of Seyval blanc in the top five of UK varieties for over fifty years is its ability to produce viable crops in years in which other varieties fail, its relatively good disease resistance and its ability to hang on and ripen fruit in conditions that would severely test other varieties. Reichensteiner likewise, whilst not as disease resistant as Seyval blanc, has also survived, mainly because in good years its higher than average crops compensate for poor years, and its grapes usually get quite high sugars and the neutral wine is adaptable and can be blended into both still and sparkling wines.

In the relatively new (and few) vineyards planted in the more northerly parts of the UK, the selection of varieties is divided into three different sections: the earlier ripening white *vinifera* varieties; old hybrids; and new interspecific crosses. The earlier ripening varieties are chosen because they (a) ripen early and therefore stand a chance of ripening on a later site and (b) tend to have lower acidity levels which make them more likely to achieve physiological ripeness.

The most widely planted are: Ortega, Madeleine x Angevine 7672, Reichensteiner, Schönburger and Siegerrebe. Of the older hybrids, chosen because they tend to be resistant to diseases and thus more likely to produce and retain a crop in difficult circumstances, Seyval blanc is of course a firm favourite, but so also are the old red hybrids Cascade, Léon Millot, Maréchal Foch, and Triomphe. It is worth noting that these old hybrids i.e. not Seyval, have long ago been weeded out of southern vineyards on the grounds of poor wine quality.

Of the newer interspecific crosses, the whites, Orion, Phoenix and Solaris and the reds, Regent and Rondo seem popular, again their better (although far from perfect) disease resistance makes them an obvious choice. These last five are now planted on slightly over 122-ha (301-acres), accounting for 8.1 per cent of the UK's planted area. The problem with almost all of these varieties is that the wine quality, even in well-sited, southern vineyards, would be considered to be behind that of say Bacchus and the Champagne varieties and if you add on to that the additional problems caused by growing vines on less-favourable sites, the wine quality is bound to suffer. Some of the newer vine varieties listed in the next paragraph might also be of interest, although many of them are probably too late for late sites.

*Breaky Bottom, Lewes, East Sussex, in the snow*

## Newer vine varieties

When I started growing vines at Tenterden in 1977, the options for 'new' varieties were fairly limited. Although I stuck with Müller-Thurgau and Seyval blanc as my two main commercial varieties (along with most of the other growers at the time), I also planted 1,250 Reichensteiner vines and the same number of Gutenborner, then a variety only being grown by one other UK grower (Carr Taylor) but which had been recommended to me by Geisenheim's Professor Kiefer who had been helping with the establishment of the nearby vineyards at Lamberhurst. These four varieties made up the bulk of the 2-ha (5-acres) I planted. My almost two years at Geisenheim had not only been spent in learning how to grow grapes and the rudiments of winemaking, but I had also spent a considerable time researching into vine varieties in an attempt to discover if there were any that were then unplanted in the UK, but which might be suitable. I remember very well going to see Professor Becker one afternoon with a list of thirteen varieties I thought of as 'possibles' for the UK, to ask his advice. He more or less grabbed the list and said 'come back on Thursday' which I took to be a signal that he was too busy to discuss the topic, but might have time later in the week. I duly turned up on Thursday to find that his assistant, Ernst Abel (who had been over to Lamberhurst to help make their maiden vintage, the 1976), had been instructed to get a bottle of wine made from every one of the varieties that I had listed (the research cellar made trial batches of wine from hundreds of varieties each year) and had them lined up in the cellar for me to taste! The result of this was that I planted one hundred vines each of Ortega, Schönburger, and Rabaner, plus twenty-five vines each of Ehrenfelser, Huxelrebe, Kerner, Optima, Siegerrebe and a Riesling x Sylvaner cross called Gm 4-46. One of the varieties I had on my list and tried at the tasting was Bacchus and I noted on my tasting notes (which I still have, dated 15 Nov 1976) 'Acid too high. Wine not good if under 75°OE' and was advised not to plant it! In my trial plot I also planted a range of other varieties: Auxerrois, Black Hamburgh, Chasselas Rosa, Dunkelfelder, Gewürztraminer, Gold Riesling, Léon Millot, Meunier, Pinot blanc, Pinot gris,

and Pinot noir. It was an ambitious list, but I thought that I would try and create a mini-research station of my own.

Today, if faced with the same task, to select some new, untried varieties for planting in the UK, it would be considerably harder to choose a reasonable number, given the huge range of different varieties now available. Most of the work on new varieties has been directed towards disease resistance and in breeding new varieties which require no pesticides, even in high disease pressure regions. Gene mapping of vines has allowed researchers to identify the genes responsible for conferring resistance to the two greatest vine diseases, Powdery and Downy Mildew. The gene conferring resistance for Powdery is called RUN-1, after 'resistance to *Uncinula necator*', and to Downy, RPV-1 after 'resistance to *Plasmopara viticola*'. These genes have been isolated from the wild American vine species *Muscadinia rotundifolia*, which is native to the south-eastern part of the USA and almost totally resistant to these two diseases. By making crosses over several generations, the RUN-1 and RPV-1 genes can be locked into a new variety, conferring resistance. The other major disease, *Botrytis*, is impossible to control in this manner as it is a disease that grows on dying and dead tissue and there is no known resistant gene. The defense against this disease is to change the bunch architecture through selective breeding so that bunches are looser and berries further apart. This will allow for better air circulation and less humidity, both of which will lessen the incidence of *Botrytis*. In *Les cépages résistants*, the 2011 book from the ICV Group (*Institute Coopératif du Vin*), there are fifty-six interspecific crosses which are considered to be worthy of a full write up and a total of almost 400 described in table form. And, if you look in the *Taschenbuch der Rebsorten, PIWI Rebsorten,* and *Wine Grapes,* you can certainly find plenty more, as yet, untried varieties that might suit UK conditions.

In order to suggest new varieties for the UK, we have to get over the age-old problem which all new variety recommendations suffer from: none of them has been bred specifically for UK climatic conditions and very few have been tested in the UK. We have therefore, to sift through the claims made for each variety and decide for ourselves how they relate to UK problems. Disease resistance is obviously a desirable trait, but I don't feel that it should be the deciding factor. If you had a choice between a variety that cropped well, produced ripe grapes with moderate acidity that made good wine, yet required a modest spray programme, compared to say a variety that cropped well, did not require spraying at all, but whose wine was of a lower quality, which would you choose? For me, the first attribute for a variety to be preferred over the ones we currently grow is the quality of its wine. A reasonable yield is very welcome, disease resistance is admirable, but without wine of sufficient quality to lift it over the problems associated with introducing a new variety to the wine trade and the wine buying public, the variety is going to struggle.

This problem is not a new one. Varieties already mentioned such as Faberrebe, Kerner, Kernling, and Würzer, plus others such as Findling and Optima have all been tried in the UK, found lacking and are slowly being grubbed. The new varieties that have found favour in UK vineyards – Acolon, Orion, Phoenix, Regent, Rondo, and Solaris – which together are planted on 129.1-ha (319-acres) – are, with the exception of Acolon – all modern interspecific crosses. The reds, Acolon, Regent and Rondo, are successful (or at least, have been quite widely planted) because they are relatively disease resistant and produce wines with plenty of colour. If you are hell-bent on producing red wine in a cool climate, then these are as good varieties as you can find (at the moment anyway) and better than the old hybrids Cascade, Léon Millot, Maréchal Foch and Triomphe. The others, all whites, have mainly been planted in vineyards in the more climatically challenged areas of the UK, again because of their resistance to disease and their suitability for cooler climates.

For the future, there are several next-generation interspecific crosses which are already on trial in the UK. Several of them are from the breeding programme developed by a private Swiss vine breeder, Valentin Blattner, who is working with German, French and Spanish vinegrowers to develop ultra-resistant varieties which require no pesticide applications at all. Much of the breeding work Blattner carries out takes place in Thailand where the climate allows two harvests a year, thus accelerating the development of new varieties. In early September 2013 I visited his '20:20' vineyard – 'twenty hours work a year and twenty tonnes a hectare' – near Bezier in the south of France which belongs to Domaine La Colombette (www.lacolombette.fr). This vineyard receives no pesticide applications, is machine pruned, irrigated with sub-soil irrigation, machine harvested and whilst perhaps not quite 20-tonnes per hectare, crops very well and produces very acceptable wine. Varieties from Blattner which are either already on trial in the UK or being considered are:

- Cabernet blanc – a 1991 white, Cabernet Sauvignon x unknown crossing with Sauvignon blanc characters. Ripens after Pinot blanc, so relatively late in the UK. Has both small and large berries.
- VB Cal. 6-04 – a 1991 white, (Sauvignon blanc x Riesling) x unknown crossing with loose bunches which ripens 'ten days before Riesling' in Germany. Good resistance against diseases.
- VB 32-7 – a 1998 white, Cabernet Sauvignon x unknown crossing with Sauvignon blanc characters. Ripens mid-season in Germany, so probably late in the UK.
- Cabernet Jura – a 1991 red, Cabernet Sauvignon x unknown crossing with deep red wine. Ripens 'early to mid-season' in Germany, so probably towards the end of the season in the UK.
- VB 91-26-29 – another 1991 red, Cabernet Sauvignon x unknown crossing with deep red wine, similar to Cabernet Jura.
- Réselle – a white, Bacchus x Seyval blanc crossing which produces a light, fruity wine. Could be good in the UK for blending with a spicy variety.

Varieties from German vine breeding institutes already on trial in the UK include:
- Bolero – a 1982 red, Gm 6427-5 x Chancellor crossing from Geisenheim crossing produced in Prof. Becker's era, which is said to ripen early and has lowish acidity. Gm 6427-5 is Rotberger x Reichensteiner.
- Cabernet Dorsa – a 1971 red, Dornfelder x Cabernet Sauvignon crossing (therefore a *vinifera*) from Weinsberg. I fear this might be too late for the UK, but time will tell. In Germany there were 252-ha (623-acres) in 2012.
- Muscaris – a 1987 white, Solaris x Muskateller crossing from Freiburg which ripens around the same time as Pinot noir. Has lowish acidity and is said to produce very spicy wine. Solaris (see later in this chapter) is a complex *Amurensis* crossing.
- Souvignier gris – a 1983 white, Cabernet Sauvignon x Bronner crossing (Bronner is a *Vitis amurensis* crossing) from Freiburg with dark pink grapes and produces 'lightly fruity' wine.
- Villaris – a 1984 white, Sirius x Villard blanc crossing from Geilweilerhof, said to ripen at the same time as Müller-Thurgau and produce similar wine.

As for other varieties that might succeed in the UK, the field is wide open. When I look at the other major cold-climate European winegrowing regions – Belgium, Denmark, Estonia, Germany's Baltic region, Holland, Latvia, Poland and Sweden – who between them have over 1,000-ha (2,500-acres) of vines – varieties such as Bianca, Cabernet Cortis, Garanoir, Gamaret, Helios, Hibernal, Johanniter and Merzling appear quite often. The truth, of course, is that there are far too many new varieties available for any private grower to carry out any meaningful trials. It would be good if an institution (Plumpton College or East Malling Research perhaps?) could have done some investigation into what might be successful and plant a small test-bed of possible varieties for the future, but I guess that is just wishful thinking.

Of course, whether the UK actually needs many new varieties is open to question. Perhaps we ought to concentrate on getting better at growing the ones we already have first?

## Vine variety descriptions A-Z

| Variety | Ha 2013 | % 2013 | Variety | Ha 2013 | % 2013 |
|---|---|---|---|---|---|
| Acolon | 6.88 | 0.46% | Phoenix | 23.59 | 1.57% |
| Auxerrois | 9.78 | 0.65% | Pinot blanc | 25.36 | 1.69% |
| Bacchus | 130.79 | 8.70% | Pinot gris | 15.17 | 1.01% |
| Chardonnay | 326.99 | 21.75% | Pinot noir | 305.22 | 20.30% |
| Dornfelder | 19.21 | 1.28% | Pinot noir Précoce | 20.24 | 1.35% |
| Dunkelfelder | 2.76 | 0.18% | Regent | 24.28 | 1.61% |
| Faberrebe | 4.31 | 0.29% | Regner | 4.50 | 0.30% |
| Huxelrebe | 17.59 | 1.17% | Reichensteiner | 80.49 | 5.35% |
| Kerner | 5.92 | 0.39% | Riesling | 3.03 | 0.20% |
| Kernling | 4.92 | 0.33% | Rondo | 47.39 | 3.15% |
| Léon Millot | 2.60 | 0.17% | Sauvignon blanc | 4.64 | 0.31% |
| Madeleine x Angevine 7672 | 45.87 | 3.05% | Schönburger | 34.54 | 2.30% |
| Merlot | 2.05 | 0.14% | Seyval blanc | 92.05 | 6.12% |
| Meunier | 68.55 | 4.56% | Siegerrebe | 14.28 | 0.95% |
| Müller-Thurgau | 55.99 | 3.72% | Solaris | 16.14 | 1.07% |
| Orion | 10.82 | 0.72% | Triomphe | 14.67 | 0.98% |
| Ortega | 34.53 | 2.30% | Würzer | 4.54 | 0.30% |

The thirty-four varieties listed above are those grown in the UK (2013) on an area of 2 ha or more. Together they amount to 1,480-ha which is 98.5 per cent of Vine Variety data total of 1,503-ha.

**Notes to variety descriptions:**

• **Synonyms:** In general I have used French variety names wherever possible as these are the names most likely to be found on bottles of UK wine and in vineyard literature. Thus you will find references to Pinot rather than Burgunder or Spätburgunder, Meunier rather than Schwarzriesling or Müllerrebe, Pinot gris rather than Pinot Grigio, Ruländer, or Grauburgunder and Pinot noir Précoce rather than Blauer Früburgunder.

• **Madeleine x Angevine 7672:** I have used the name Madeleine x Angevine 7672 and the abbreviation MA in the following pages, even though this name is not strictly correct. Please refer to the entry on this variety for the reasons why.

• **Meunier:** I have used Meunier, the correct name for the variety often called Pinot Meunier or even Wrotham Pinot.

• **Müller-Thurgau:** When referring to Müller-Thurgau in the individual variety descriptions I have used the abbreviation MT.

• **Sylvaner:** I have kept to the old spelling of Sylvaner when referring to both 'Madeleine x Sylvaner III 28/51' and 'Riesling Sylvaner' (Müller-Thurgau or Rivaner) in preference to the modern German spelling 'Silvaner', except where this variety was one of the parents of another variety. The Swiss (and others) continue to use the spelling Sylvaner.

• **German vine-breeding establishments:** References are made in the variety descriptions of the following vine-breeding establishments, all of them in Germany:
Alzey, Rheinpfalz
Freiburg, Baden-Württemberg
Geilweilerhof , Rheinpfalz
Geisenheim, Rheingau
Oppenheim, Rheinhessen
Weinsberg, Baden-Württemberg
Würzburg, Bayern

• **Sugar and acid levels:** Sugar levels are usually given in per cent potential alcohol. Most UK growers and winemakers use degrees Oechsle (°OE). As in almost all other countries – France and French-influenced regions being the annoying exception, where levels in sulphuric acid are used – total acid levels in the UK are expressed in grams per litre of acidity as tartaric. To convert, multiply tartaric by 0.66 or multiply sulphuric by 1.52.

## Acolon

Type: *Vinifera*
Colour: Red
Area in the UK: 6.9-ha (17.0-acres), 0.5 per cent of the planted area in 2013
Origin: Limberger x Dornfelder

Acolon is newish German *vinifera* cross bred in 1971 at Weinsberg by Bernd Hill and its parents – Blauer Limberger (known also as Blaufränkisch in Austria) and Dornfelder – are both staples of German red wine production. Dornfelder itself is Helfensteiner (Blauer Frühburgunder x Black Hamburg) crossed with Heroldrebe (Portugieser x Limberger), so its antecedents are impeccable. In Germany, plantings have grown from its release in 2000 to a total of 428-ha by 2005, but have then risen more slowly to 482-ha in 2012. In Germany it is planted as it is a deep coloured variety that adds colour to Dornfelder wines of which there are plenty – there are 8,197-ha of Dornfelder in Germany – with higher sugars and a slightly lower yield.

In the UK, it has been planted for only a short time, New Hall Vineyards being the first to plant, and even now it is only found in around twelve vineyards, including several in the more northerly regions. The area planted has risen slowly from 4.6-ha in 2009 to 6.9-ha in 2013, but that is hardly a vote of confidence.

As to whether it is a good variety for the UK – who can tell? To date there have been very few single-variety wines made from Acolon. My guess is that it will not take over from the more mainstream reds and as (if?) the climate continues to improve, Pinot noir, with its heritage, class and consumer acceptability, will continue to be the red variety of choice.

## Auxerrois

Synonym: Pinot Auxerrois
Type: *Vinifera*
Colour: White
Area in the UK: 9.8-ha (24.2-acres), 0.7 per cent of the planted area in 2013
Origin: Original variety

Auxerrois, an ancient variety, related to Chardonnay and Pinot blanc, is widely grown in Alsace where it is usually blended into *Edelzwicker* (although in Alsace it can also be labelled as Chardonnay or Pinot blanc) or used for sparkling wine. It can also be found in Burgundy and Luxembourg in the Old World and Canada, New Zealand and the USA in the New World. Geisenheim has produced some more productive clones and in 2008, 185-ha were being grown in Germany. It was included on the original list of 'Recommended' varieties for the UK submitted to the EU in 1973, even though it was not then widely grown and had not been suggested by the EVA.

Auxerrois is a variety of moderate vigour, fairly resistant to *Botrytis* and ripens its wood well. It is quite a late variety, ripening in the UK after MT but before Seyval blanc. As a neutral Pinot blanc/Chardonnay style variety which would be useful for barrel ageing or for sparkling wine base, it should be more widely planted in the UK – perhaps on the more challenging sites – as it has lower acid levels than other similar varieties. It is a steady yielding variety and it is a pity that it appears to have fallen out of favour in the UK, but I guess that if you can ripen Chardonnay, why would you want to grow Auxerrois? There were 9-ha in 2009 and 9.8-ha in 2013, so it is barely expanding. One to watch and well worth a trial.

## Bacchus

Type: *Vinifera*
Colour: White
Area in UK: 130.8-ha (323.2-acres), 8.7 per cent of the planted area in 2013
Origin: (Silvaner x Riesling) x Müller-Thurgau

Bacchus, a crossing made by Peter Morio and Prof. Husfeld at Geilweilerhof in 1933, was first registered in 1972 and was known in the Rheinpfalz as the 'Early Scheurebe'. Its parentage is the same as Optima. Bacchus is the second most popular white *neuzüchtung* (new-crossing) in Germany (after Kerner) and in 2012 there were 1,841-ha, down slightly from the 2008 area of 2,015-ha, but down considerably from the 1990 area of 3,500-ha. It first appeared in the UK in the Wye College vineyard[6] in 1973 and was upgraded to 'Recommended' in 1998. Bacchus, as a variety for the UK, is here to stay (unless it warms up another notch or two so that we can start growing *echt* Sauvignon blanc). The area under cultivation in the UK has risen from 76-ha in 1990, via 118.75-ha in 2009, to 130.8-ha in 2013 and is the third most widely planted variety. In terms of percentage of the UK vineyard area it has fallen slightly since 2009 from 9.8 per cent to 8.7 per cent. This must not be seen as a failure on the part of Bacchus, but rather a reflection of the rush into sparkling wine.

Bacchus is the best white variety being grown in the UK today for the production of still wines and it regularly wins many of the major prizes. In growth habit it is similar to MT, although perhaps not quite as vigorous, but just as prone to *Botrytis*. It appears to ripen readily in most years with 8–10 per cent natural alcohol achievable. Acids can be high and care needs to be taken that they are not too high in the bottle, especially with wine made from grapes harvested at lower sugar levels.

In the bottle, Bacchus falls into two camps: what one might term the *Sauvignon de Touraine* or pretend *Sancerre* camp, where the wine is light, fruity, with a modest spiciness, but of no great weight; and the full-on Marlborough Sauvignon style with luscious spicy, even catty, fruit with enough body and weight to carry the flavour. These tend to be the riper (higher natural sugar) examples and are best when they are bottled with perhaps a few grams of residual sweetness (as are many Marlborough wines). Chapel Down's *Bacchus Reserve* is often a fine example of this latter (and to me, more preferable), style. I like Bacchus as a variety, both to grow and to consume. With top Bacchus wines selling for £12-£15, this is a variety that can make money. The one *really* good thing about Bacchus is the name – none of your funny Teutonic names complete with umlauts and *burger* or *rebe* at the end – just a name everyone recognises and thinks has something to do with wine. Who was that Bacchus guy anyway, some sort of God?

## Chardonnay

Type: *Vinifera*
Colour: White
Area in the UK: 327.0-ha (808.0-acres), 21.7 per cent of the planted area in 2013
Origin: Original variety

With its origins lost in the mists of viticultural time, Chardonnay is now found in virtually every grapegrowing region in the world, from the hottest parts of Australia, South Africa and California to the coolest of all growing regions, the UK. With it being the dominant (often the only) variety in white wines from Burgundy and of course Champagne, it is not surprising that early vineyard owners in Britain were seduced into thinking that it would do well here. Brock had it in his collection at Oxted, but could never get it to ripen properly. Salisbury-Jones planted it at Hambledon in the late 1950s and had the same problems: excessively high acid levels and low natural sugars. Ian and Andrew Paget at Chilsdown planted Chardonnay and I seem to recall one year (1981?) when the acidity (in grams per litre as tartaric) was higher than the degrees Oechsle! Ouch. Extreme unripeness was a common finding among those early growers who persevered with it, although most decided to give up and removed the offending variety. Only in really hot years would it produce anything like ripe grapes and tolerable wine.

In the late 1980s, some growers – New Hall, Surrenden and Nyetimber – started to plant Chardonnay for the production of bottle-fermented sparkling wines using better clones, ones perhaps more suited to our climate. In the 2001 edition of this book I wrote: '*through a combination of good site selection and traditional training systems (aided by a degree of global warming) they have started to produce some interesting results. While acids are still high at harvest (15 g/l is not uncommon) the combination of a full malolactic fermentation and the traditional secondary bottle fermentation, renders them manageable'*. Well, the 'interesting results' turned out to be more than interesting and since then some extremely good wines, almost all sparkling, and very occasionally (2003, 2009 and 2011 come to mind) some respectable still wines, have been produced. High acids are a problem and growers, especially those with less than perfect sites, need to make sure they select the right clones and rootstocks, plus prune and canopy manage, to get acids down. Chardonnay plantings have gone from 7.0-ha in 1988, via 33.5-ha in 2002 and 119.6-ha in 2007 to 327.0-ha in 2013, making it the UK's most widely planted variety and accounting for almost 22 per cent of the planted area. I cannot see this rate of expansion slackening off given the quality of the sparkling (and occasionally still) wines being produced.

As a variety for the UK, Chardonnay appears to be more and more at home. Viticulturally it is no more demanding to grow than most varieties. It buds up quite early and in frost prone sites this can be a problem. It is susceptible to Powdery and Downy Mildew and *Botrytis* and vines almost always need spraying in their year of planting. Until it can be demonstrated otherwise, simple *Guyot* single or two-cane pruning appears to work well. While we might like to have them, we do not get the very high yields common in Champagne (15–20 tonnes-ha is not uncommon), so I don't think Cordon pruning is required. It benefits from an open canopy and deleafing both after flowering and pre-*véraison*. It will also get late-season Downy Mildew, which will affect the ripening process, so protection needs to be kept going until the bitter end.

Chardonnay ripens late and is usually not harvested until the third or even fourth week of October. In a very late year – such as 2013 – it was still being picked on 20 November which must be the latest UK harvesting date ever. Of course, 'late' is subjective and having rarely enjoyed sharing Guy Fawkes night with my children in the late 1970s and 1980s as I was always pressing Seyval blanc, today's Chardonnay growers shouldn't complain too much. Sugar levels are usually in the 8–10 per cent region – ideal for sparkling wine – although in cool years and late sites 7-8 per cent is quite common. Acid levels are typically 12-15 g/l, although in cool years and late sites, 16-17 g/l is quite common and even higher not unheard of. In 2013, some growers harvested Chardonnay at very low sugars and high acids and one has to wonder what sort of wines these grapes will make. However, I suspect that with some de-acidification, malolactic fermentation (assuming you can get it started), blending with lower acid varieties, an extended *sur latte* ageing and an appropriate dosage, the effect will be minimal. However, I should not want to harvest grapes at this level of acidity every year.

For UK sparkling wines, Chardonnay is an indispensable component and no serious grower can be without it. Ridgeview produce some great Chardonnay wines and for me, their 100 per cent Chardonnay *Grosvenor Blanc de Blancs* is very often their best wine. Their 2000 and 2001 magnums of this wine I believe are absolutely magnificent and I have several still *sur latte* awaiting a suitable occasion to drink them. Ridgeview's 2006 *Grosvenor Blanc de Blancs* will go down I am sure as one of their best wines and its winning of the Decanter World Wine Awards 'International Sparkling Wine Trophy' (beating four very prestigious Champagnes in the process) was a real affirmation of the quality of UK sparkling wines. There are today many other UK growers making good to very good *blanc de blancs* sparkling wines and this can only enhance its reputation as a must-have variety.

For the production of still wines, Chardonnay has shown that with a suitable site, correct canopy management and, most importantly, the right level of crop, very good wines can be produced in the UK. I have already mentioned *Gusbourne Estate's 2011 Guinevere Chardonnay* and *Chapel Down's 2011 Kit's Coty Chardonnay*, two still wines which I believe are pointers to the future of this variety. If growers can make still wines that sell at the same sort of prices as middling Chablis and white Burgundy, then we will see even more Chardonnay planted in years and decades to come. For still wines, I regard clones 75, 76, 95 and 548 as suitable for the UK. Clones 121 and 131 have also been recommended for still wine, but acids are said to be higher. However, given that in France alone, thirty-one clones of Chardonnay are registered for use and in other countries there are tens of dozens more (some of them duplicates admittedly), I am sure there are other clones suitable for UK vineyards yet to be trialled and proved.

The combination of a classic name, its Champagne heritage and many excellent sparkling (and a few still) wines, have made Chardonnay indispensable for any UK vineyard with pretensions to seriousness. I am not convinced that it suits all the sites it has been planted on in the last ten years, and some growers may yet struggle to ripen it and/or find that their wines need years (5+) in the bottle to come round – not a recipe that I think will guarantee financial success.

**Note:** See the separate section towards the end of this chapter on: *Clones of Chardonnay, Pinot noir and Meunier for sparkling wine*

## Dornfelder

Type: *Vinifera*
Colour: Red
Area in the UK: 19.2 ha (47.5-acres), 1.30 per cent of the planted area in 2013
Origin: Helfensteiner x Heroldrebe

Dornfelder is one of the new(ish) wave of German crossings, bred at Weinsberg in the heart of Germany's red wine producing region, Württemberg. Here, the traditional varieties – Trollinger (Black Hamburg) and Limberger – suffer from a lack of colour and substance and Dornfelder was bred to produce more of both. The crossing was made in 1955 by August Herold and released to growers in 1980. Dornfelder's parents are two other Weinsberg varieties: Helfensteiner (which is Blauer Frühburgunder x Black Hamburg) and Heroldrebe (which is Portugieser x Limberger). Now the most widely grown 'new variety' in Germany, its 8,197-ha (2012) occupy 22 per cent of their red vine area and 8 per cent of their total vine area. It is capable of producing some good wines, albeit in a spicy Rhône style, rather than a classic Bordeaux style, although some German examples can be fairly light and insubstantial, probably due in part to high yields: 120-150 hl-ha is not unknown.

Dornfelder first appeared in the UK in the late 1980s and is able to produce tolerable red wines, especially in blends with other varieties. It is no more difficult to grow than other *vinifera* varieties and in good years can produce quite heavy crops. Very few 100 per cent Dornfelder wines have been produced in the UK and it is mainly blended. Plantings have only expanded by 1-ha since 2009, an indication of its lack of popularity amongst growers and I suspect that it is due for a slow lingering death. For true reds, Regent and Rondo are preferred. My advice: no need to rip it out, but think twice before planting any more.

## Dunkelfelder

Type: *Vinifera*
Colour: Red
Area in the UK: 2.8-ha (6.8-acres), 0.2 per cent of the planted area in 2013
Origin: Crossing of unknown parents

Dunkelfelder is a crossing made by Gustav Adolf Frölich in Edenkoben in the Rheinpfalz in the early 1900s and its exact parentage is unknown. It was discovered in the Geisenheim vine collection in the 1930s and clonally selected in the 1970s. It was officially classified for wine production in Germany in 1980 and in 2012 there were 314-ha, down from 352-ha in 2008. Few varietal wines are made from it in Germany and it is primarily used as *deckwein* (colouring wine).

Dunkelfelder first appeared in the UK in mid-1980s (I believe I was the first grower to plant it) and in 1990 there were 3.5-ha. Today it is down to 2.8-ha which probably sums up its attractiveness to UK growers: small and falling. Viticulturally it is undemanding with fairly low vigour, but does not usually run to large crops. It needs regular spraying and *Botrytis* can be a problem. It ripens very early and is susceptible to bird and wasp attack. However, it is the best *teinturier* variety grown in the UK and can produce massive colour. On its own, the wine is fairly neutral with low acidity and is best blended with other red varieties. As part of a red blend it is fine, but it is never likely to be anything else. Perhaps a variety that red and rosé winemakers should have a few rows of to liven up the colour of their wines.

## Faberrebe

Type: *Vinifera*
Colour: White
Area in the UK: 4.3-ha (10.7-acres), 0.3 per cent of the UK planted area in 2013
Origin: Pinot blanc x Müller-Thurgau

Faberrebe (often incorrectly called Faber) is a crossing made by Georg Scheu at Alzey in 1929. It is valued in Germany for its high sugars and crisp fruity acidity and is used for blending with MT, although the area under cultivation has fallen quite quickly: 1998 1,657-ha, 2008 587-ha, 2012, 453-ha.

In the UK it is down from its peak of 10.3-ha in 1990 to 4.3-ha in 2013 and has probably had its day. It's a late variety, prone to high acids and the wine is OK, but nothing special. Bacchus makes better wines, is easier to grow, far easier to ripen and has a more user-friendly name. My advice: leave it there if you have it, but don't plant any more.

## Huxelrebe

Type: *Vinifera*
Colour: White
Area in the UK: 17.6-ha (43.5-acres), 1.2 per cent of the planted area in 2013
Origin: Chasselas x Courtillier Musqué

Huxelrebe is another Georg Scheu crossing (Alzey 1927) and named after Fritz Huxel, a grower from near Worms who first recognised its potential. Courtillier Musqué (also known as Muscat Précoce de Saumur) is a 'selfling', i.e. self-pollinated seedling of Pinot noir Précoce. In Germany (635-ha in 2008 and 548-ha in 2012), it is capable of producing very large yields of grapes (or as the Germans say *'trägt wie ein Esel'* – 'carries like a donkey'), with high natural sugars.

Huxel – as it is usually called – was first introduced to the UK via the Wye College vineyard in 1972 and on account of its higher yielding ability was quite widely planted. In 1990 there were 43.9-ha, but since then the area has fallen and is today down to 17.6-ha, although this has barely changed since 2009.

Huxel can be extremely vigorous, with great fat canes and very large leaves and is probably best grown on a spur pruned system (GDC) where vigour can, to a certain extent, be tamed. Bunches are very large and contain an unusually high number of seedless grapes which ripen readily and achieve very high natural sugars, although loved by wasps. It undoubtedly benefits from thinning and pre-harvest deleafing as it suffers badly from *Botrytis*. When really ripe, the wine can be very fruity with a pronounced Sauvignon blanc character, although acid levels can be high and to obtain the best wines, the grapes must be allowed to fully ripen. Unripe examples can be rather too herbaceous and catty and can be detected even when disguised in a blend. It has been used for a few late-harvest sweet wines, but only when *Botrytis* has got the better of it. In 2001 I wrote: *a variety that is probably worth persevering with on account of its good quality wine & higher than average yields. With a new generation of anti-Botrytis fungicides now available, will Huxelrebe become more viable to grow?* Well, twelve years on, I can answer the question: no. It is still a pushy monster in the vineyard, overcropping when it feels like it and suffering from wasps and rot in equal measure. Its falling area sums up its attractiveness to UK growers and I cannot see it lasting that much longer and no one is planting it now.[7]

## Kerner

Type: *Vinifera*
Colour: White
Area in the UK: 5.9-ha (14.6-acres), 0.4 per cent of the planted area in 2013
Origin: Trollinger (Black Hamburg) x Riesling

Kerner is a crossing made in 1929 by August Herold at Weinsberg. It is popular in Germany where, over Riesling, it has several advantages: it ripens more easily, has a lower acidity and better frost resistance, yet still retains the wine quality of the noblest of its parents, Riesling. It is Germany's sixth most planted white variety (3,712-hectares in 2008, 3,131-ha in 2012) and, after Dornfelder, the second most popular of the 'new crosses'. It is also popular with growers in Italy's Alto Adige region and the wines from there can often be very good.

Kerner first appeared in the UK in the Wye College vineyard in the mid-1970s and was widely promoted as a quality variety, although just why I am still not sure. It was always extremely vigorous with great big, dark green, leaves and lots of side-shoots. Acids were always high and the wines, which seldom did well in tastings, were always fairly hard and uncompromising. With time, some of them came round, but who wants to wait for a Kerner to come round? The area has dropped from 21.4-ha in 1990 to under 6-ha today – a fair measure of its popularity. Another one for the history books and if I had any I would pull it up.

## Kernling

Type: *Vinifera*
Colour: White
Area in the UK: 4.9-ha (12.2-acres), 0.3 per cent of the planted area in 2013
Origin: Mutation from Kerner

Kernling is a mutation from Kerner selected by Ludwig Hochdörfer from the Pfalz, Germany and first registered in 1974. It is said to be similar to Kerner, but without the excessive side-shoots that make Kerner difficult to grow. It was introduced into the UK in the late 1980s as an alternative to Kerner and promoted quite strongly in the West of the UK by certain viticultural consultants in that region. However, despite being planted on quite a large area in 1990 (21.4-ha), very few wines of note have ever been produced and its high acidity and unsympathetic wine did not find favour with wine drinkers. Today it is down to 4.9-ha and, I predict, destined for the dustbin.

## Léon Millot

Type: Hybrid
Colour: Red
Area in the UK: 2.6-ha (6.4-acres), 0.2 per cent of the planted area in 2013
Origin: *Riparia-Rupestris 101-14* x Goldriesling

Léon Millot is an old French-American hybrid bred by Eugène Kuhlmann (1858–1932) in the late 1890s and popular at one time in France. It can still be found in many vineyards in the United States. Its father is the rootstock variety 101-14 *Millardet et De Grasset* and its mother Goldriesling, which is Riesling x Courtillier musqué. The varieties Maréchal Foch and Lucie Kuhlmann have the same parentage. Originally known as Kuhlmann 194.2.

Introduced into the UK by Brock at Oxted in the early 1950s, it was one of the first red varieties to be grown commercially. It is, like many red hybrids, very vigorous and canopies can be extremely dense, although it is very resistant to disease and can be grown with minimal spraying. The bunches are small, as are the grapes on them, and yields are never that high. Colour is good – the skin, flesh and juice are all red – and the variety is useful for adding colour to a blend of different red varieties or for a rosé with other white varieties. Its flavour, while not 'foxy', does have a certain non-*vinifera* element which must be counted against it.

In 1990 there were 2.0-ha and today (2013) 2.6-ha. For the UK, it has certainly now been superseded by better red varieties and no one is planting it, although it might still have a future in organic vineyards or on more challenging sites. There is undoubtedly some clonal variance in the variety and anyone considering planting it would do well to look into this aspect before planting.

## Madeleine x Angevine 7672

Type: *Vinifera*
Colour: White
Area in the UK: 45.9-ha (113.4-acres), 3.1 per cent of the planted area in 2013
Origin: Freely pollinated seedling of Madeleine Angevine.

The variety we loosely call 'Madeleine Angevine' is more properly called Madeleine x Angevine 7672 for reasons which I will explain. In 1957 Brock at Oxted was sent cuttings of several varieties by Dr Zimmerman from Alzey and one of them was labelled 'Sämling [seedling] 7672'. Just when this crossing was made is not known, although the timing would suggest that it was while Georg Scheu – responsible for varieties such as Huxelrebe, Faberrebe, Kanzler, Regner, Scheurebe, Septimer, Siegerrebe and Würzer – was the Alzey Institute's Director.

By 1960 Brock was able to report that it was: *giving large crops which ripen with Riesling Sylvaner* [MT]. *Considered to be a promising variety.* Not having been given the crossing details of Sämling 7672, Brock wrote to Zimmerman and asked for them. He was informed that it was a 'freely pollinated seedling of Madeleine Angevine'. When Brock started to sell cuttings of the variety (as he did with all promising varieties) he gave it the name Madeleine x Angevine 7672 and it was under this name that it was known for many years. As it became quite popular, the name on wine labels became shortened to simply 'Madeleine Angevine'. This was an unfortunate name as another variety already existed under this name. There is also another variety to cause further confusion called Madeleine Angevine Oberlin, a crossing between Madeleine Angevine and Bouquettraube.

The true Madeleine Angevine (also sometimes called Madeleine d'Angevine), is a female only table grape variety, for many decades said to be a crossing of Madeleine Royale[8] and Précoce de Malingre made by Pierre Vibert at the Moreau-Robert nurseries in Angers in 1857 (some reports say 1859), but described in *Wine Grapes* to be a crossing of a Chasselas-based table grape variety called Circé and Madeleine Royale. It is one of the earliest table grape varieties for open cultivation in France and named after St. Madeleine's Day (22 July), said to be the date on which it can be picked. Having only female flowers and being very early, it has been used by plant breeders in a number of crosses over the years. Morio and Husfeld used it for Forta and Noblessa and it is one grandparent of Reichensteiner. Scheu himself used it to produce Siegerrebe and interestingly, this variety, which at one time was credited with being a Madeleine Angevine x

Gewürztraminer crossing, was unmasked by Heinz Scheu, Georg's son, as also being a freely pollinated Madeleine Angevine seedling. It is conceivable that the variety we now grow in the UK as Madeleine x Angevine 7672 comes from the same crossing programme that produced Siegerrebe. In 1992, I asked Professor Alleweldt (or Professor Dr. Dr. h.c. Diplomlandwirt Gerhardt Erich Alleweldt to give him his full title), then head of the Geilweilerhof State Institute for Grapevine Breeding, to see if he could discover more about our Mad Angie (as it is often known). He located Georg Scheu's old breeding books in the Alzey archives and found that 'Sämling 7672' was – as Brock was originally told – an 'open pollinated progeny of Madeleine Angevine'.

Madeleine x Angevine 7672 found favour with many of the early UK growers and it became fairly widespread. At one time it was the third most popular variety (after MT and Seyval blanc) and Gillian Pearkes, one of the pioneers of UK grapegrowing who was an influential character in the West Country, thought highly of it. Unfortunately, owing to the confusion over the name and the fact that this variety was not available from any other source other than Brock's original stock or vineyards planted with vines obtained from Brock, some growers were sold vines of the true table grape variety Madeleine Angevine, which was barely suitable for the UK, except in the very best years. Unless it was being grown in proximity to other early varieties for pollination, it seldom set a good crop and in some years, ripened at the end of August. The wines from this variety were flabby and never really acceptable except for blending. The confusion over this variety – foreseen in a rare moment of sanity (as far as rules and regulations governing UK viticulture is concerned) by the EU Commission in 1973 when MAFF submitted vine varieties for classification – has meant that it gained something of a chequered reputation.

Today, the area planted is 45.9-ha accounting for 3.1 per cent of the UK's planted area – down very slightly from 46.8-ha in 2009 – and this reflects the support it has from existing growers of the variety. It is easy to grow, ripens early, gives good crops and the wines have a light Muscat tone and low acidity. In 1988 I took wood from genuine Madeleine x Angevine 7672 vines growing in Robin Don's Elmham Park vineyard in Norfolk, now grubbed, which Robin had planted with cuttings supplied by Pearkes (who had got her's directly from Brock). Buds from this wood were then sent to France and grafted on to resistant rootstock. The resultant grafted vines were sold to various growers around the country. Sharpham Vineyard in Devon is probably the best known and their wine made from 100 per cent MA, *Sharpham Estate Selection Dry,* is a regular prize winner. I note that their 2011 was voted 'Best wine in Devon to go with crab'!

For the long term, I suspect that Mad Angie will not survive the Pinot-Chardonnay storm-troopers lining up against her and as her growers get older and give up, sell up or go to that vineyard in the sky, the area will dwindle. Pity, as it can make good wine. For growers with more challenging sites, it is probably a variety worth considering, but they are advised to make sure they know where the bud-wood comes from before buying any vines.

### Merlot

Type: *Vinifera*
Colour: Red
Area in the UK: 2.1-ha (5.1-acres), 0.1 per cent of the planted area in 2013
Origin: Original variety

Merlot is of course one of the best known red vine varieties and with Cabernet Sauvignon, responsible for producing some of the world's most highly priced wines. On its own it reflects very much the climate it is being grown in, tending towards the flabby in warmer climates and towards the undrinkable in cool climates.

Quite what Merlot is doing in UK vineyards is open to question! It has long been grown by Mark Sharman under polytunnels at Beenleigh Manor where it has quite often produced some interesting wines which have won the UKVA red wine trophy on several occasions. The 0.2-ha planted in 1990 referred to this vineyard. Since 1990, the area increased to 1.1-ha in 2009 and to a heady 2.1-ha in 2013. Many of the extra plantings appear to be in conjunction with Cabernet Sauvignon, so I assume these are also tunnel grown. The only serious grower I know with Merlot in the open air is Bolney Estate in West Sussex. In (very) good years it is a component of one of their reds; in middling years it makes a rosé; and in poor years (2011, 2012 and 2013) it doesn't get picked. For UK vineyards I would suggest it's not a suitable variety, although as a talking point it may have some merit.

### Meunier

Synonym: Pinot Meunier, Schwarzriesling, Müllerrebe – and in the UK only – Wrotham Pinot
Type: *Vinifera*
Colour: Red
Area in the UK: 68.5-ha (169.4-acres), 4.6 per cent of the planted area in 2013
Origin: Original variety

Meunier, one of the numerous of the mutations that go to make up the Pinot family, accounts for around one-third of the plantings in Champagne (the actual percentage appears to be a closely guarded secret) and while it is seldom spoken about in the same breath as its nobler companions – Chardonnay and Pinot noir – and is not allowed in *Grand Cru* wines, it is used in some of the finest *cuvées* (Krug for example). In Champagne it is favoured for its higher acidity than Pinot noir, its ability to withstand spring frosts and higher yields and is found in the cooler sites. It is characterised by its white tipped shoots and its hairy leaves, especially on the underside, which give it the 'dusty' look from which the name – which means 'miller' in French – stems. Like many of the Pinots, it can show reversions back to the true Pinot noir and it is quite possible to have vines with both hairy and non-hairy leaves on different shoots in one year, which disappear in another year.

In the UK, Meunier has had a somewhat chequered career. In the early 1950s, Edward Hyams, one of the early pioneers of UK grape growing, discovered a vine growing on a cottage wall at Wrotham which he named Wrotham Pinot and which he gave to Ray Brock at Oxted. Given that this foundling had the classic dusty and red-edged leaves of Meunier, Brock assumed, wrongly or rightly, that it probably was a Meunier, although he reported that it had: *a higher natural sugar content and ripened two weeks earlier* than supplies of Meunier obtained from overseas. Brock sold cuttings and it became quite popular with some of the early vineyards. It is doubtful now whether any cuttings from Hyams or Oxted still survive in British vineyards and all plantings of Meunier stem from France or Germany (where it is known as Schwarzriesling or Müllerrebe). However, the name Wrotham Pinot is still a permitted synonym for Meunier in the UK.[9]

Although it has been grown for over 50 years in UK vineyards, Meunier has never really shone as a variety capable of making interesting wines on its own and most of it has been blended with other varieties. However, the rise in the planting of Champagne varieties has meant a resurgence of interest in the variety and my experiences to date, despite my former misgivings about its suitability for our climate, have been favourable. The quality of the Nyetimber *2003 Blanc de Noirs Pinot Meunier* which won a Gold Medal in both the 2006 and 2008 EWOTYC and for me (and for Tom Stevenson) was the best wine in the *Decanter Magazine* March 2008 mega-tasting of UK sparkling wines, has opened my eyes to its possibilities. In 1999 there were only 5.5-ha being grown in the UK, most of it fairly old and unloved I suspect, but since 2006, when the area stood at 22.5-ha, plantings, have shot up and today there are over three times that at 68.5-ha. There is no doubt now that it is seen as an indispensable part of many *classic cuvée* sparkling wines and often accounts for 15-20 per cent of Champagne variety plantings.

In most years, Meunier is unsuitable for still red wines, and, given that I suspect that all Meunier growers will also be growing Pinot noir, why would they want to make reds from it? Having said that, given its slightly lower cropping level (than Pinot noir) it can get very ripe and colours are no worse than Pinot noir, so it might be quite interesting, in a good year, to make red wine from it. A variety that, in time, I can see becoming the UK's third most widely planted variety.

**Note:** See separate section in this chapter on: *Clones of Chardonnay, Pinot noir and Meunier for sparkling wine.*

### Müller-Thurgau

Synonym: Rivaner, Riesling Sylvaner
Type: *Vinifera*
Colour: White
Area in the UK: 56.0-ha (138.4-acres), 3.7 per cent of the planted area in 2013
Origin: Riesling x Madeleine Royale

Professor Dr Hermann Müller, a Swiss from the canton of Thurgau near Zurich, produced this crossing while working at Geisenheim in 1882. Returning to Switzerland in 1891 to become Director of the Wädenswil Research Institute, Prof. Müller asked for 150 of his best crossings to be sent to him at Wädenswil, including No.58, which was eventually to become MT. Owing to some confusion with the labelling at the time the crossings were delivered, the true parentage of No.58 was never discovered and it eventually became known as 'Riesling Sylvaner' on account of its wine style, said to resemble a blend of Riesling and Sylvaner. Professor Becker, head of Geisenheim in the 1970s and 1980s, attempted to recreate the variety by making multiple Riesling and Sylvaner crossings, but failed. He was, however, of the opinion that it more resembled a Riesling x Riesling crossing than any other.

In 1996 an Austrian, Dr Regner from the viticulture school in Klosterneuburg, proved that the crossing was between Riesling and a member of the Chasselas family, a table grape vine variety that (he thought) was called *Admirable de Courtiller*. It was then discovered that the reference vine of this variety in Klosterneuburg's collection was in fact another variety altogether – it turned out to be Madeleine Royale (a Chasselas seedling variety). In 2001, two researchers in Germany, Erika Dettweiler and Andreas Jung, were able to unravel the DNA in MT and prove that it was indeed a crossing between Riesling and Madeleine Royale: after 119 years MT's parents were finally found. Madeleine Royale is itself Pinot x Black Hamburg (*Wine Grapes*).

In 1912, wet-sugaring (the use of sugar in solution to chaptalise wines) was forbidden in Switzerland and MT started to replace Elbling, up until then a widely grown variety, but high in acid. MT then began to find favour in Germany and, in the early 1920s, was taken up by Georg Scheu, then at Alzey in the Rheinland-Pfalz. He subjected it to clonal selection and helped improve its yield. Following the Second World War, when many vineyards were suffering from *Phylloxera* as well as the ravages of the war, MT was widely planted and its large yields, early ripening and soft wines, lower in acidity than either Riesling or Sylvaner, were much appreciated.

It is still today Germany's second most widely planted vine variety after Riesling and in 2012 there were 13,108-ha, 20.0 per cent of the white vine area and 12.8 per cent of the total vine area. although this is considerably down from the 1999 area of 20,672-ha when it occupied 20 per cent of the total German vineyard area. In Luxembourg – where it is called Rivaner – it is still a popular variety, occupying 27 per cent of their total vine area in 2011 (and cropping at 136 hl-ha). Until 1987, it was New Zealand's most widely planted variety and accounted for 42 per cent of their vineyard area although plantings have now almost disappeared and in 2013 only 11-ha remain. It is popular in high-altitude vineyards in Italy's German-speaking Alto Adige (*Sud Tyrol*) region, where it can make very fine wines. It is also to be found in many Eastern European countries, such as Slovakia and the Czech Republic. EU regulations forbid the use of the name Riesling Sylvaner, although this name can still be found in non-EU countries such as Switzerland.

Its introduction into the UK stems from Ray Brock's visit to Switzerland in 1946 when he met Mr Leyvraz at the Swiss Federal Vine Testing Station at Caudoz-sur-Pully. In 1947 vines of various varieties were sent by Leyvraz to Brock, including 'Riesling Sylvaner'. Brock gave cuttings to Edward Hyams in 1949 and they both trialled it for a number of years. Brock first harvested grapes from MT on 14 October 1950. In Hyams' 1953 book *The Grapevine in England* Brock wrote in his chapter on vine varieties that: *Riesling Sylvaner is known to give an outstandingly fine wine in cool climates*.

When Jack Ward was looking for vines for the Horam Manor vineyard, planted in 1954, he was recommended MT, and it became a staple of all the early UK vineyards. Ward was a very influential figure in the early days of the revival (the EVA's first Chairman) and undoubtedly did much to persuade growers to plant MT. Ward's company – the Merrydown Wine Company – sold vines and gave advice and ran a winemaking co-operative between 1969 and 1979 to which many of the early growers belonged. MT was top of my list when I selected varieties for planting in 1976-7 and it was almost unthinkable to plant a vineyard in the UK then without it. Most German wine and viticulture experts considered England to be a country of mists and not-very-mellow fruitfulness and thought that a high-cropping, early ripening, low acid variety (which is what MT is in Germany) was just what we needed.

MT is a vigorous variety, especially in its early years, and it will grow thick canes and large leaves leading to excess shading. This often results in poor cropping, especially in years with low light and heat levels in the previous season. It suffers from *Botrytis*, Powdery and Downy Mildew and requires regular spraying and must be deleafed after flowering and then again around *véraison*. In heavy-yielding years, stem-rot can be a problem. The wood often ripens poorly and does not over-winter well, often showing active *Botrytis* in mild winters. It is probably a variety best avoided by organic growers. Since the advent of better anti-*Botrytis* chemicals such as Scala, Teldor and Switch, disease control has become easier (if more costly) and clean crops of MT are the norm, rather than the exception they were in the 1970s and 1980s.

MT grapes can have good fruity flavours with light Muscat hints and at their best, the wines made from them can be very good. However, when less than fully ripe, they tend towards the herbaceous and catty. The acidity is usually average to low and with some balancing residual sugar, the wine can be very attractive and fresh when young and will keep well, although probably best drunk within two to three years after bottling. Picked early with sufficient acidity and when the fruit flavours are more neutral, it can be used for sparkling wine and Chapel Down have always used it in their entry-level *Vintage Brut Reserve*, although over the years, the percentage in the blend has come down, to be replaced with pressings from Chardonnay and Pinot noir.

In 1984, MT was by far the largest single variety being grown in the UK with 149.0-ha, accounting for 35 per cent of the UK planted area. Over the intervening years however, it has slowly fallen to 61.5-ha in 2009 and 56.0-ha in 2013, which is just under 4 per cent of the UK planted area. It would appear that a few growers are hanging on and no doubt, in these warmer times, getting good enough crops to justify its existence. However, no one is planting it anymore and over time, it will continue to dwindle.

With hindsight, it was a variety that the UK could

probably have done without, although one must not forget that the most popular wine at the time it was being planted was the light, fruity *Liebfraumilch* style that MT is so suitable for. Its extreme vigour, especially in the early years, coupled with its on–off cropping pattern and disease problems, make it a difficult variety for UK conditions.

## Orion

Type: *Vinifera* (complex hybrid)
Colour: White
Area in the UK: 10.8 hectares (26.7-acres), 0.7 per cent of the planted area in 2013
Origin: Optima x Seyve Villard 12-375

Orion is one of the many crossings made by Prof. Dr Alleweldt at Geilweilerhof. It dates from 1964 and was first registered in 1994. It is a crossing of another Geilweilerhof crossing, Optima, which is [(Silvaner x Riesling) x MT], and Seyve Villard 12-375 which is known as Villard blanc. Orion is one of the new generation of complex interspecific-crosses (now known as PIWI varieties[10]) which have been bred for both wine quality and disease resistance. It is not as resistant to fungal attack as some of the older hybrids (Seyval blanc for instance) and usually requires spraying against Powdery Mildew, but is good against *Botrytis* and ripens its wood well. It also shows better resistance to winter frost damage than MT (not often a problem in the UK) and its basal buds are said to be very fruitful. Orion was introduced to the UK in the late 1990s and by 1999 there were 8.4-ha being grown. This area has grown very slowly since then, to 10.8-ha in 2009 from which point it has not changed, it being 10.8-ha in 2013. Wines made from 100 per cent Orion seldom surface, so it is difficult to judge its true worth, but the wine is said to be fruity and aromatic. I don't see it expanding much more, although some of the more northerly vineyards seem to like it.

## Ortega

Type: *Vinifera*
Colour: White
Area in the UK: 34.5-ha (85.3-acres), 2.3 per cent of the planted area in 2013
Origin: Müller-Thurgau x Siegerrebe

Ortega is a crossing made by Dr H. Breider at Würzburg between MT and Siegerrebe. Siegerrebe is a freely pollinated Madeleine Angevine seedling with Gewürztraminer the most likely culprit as father. Ortega was first registered in 1971 and is named (somewhat curiously) after the Spanish philosopher José Ortega y Gasset, (but good for pub quizzes when 'what's the name of a famous Spanish philosopher' comes up.)

In Germany there are 561-ha (2012) mostly in Rheinhessen and the Pfalz. However, it is a declining variety (down from 951-ha in 2001), so falling in popularity. In Germany, it ripens early, achieves high natural alcohol levels and low acidity levels and with its rich, spicy tones, makes a good blending partner for higher acid varieties such as Riesling.

In the UK, Ortega was introduced by Jack Ward who planted it at Horam Manor in 1971 and it has slowly grown in popularity. It ripens early – just after Siegerrebe and Optima – has high sugars, low acids and plenty of flavour. An early bud burst makes it susceptible to spring frost damage and it is sensitive to poor flowering conditions and will suffer from *coulure* in poor years. It can be quite vigorous and canopy management needs to be good to get the best fruit. It will also get *Botrytis* towards the end of ripening which will turn to 'noble rot' if sugar levels are high enough. Given good canopy management and timely attention to spraying, this variety can provide high quality grapes, useful for both normal still wines and dessert wines. Growers report that its bunches tend to get tangled up with each other and with the canes and wires and picking can take twice as long as for other varieties.

When fully ripe, wines made from Ortega are rich and zesty with good balance, although warm years may result in wines with rather low acidity and care needs to be taken to pick at the correct time. Biddenden Vineyards have won numerous gold and silver medals with Ortega wines and won the Gore-Browne Trophy with one in 1987. Surprisingly it takes to new oak well and Chapel Down used to make a very good barrel-aged *Condrieu*-like wine from Ortega. Growers of Ortega seem to like the variety and the area has risen from 29.5-ha in 1990 to 34.5-ha in 2013. This must be seen as a positive vote in its favour. I suspect that it will remain as one of our important, albeit minor, varieties and, as vineyards creep ever northwards, might find favour there.

## Phoenix

Type: *Vinifera* (complex hybrid)
Colour: White
Area in the UK: 23.6-ha (58.3-acres), 1.6 per cent of the planted area in 2013
Origin: Bacchus x Seyve Villard 12-375

Phoenix (and not Phönix) is another of the many complex hybrid crossings made by Prof. Dr Alleweldt at Geilweilerhof and is Bacchus x Seyve Villard 12-375 (Villard blanc). It was first registered in 1984 and listed for general growing in 1992. In Germany there were 24-ha in 1999 and 48-ha in 2012. Although not as resistant to fungal attack as the older hybrids, it ripens its wood well.

Phoenix first appeared in the UK in the late 1990s – there were only 1.9-ha planted in 1999 – and it has risen very slowly to cover 23.6-ha in 2013, which, all things considered, is relatively respectable. Although only planted on a few sites in the UK, the wine quality can be good (Three Choirs' is usually the best), with higher sugars and lower acids than MT and is Bacchus-like, although not as powerful. It is one of the several complex hybrids that can be made into Quality Wine in the UK. Whether Phoenix really has a place in UK vineyards when Bacchus is now easier to grow, given the warmer summers and better fungicides, is open to question. Its rate of increase over the last decade has been steady, suggesting that it has some positive attributes and I suspect that it is better suited to more challenging sites and as such, will remain a useful, but minor variety.

## Pinot blanc

Synonym: Weißer Burgunder
Type: *Vinifera*
Colour: White
Area in the UK: 25.4-ha (62.7-acres), 1.7 per cent of the planted area in 2013
Origin: Original variety

Pinot blanc is one of the most widely distributed of varieties across Europe and is one of the vast family of Pinots. It is often confused (one suspects mostly on purpose) with Chardonnay – the style of wine they produce can be similar – and in general terms it is less demanding than Chardonnay, will ripen more easily and has a higher yield. In Germany it is increasing in popularity and there were 4,449-ha in 2012, making it the fifth most widely planted white variety. It is to be found in France, Alsace especially, and in many Italian regions in great quantity and in many other cooler regions.

In the UK it is a fairly new introduction (since 1990) and has grown steadily from 6.2-ha in 2006 to 25.4-ha in 2013. It is mainly used for the production of sparkling base-wine and very few 100 per cent varietal wines exist, although Chapel Down's version (made from grapes grown in Hampshire, Essex and Kent) is one of their best wines and more growers should follow their example. Like Chardonnay, it requires a good site and careful management to ripen it fully and get the acids down. It will find a good home in sparkling wine blends and it deserves to be planted a bit more. In 2008 I said 'I cannot really see it expanding much more, given the onward march of Chardonnay' but since the area continues to rise, someone is planting it and maybe, that as an alternative to Chardonnay for more marginal sites, especially for still wines, it will eventually come into its own in the UK. Another important, but minor, variety.

## Pinot gris

Synonym: Ruländer
Type: *Vinifera*
Colour: White
Area in the UK: 15.2-ha (37.5-acres), 1.0 per cent of the planted area in 2013
Origin: Original variety

Pinot gris is another variety from the large Pinot family and it appears to have almost as many clones as there are winegrowing regions that use it. In Alsace, its most respected home (where until recently it was known as Tokay d'Alsace), it is capable of producing exceptionally fine late-harvest dessert wines. In Germany – where it is known as Ruländer for wines with residual sugar and Grauer Burgunder or Pinot gris for dry wines – there were 5,042-ha in 2012 making it the fourth most widely planted white vine variety and it makes an easy-drinking soft wine. In Italy (as Pinot grigio), where there are almost 7,000-ha (17,290-acres) of the variety, it makes a very neutral, quite crisp wine, ideal with food. It seems to be able to change its style to suit the region.

In the UK, where it has been grown since the late 1970s, it is making slow progress from 6.0-ha in 2007, via 10.6-ha in 2006, to today's total of 15.2-ha. It is not the easiest variety to grow and requires a good site and careful canopy management to make the best of it. Yields are not the highest and need to be kept under control to produce the best grapes. Some reports talk of a prolonged flowering, resulting in picking in two or more passes. To date, very few single variety still wines have been made from Pinot gris, although Meopham Valley, New Hall and Stopham vineyards have all won medals and awards with it. Stopham, in particular, made good Alsace-style wines from the variety in 2010 and 2011 which were very well received and I am told that the 2013 vintage is also very good. It has also been used in sparkling wines, but, except in a blend, I cannot see it becoming an important variety for this type of wine.

Assuming that the climate continues to improve and as more single varietal wines become available and achieve success, I can see Pinot gris making steady progress and becoming a minor, but useful, variety for UK growers.

## Pinot noir

Synonym: Blauer Spätburgunder
Type: *Vinifera*
Colour: Red
Area in the UK: 305.2-ha (754.2-acres), 20.3 per cent of the planted area in 2013
Origin: Original variety

Pinot noir is one of the most ancient of varieties and probably has more clones and variants than any other variety. While its home is often thought of as Burgundy, where undoubtedly many of the finest examples can be found, it seems to thrive in both very warm and very cool climates and good examples can be found in Australia, California, Chile, Germany, New Zealand, South Africa, and Spain. Norway's only vineyard – yes, Norway – is planted with Pinot noir and the wine can (so one is told) be very good. In Germany, the area planted has gone from 7,607-ha in 1995, to 11,769-ha in 2012, making it the most widely planted red vine variety occupying 32 per cent of the red wine area and 11.5 per cent of the total vine area. It is also of course not only used for still red wines, but is also one of the classic sparkling wine grapes, found not only in Champagne, but wherever good sparkling wines are made.

In the UK it was one of the earliest varieties to be grown. Brock trialled it at Oxted, but was not pleased with it and by 1961, when he issued *Report No.3 Progress with vines and wines,* he stated that Pinot noir: '*appears to be very much later* [than on the continent] *in this climate ... and has been discontinued*'. His lack of success was probably due to the fact that, at the vineyard's elevation of 125–137 metres above sea level, the site was just too cool. In addition, Brock was not, at least not in the early years, looking to make sparkling wines, although he did make some later on. Jack Ward was likewise somewhat dismissive of the variety and also thought it too late.

Despite the reservations of these pioneers, it seems to have been planted quite widely, if not in any great quantity. Many of the early growers seemed to limit their investigation of continental vineyards to a quick visit to

Champagne and returned enthused with the idea that Pinot noir, and for that matter Chardonnay, were naturals for our climate. The truth of the matter is that in those early days they were not, and good wines made from them were *very* few in number. Whatever Bernard Theobald claimed in the 1970s and 1980s, Pinot noir was *not* the best variety to be growing then. What I wrote in 2001 (I hope) bears repeating:

> *'The rise in interest of bottle-fermented sparkling wines and the results to date, from those vineyards that have gone into the job seriously, is impressive. There have also been a number of very creditable red wines made from the variety in recent years – only it has to be said in the warmer years – but it is an exciting trend. There are a number of factors which might make Pinot noir a more acceptable variety for the UK. There is no doubt that vine breeders have done much to change Pinot over the last 50 years. Clones are available now that ripen earlier, are more consistent, produce better quality wines and are more disease resistant. The upsurge in interest in making bottle-fermented sparkling wines seems set to continue and Pinot noir must be considered as a major variety in this respect. Today's fungicides, especially for the control of Botrytis are markedly better than they were only a decade ago and this undoubtedly allows growers to leave their grapes to hang for longer and to ripen more fully.*
>
> *Whether or not global warming is affecting the UK now – or will do in years to come – is open to debate. However, most winegrowers sense that weather patterns are changing and we are now experiencing earlier budbursts (although this is coupled with a higher incidence of spring frost damage) and therefore longer growing seasons. This does mean that the more marginal varieties – of which group the Pinots and Chardonnay are members – may fare better in the next decade than the last. One other factor to be considered is that of marketing. There is no doubt that the public will buy wines bearing names that they recognise and Pinot noir is one that has its devotees'.*

The upsurge in plantings since 1984, when 11-ha were recorded as being planted in UK vineyards, via 46.6-ha in 2002, to today's 305.2-ha, occupying 20.3 per cent of the planted area, is impressive and speaks volumes about the ease with which it can be grown, its relatively good crops and its suitability for turning into fine sparkling wines. It is also due to three other factors: what I have called the 'Nyetimber effect', the weather and the name. The first factor showed that good, even great, sparkling wines could be made using the classic varieties, of which Pinot noir was an important component (although the first Nyetimber release was actually a *Blanc de Blancs*). Since then, all of the major players in the UK sparkling wine business have shown that this was no fluke. The second factor has meant that the acids are manageable and – if you want some colour – colours are acceptable. It has also meant that it crops adequately – another not-to-be-forgotten aspect of the variety. Thirdly, the very name 'Pinot noir' has a magic which cannot be denied, partly because it can make

some of the best wines in the world, but also because it is such a chameleon, making both great red still wines and great (white) sparkling wines. Everyone talks about it being a 'difficult' variety and a 'heartbreaker' which further adds to its mystique.

On the red wine front, I am more convinced now than I used to be about its suitability to make good red wines in the UK. Pinot noir wines have won The Bernard Theobald Trophy for the Best Red in the EWOTYC in ten of the eleven years between 2002 and 2013 (five times by Chapel Down and once each by Biddenden, Plumpton College, Sharpham, Sandhurst and Titchfield), although these wines were the exceptions rather than the rule. Too many UK red Pinot noir wines are just thin, acidic and very poor value for money. The best are generally light in colour (although no lighter than many top-class Burgundies) and have simple red-fruit bouquets, perhaps with a touch of oak, adequate tannins and a fresh, fruity crispness about them that says 'attractive' rather than 'serious'. They are not usually very substantial wines and must be put in context with wines from other cooler growing regions: the Loire (Sancerre especially), Burgundy and even Alsace. Against wines from warmer climes they stand no chance. Many UK-grown Pinot noirs would be much better presented as light, fruity rosés with a touch of sweetness and a very light *petillance*. However, in 2011, when sugars were high, there were a couple of very good examples – Gusbourne Estate's being the best – which made me think that maybe, just maybe, we were turning a corner for red wines from this variety.

Viticulturally, Pinot noir presents no great problems to the seasoned grower. It buds up quite early, making it susceptible to damage on frost-prone sites, but it will shoot from secondary buds. It gets all the usual ailments and requires good management to keep it *Botrytis* free if the fruit is needed for whole-bunch pressing or for fermenting on the skins as a red wine. With a good spray regime and deleafing at the appropriate times, 100 per cent clean fruit is achievable in every year. On the cropping front, I have been very impressed by the level of the yields and whilst years such as 2007, 2011 and 2012 might set the averages back, 10 tonnes-ha (4 tonnes-acre) would appear to be achievable in 'normal' years and even higher in better years, fine for sparkling wine. For still red wine production, the quality of the site and the year will play a major rôle in fruit quality, but it is probably wiser to aim for nearer half this figure if good wines are to be made.

Clonally, Pinot noir is very diverse and I have no doubt that in the UK we have only scratched the surface of this aspect of growing. It is a great pity that not more work has been done in the UK on clones suitable for our unique growing conditions (another job for Plumpton College perhaps?) We can only, therefore, take anecdotal evidence gleaned from existing UK growers, plus take notice of recommendations offered to overseas growers.

## Pinot noir clones

Pinot noir clones are loosely divided into four types:
• Clones with compact bunches, also often with small berries. These are favoured by still red wine producers. Yields tend to be lower than other clones. They are also

called *Pinot Fin* clones.

• Clones with loose bunches, often with larger berries, and higher yields. German growers have planted these widely as they are more *Botrytis* resistant. Probably not the best for sparkling wines. Also sometimes known as Mariafeld or Wädenswil clones which stem from Switzerland.

• Upright clones (*Pinot droit*) have more erect foliage, favoured by some growers, and often have tight bunches. They tend to be less *Botrytis*-prone. Good for sparkling wines, although can be later to ripen than other clones.

• Clones with small berries. German research stations (principally Geisenheim and Freiburg) have developed these clones which tend to have large bunches and high yields. Good for still red wine in the German style, but not much favoured in other regions.

• There are also several 'mixed' clones, as well as various *selection massale*[11] which many Burgundian growers now prefer.

The question of *Botrytis* resistance has to be understood and taken into account when considering descriptions and recommendations in publications and on websites, all of which are based upon non-UK conditions. As I point out in *Chapter 16: Pests and Diseases*, the incidence of *Botrytis* in well managed UK vineyards is actually far less than it is in the regions of Germany and France where they grow Pinot noir. In Germany for instance, where yields are high and grapes are often very tightly packed together inside the canopy, *Botrytis* is a major concern. As will be seen in *Chapter* 16, some German growers practice *traubenteilen* – the cutting of the bunch in half – which causes the shoulders of the bunch to droop, loosening the bunch and opening it up. Many clones have therefore been selected for their resistance to *Botrytis*, mainly based upon the clone having large, loose bunches, so that individual grapes are not packed tightly together and air and light, plus chemical sprays, can penetrate the bunch easily.

Another aspect which also needs to be borne in mind when looking at Pinot noir clones is the question of colour. Deep coloured red Pinot noir wine is not something that traditional Burgundian growers set much store by and in fact many old hands in the wine trade, on seeing a dark red Burgundy, will immediately suspect that it has been 'Hermitaged' – the practice of beefing up wines by the addition of Syrah-based Hermitage wine. Many German and New World growers believe that light coloured, slightly brick-red Pinot noir wines are to be avoided and thus select clones giving good colour. They also like clones producing wines with plenty of good fruity characters and one often sees the word 'cherry' mentioned in relation to non-French clones. Whether UK growers require *Botrytis* resistant Pinot noir clones producing fruity, dark red, wine is open to question. For the production of high-acid, white sparkling wine, the answer is probably 'no'. For non-French clones, the German nursery Reben Sibbus has some interesting data:
http://www.sibbus.com/en/vine-nursery/varieties/red-wine-varieties/pinot-noir.html#

For still red wines, the most successful clones in UK vineyards appear to be the compact bunch French clones

113, 114, 115, 667 and 777. There are also good reports of two Geisenheim clones, Gm 20-13 and Gm 20-19 and an Italian clone SMA 201. I personally prefer 667 and 777. There is also a *teinturier* clone of Pinot noir, called (not unsurprisingly) Pinot Teinturier – also known as *Pinot tête-de-nègre* – which a few UK vineyards have tried and which gives both good wine and very good colour. Grafted vines of these clones are hard to come by, but it is worth trying if still red wines are the aim. There are several sub-clones including Bury, Guicherd, and Marsellein clones.

If you start looking into Pinot noir clones, you will find a huge amount of information, much of it confusing and contradictory. Given that there are forty-five Pinot noir clones registered for use in France (including eighteen in Champagne), eight-hundred in total in collections in Alsace, Bourgogne and Champagne, dozens (if not hundreds) in other countries and that many nurseries have their own 'selections', this is a vast unfathomable subject. Find a great site, get the density right, plant a couple of the clones recommended above, and when they start cropping, manage the yield and canopy properly and given a fair year, you will produce something interesting – maybe a light red, perhaps a decent rosé. Only time will tell you if you have the right combination for great still red Pinot noir.

For sparkling wine, I am not as concerned about the question of clones as I am with still wine. There is so much that happens in sparkling wine production between picking and drinking that can substantially alter the nature, flavour, style and quality of the wine (blending, *sur latte* ageing and *dosage* being the main ones) that the clone is of secondary importance. It would be nice to plant those clones with the lowest acidity and highest yield and in time these will hopefully make themselves known.

Pinot noir is undoubtedly here to stay and given its success in making some great sparkling wines and the beginnings of what may well be some great still red wines, I can only see its importance to UK growers increasing.

**Note:** See the separate section at the end of this chapter on: *Clones of Chardonnay, Pinot noir and Meunier for sparkling wine.*

### Pinot noir Précoce

Synonym: Blauer Frühburgunder
Type: *Vinifera*
Colour: Red
Area in the UK: 20.2-ha (50.0-acres), 1.3 per cent of the planted area in 2013
Origin: Original variety

When growers started planting Pinot noir in earnest in the UK, the search went out for the earliest ripening clones in the belief that it was a late ripening variety (it's not, but that's another matter) and they were offered what many thought was an early German clone of Pinot noir by some UK vine suppliers. This was what the Germans call Blauer Frühburgunder. Vines were imported and planted and the wine was sometimes called by its correct name, (Blauer) Frühburgunder, but was more usually called Spätburgunder or Pinot noir, occasionally Early Pinot noir.

All was fine and dandy until some eagle-eyed WSB inspector noticed Blauer Frühburgunder on a wine label and realised that this variety was not on the list of permitted vine varieties for the UK and therefore any wine made from it could only be sold as UK Table Wine. After some discussion with the industry, the WSB agreed that the synonym Pinot noir Précoce (PNP) would be a permitted name (as it is already called this in other EU Member States and it is so much nicer than Blauer Frühburgunder) and growers with this variety were asked to confess their misdeeds and re-register their vineyard parcels containing this 'clone'. This is why it has suddenly appeared from nowhere on the variety lists.

In fact, Frühburgunder is a relatively old variety, planted in the 1800s in the Ahr wine region, Germany's most northerly winegrowing area. The region is named after a tributary of the Rhine which joins the main river just south of Bonn. By the 1900s the variety had migrated to the town of Ingelheim am Rhein, '*Die Rotweinstadt*' (the red wine town) and it became that town's dominant variety for which they became very well known.[12] Geisenheim has done some work on it, cleaned it up (the old clones had Leaf Roll and cropped very poorly) and today there are five clones listed that are worth growing (in Germany). In Germany there are 262-ha (2012).

Whether PNP is a suitable variety for the UK is another matter. It ripens up to two weeks earlier than Pinot noir and is said to achieve better sugars and better colour. It is just as *Botrytis* prone and offers no other advantages. Its drawback is the name. Pinot noir Précoce sounds a bit odd and Blauer Frühburgunder dreadful. It may well turn out to be a great blending partner for Pinot noir and kept below 15 per cent of the blend, would not upset the WSB's labelling hounds. In the 2008 edition of this guide I wrote: *I don't anticipate a huge surge in plantings, although I suspect that more will emerge over the next few years as the WSB ask growers to look back and see what they actually planted. Luckily, ampelographers are fairly thin on the ground in the UK.* The fact that the area has gone from 8.2-ha in 2007 to 20.2-ha in 2013 is something of a vote of confidence, but mainly I suspect by growers with more marginal sites (probably those northern counties again), hoping that it will ripen more easily than straight Pinot noir. Just how good the wines are is open to question although there have been a few medals at the EWOTYC (three silvers, one bronze and one highly commended). I don't expect the UK area to increase very quickly, but it will probably slowly increase. If I had a good site, I would plant Pinot noir. If I had a poor site, I would steer clear of red varieties.

## Regent

Type: *Vinifera* (complex hybrid)
Colour: Red
Area in the UK: 24.3-ha (60.0-acres), 1.6 per cent of the planted area in 2013
Origin: Diana x Chambourcin

Regent (pronounced in German *Ray-ghent* with a hard g as in Ghent, not as in Regent Street) is another of Prof. Dr. Alleweldt's Geilweilerhof crossings (see Orion and Phoenix). Its parents are Diana, a Silvaner x Müller-Thurgau crossing (and not the native Catawba variety grown in the US of the same name) and Chambourcin, a Joannès Seyve crossing of Seyve-Villard 12-417 and Chancellor. The crossing was made in 1967 and in Germany it was released in 1995 and it has become popular with growers and at 2,047-ha (2012) is their sixth most widely grown red vine variety. It has very good colour, is more disease resistant than *viniferas* and the wine quality is usually quite good (always a help). In 1996, despite not being 100 per cent *vinifera,* it was authorised for the production of quality wines in Germany, the first modern interspecific-cross to be allowed to do so. According to *Wine Grapes* it is named after *Le Régent*, the 140.5 carat diamond found by a slave in the Golkonda mine in India and eventually placed in the crown of the French King Louis XV when he was crowned in 1722.

In the UK, Regent has only been around since the 1990s and by 2006 there were 12.6-ha. Today, it has grown to 24.3-ha and is the second most widely planted purely red variety (i.e. ignoring Pinot noir and Meunier). It requires a good site, good management and deleafing at the right times, but no more so than other red varieties. It is certainly less disease prone than Dornfelder and Rondo, so on that score alone, it could be a better bet for a deep red wine variety, but is susceptible to Downy Mildew. It usually yields quite well and 7.5-10 tonnes-ha (3-4 tonnes-acre) are achievable on a good site. For deep red wines, it has a higher quality than wines made from Dornfelder or Rondo, although it probably best used in a blend of all three. It takes oak well, has great colour, soft tannins and acids are manageable. Its continuing expansion would suggest that it is a valuable variety for those wanting to produce deep-coloured blended red wines.

## Regner

Type: *Vinifera*
Colour: White
Area in the UK: 4.5-ha (11.1-acres), 0.3 per cent of the planted area in 2013
Origin: Luglienca bianca x Gamay Früh (Early Gamay)

Regner is an Alzey crossing from Georg Scheu, made in 1929 and first released in 1978, and is another of Scheu's crossings that used a commercial table grape (Luglienca Bianca, known as Gelbe Seidentraube in Germany) as one parent and a *précoce* clone of Gamay as the other. It is not widely planted in Germany and has fallen from 124-ha in 2001 to 31-ha in 2012.

Regner first appeared in the UK in the Wye College vineyard and quickly proved capable of good yields with grapes that ripened mid-early (before MT) with high sugars and low acid levels – in short – an ideal variety for our climate. I have long felt that it had a place in the UK and when I was winemaker at Lamberhurst, we used to buy it from a local vineyard and make good wine from it. Jon Leighton at Valley Vineyards (now Stanlake Park) used to grow it and was always pleased with the results and Wroxeter Vineyard in Shropshire have it and like it very much. The UK area has remained fairly stable over the past few years, but I feel it is due for a modest revival.

## Reichensteiner

Type: *Vinifera*
Colour: White
Area in the UK: 80.5-ha (198.9-acres), 5.4 per cent of the planted area in 2013
Origin: Müller-Thurgau x (Madeleine Angevine x Calabreser-Froelich)

Reichensteiner is a Geisenheim cross produced by Prof. Henrich Birk in 1939 by crossing Müller-Thurgau with a cross between two other varieties: Madeleine Angevine, the female French table grape used by Scheu (among others) for a number of his crossings, and Calabreser-Froelich, an early white Italian table grape. Together, these have combined to produce an early ripening variety, capable of producing large crops of relatively neutral grapes, high in natural sugars and low(ish) in acidity.

In Germany, Reichensteiner was seen as a substitute to the practice of 'wet-sugaring' (where up to 20 per cent by volume of water could be added to the must during the enrichment process in order to lower the acidity) – a practice that only came to an end in the late 1970s. In Germany, the area has fallen from 257-ha in 1999 to 79-ha in 2012 and it is undoubtedly on the way out. In warm climates, it is capable of producing massive crops – up to 200 hl-ha (12 tonnes/acre) is not uncommon – and it is used as a blending partner for varieties with more acidity. Apart from a small area in New Zealand (where in 2013, 11-ha produced 183 tonnes at 16.6 tonnes-ha or 6.7 tonnes-acre ), its only other real home is the UK.

Reichensteiner was introduced into the UK by Jack Ward when he extended his Brickyard vineyard in Horam in 1971. Early results showed that it was a consistent cropper, with good yields and high sugars. Although it can be vigorous in its youth, it settles down after a few years and is less vigorous than MT at the same age. It has a good open habit and a leaf-wall that is less crowded and better ventilated than MT, both of which help disease control.

As a varietal wine, it does not have the character of fruitier varieties, but has lower acid levels, more body and extract and higher natural sugars. It is probably best used in a blend. It has been used for sparkling wine (Camel Valley, Carr Taylor, Chapel Down, Davenport, Meopham), as well as for the production of *süss-reserve*. Although it has fallen in area, from 113.9-ha in 1990, via 84.43-ha in 2009, to 80.5-ha in 2013, I believe it still has a valuable part to play in the UK wine industry on account of its reliable cropping record. Vines are difficult to obtain as no one is grafting them except to order.

## Riesling

Synonym: None
Type: *Vinifera*
Colour: White
Area in the UK: 3.0-ha (7.5-acres), 0.2 per cent of the planted area in 2013
Origin: Original variety

One of the classic 'cool climate' vine varieties (along with Chardonnay, Chenin blanc and Sauvignon blanc), Riesling is Germany's most widely planted vine variety occupying 22,837-ha in 2012 which equates to 35 per cent of their white vineyard area and 22 per cent of their total vineyard area. In Germany, it is capable of making both fruity, ready-to-drink wines at the cheaper end of the market, as well as magnificent dry, medium dry and sweet wines which are amongst some of the longest lived in the world. The key, of course, is acidity.

In the UK, Riesling has hardly ever been planted and the only planting of any size was at Denbies. For twenty years it failed to produce any wine of note, apart from the very hot year of 2003, after which the vines were taken out (although I gather some have since been replanted!). In 2012, Rathfinny planted around 1.50-ha, but they have yet to crop.

In my view, Riesling is a variety that, even with global warming, will struggle to set fruit and ripen in the UK except in the best of years and on the best of sites and should only ever be planted on a trial basis. It is also a variety that is difficult to sell to UK wine drinkers.

## Rondo

Synonym: Gm 6494/5
Type: *Vinifera* (complex hybrid)
Colour: Red
Area in the UK: 74.4-ha (117.1-acres), 3.2 per cent of the planted area in 2013
Origin: Zarya Severa x St Laurent

If ever there was a variety with a complicated, not to say convoluted, history attached to it, then Rondo has to have one of the most complex. The original *Vitis amurensis* vines from which Rondo is derived were wild vines and came from Manchuria, in the north of China, where the River Amur marks the border between China and Russia. Here, on account of the early onset and severity of the winters, wild vines need be able to withstand deep winter

temperatures and therefore colour up and ripen early. In 1910, a Russian vine breeder, Ivan Vladimirovich Michurin (1855-1935) – pictured on the left – selected an open-pollinated seedling of *Précoce de Malingre*, which was probably pollinated by a *Vitis amurensis* in Michurin's vine collection, which he called Seyanets Malengra.

Michurin was a famous plant breeder whose work was recognised by Lenin and whose private research station at Tambov, about 435-km south-east of Moscow, became the Michurin Central Genetic Laboratory in 1934. Seyanets Malengra is a female vine and used in Russia and Ukraine as a table grape variety. In 1936, two Russian plant breeders, Yakov Potapenko and E. Zakharova, working at the the All-Russia Research Institute of Viticulture and Winemaking (later called the Potapenko All-Russia Research Institute of Viticulture and Winemaking), situated at Novocherkassk in Rostov Province, crossed Seyanets Malengra with another *Amurensis* vine to produce a variety called Zarya Severa. This crossing then found its way to Lednice in Moravia, Czechoslovakia where Prof. Dr. Vilém Kraus crossed it, in 1964, with St Laurent, an old Austrian wine variety. This crossing then travelled to Geisenheim where Prof. Helmut Becker improved it and gave it a breeding number Gm 6494/5. With me so far? It was then trialled at Geisenheim and proved capable of producing good crops of early ripening, deeply coloured grapes.

In 1983 Prof. Becker gave me 50 vines to plant at Tenterden, as well as 50 to both Ken Barlow at Adgestone and Karl-Heinz Johner at Lamberhurst, to see what the results would be. From the first harvests it showed itself well adapted to UK conditions and plantings have been increasing since then. From 2-ha in 1990, it has continued to grow in popularity and stands at 47.4-ha in 2013. Ignoring Pinot noir and Meunier (from which little truly red wine is made) Rondo is the most widely planted red variety in the UK, with double the area of the next most widely planted red variety, Regent. In Germany (2012) there is a bare 11-ha, although in other cool climates such as Belgium, Denmark, Holland, and Sweden it is one of the most important varieties. For the first decade of its life in the UK it was called Gm 6494/5, but eventually we got it a name – Rondo – and persuaded DEFRA to classify it as a *vinifera* (as the Germans had done five years earlier).

Initially, Rondo had all the makings of a good variety for the UK: early to ripen, with a good crop of deep red grapes with low(ish) acidity and wine quality that was certainly better than anything else seen in the mid-1980s – Léon Millot, Maréchal Foch and Triomphe d'Alsace (as it was then called) – being the alternatives. Chapel Down made two versions: a straightforward wine and a Reserve, both from grapes from Anthony Pilcher's Chapel Farm vineyard on the Isle of Wight. The Reserve, with enough oak and some time, could be very good, although the flavour was always very slightly unusual. I always likened it to a Syrah-Tempranillo blend – the American oak helped – and I tried to persuade myself for years that it had a future. However, reluctantly, and in the face of the onslaught from Pinot noir and Regent, I don't think the wine quality is high enough for it to succeed in the long term.

It is a very vigorous variety, with big leaves (almost like the leaves of Kiwi fruit) and canes that can stretch for several metres if allowed to run. Consequently, canopies tend to be crowded and shaded and although an interspecific cross, it is still fairly susceptible to *Botrytis*. The wine colour is excellent, deeper than Dornfelder and

Regent and the quality is passable, but not of the first order and certainly not what the consumer expects of a wine of that appearance. Although the area planted has expanded – from 43-ha in 2009 to 47.4-ha in 2013 – most of this additional planting is in vineyards in the more challenging parts of the UK and I do not believe that any mainstream vineyards view it as a serious variety for the future. Although I value the direct link back to Helmut Becker and those first 50 vines, sentimentality never helped make good wine and plantings of Rondo, although they will probably expand, will do so only slowly.

## Sauvignon blanc

Synonym: None
Type: *Vinifera*
Colour: White
Area in the UK: 4.6-ha hectares (11.5-acres), 0.3 per cent of the planted area in 2013.
Origin: Original variety

Sauvignon blanc is one of the world's most popular and widespread white vine varieties and can be found in climates both cool and warm. Great wines can be produced in a variety of styles: Marlborough's high-acid, zesty pure-fruit wines, the classic lean and minimalist wines from Sancerre and Pouilly-Fumé and the full-bodied oaky offerings labelled as Fumé Blanc from California are all fine examples of this versatile variety. In Germany it has risen in popularity from nothing in 1999 to 734-ha in 2012. It is also popular in Austria, although not recorded as a separate variety in Luxembourg.

In the UK, Sauvignon blanc has risen in area from 0.5-ha in 1990 to 4.6-ha in 2013, hardly a meteoric rise and one that I think spells out its suitability for the UK. From what I have seen to date, it struggles to set fruit and ripen it, except on the very best sites and in the very warmest of vintages and to date no one has managed to make anything really worth drinking with it. However, Denbies, who claimed in 2010 when they planted 3-ha that it was a 'UK first' (it wasn't), have been very bullish about their 2013 harvest, which was picked on 31 October at 9.2 per cent, 11.4 g/l acidity and had a pH of 2.94. These are exceptionally good figures (especially given the year). The wine, however, is very grassy and perhaps 2013 was not the year for it? However, I used to say that Chardonnay was impossible in the UK for still wine, so who knows? Maybe in fifty years' time, the UK will be growing all the Sauvignon blanc and New Zealand will be sending us table grapes!

## Schönburger

Type: *Vinifera*
Colour: White
Area in the UK: 34.5-ha (85.4-acres), 2.3 per cent of the planted area in 2013
Origin: Pinot noir x IP1

Schönburger is a crossing made at Geisenheim by Prof. Dr Heinrich Birk in 1939 and first registered for use in 1980. Like many of the crosses from this era, it combined a classic winemaking variety, Pinot noir, with an early ripening table grape variety, in this case a crossing from an Italian, I. Pirovano called IP1 which is Chasselas rosa x Muscat Hamburg. The hope was that a unique German table grape could be produced. There is very little Schönburger planted in Germany (in 2012 there were only 19-ha, down from 39-ha in 1999) and countries such as Canada, New Zealand and the UK have more and some can even be found in Australia and South Africa!

It has been grown in the UK since the late 1970s and on account of its high quality, award-winning grapes, low acidity and regular crops, it became quite widely planted. Colin Gillespie at Wootton Vineyard made it his speciality and won the Gore-Browne Trophy with it in 1982 and Lamberhurst won the same trophy with Schönburger wines in 1982 and 1990. By 1990 there were 75.3-ha, making it then the fifth most planted variety. It is an undemanding variety, more disease resistant than MT and not so on–off in its cropping habits. Yields are never large, but what is picked is almost always of excellent quality, with high sugars and low acids. As they ripen, the grapes change colour from a light lime-green to, at first, light pink and then, when fully ripe, to an almost tawny brown colour. This gives a very good visual indication to the pickers as to which bunches are ripe and allows for some selective picking. This can only aid wine quality. The wines are almost always light and very fruity, with some good Muscat tones (some resemble a less powerful version of Gewürztraminer) that are best balanced with a slight amount of residual sugar. Wines age well and have been known to keep for up to seven years. Schönburger is one of the few varieties we grow that can be eaten with pleasure and although the berries are small, they are packed with flavour.

Despite all these attributes, the area being grown has fallen by 54 per cent to 34.5-ha (2013) and I suspect that this decline will continue. Why? The name is tricky – an *umlaut* and -burger on the end never helped any vine variety become popular – and in style it's just a bit too – well it has to be said – a bit too weak and wishy-washy (I was going to say 'girly' but I realise that might upset some readers). I say this even though a well-made Schönburger, with a touch of residual sweetness, nicely chilled and served as an apéritif is as good an English Wine experience as you could want – not serious, light, and slightly frivolous. Why has this counted against it? Who knows, fashion is a fickle thing and while I like Gewürztraminer, Viognier, Torrontes, and other aromatic, flowery varieties, I know that I am in the minority. Another variety that, I fear, will dwindle in years to come.

## Seyval blanc

Synonym: Seyve Villard 5276
Type: *Hybrid*
Colour: White
Area in the UK: 92.1-ha (227.5-acres), 6.1 per cent of the planted area in 2013
Origin: Seibel 5656 x Seibel 4986

Seyval blanc, a crossing made by Bertille Seyve (the younger) at the nursery of his father-in-law, Victor Villard, in St Vallier on the Rhône in 1921, was originally known as Seyve-Villard 5276. In some references, the crossing is given as Seibel 4996 x Seibel 4986, but Pierre Galet (probably the most famous ampelographer in the world) assured me in a letter that Bertille Seyve's son stated in the *Viticulture Nouvelle* of 1961 (p. 182) that the crossing was Seibel 5656 x Seibel 4986. S. 4986 is known as *Rayon d'Or*. In 1958 there were 1,309-ha in France, but plantings have declined since then and in 2008 were down to 111-ha. It can also be found in many different parts of North America, most notably in New York State and Ontario, and is also grown in Switzerland.

It was first grown in the UK by Edward Hyams who, in 1947, obtained vines directly from the Seyve-Villard nurseries (as they had become known by then) and planted them in his small vineyard at Molash near Canterbury, Kent. Brock also imported the variety from the Swiss Federal Vine Testing Station at Caudoz-sur-Pully a year later in 1948. These two pioneers tested it and soon found that it was a very suitable variety for our climate and together with MT, it became the standard variety for almost all the early vineyards. When Sir Guy Salisbury-Jones planted his vineyard at Hambledon in 1952 he chose Seyval blanc on the advice of a helpful Burgundian grower to whom he sat next at a *Confrérie des Chevaliers du Tastevin* dinner.

Seyval blanc has many attributes. It sets good crops even in cool years, is not vigorous and has a good open habit with small leaves and only a few side-shoots. It is unusual in that the flowers appear and are very prominent before many of the leaves really develop. It is almost totally resistant to disease, although *Botrytis* will occur in riper years, and it yields well – in some years very well. Although the grapes are never very high in natural sugar (I remember plenty of years in the 1970s and 1980s when only 5–6 per cent natural alcohol was reached), wine quality can be good *if* the winery knows what it is doing. On the downside, apart from the low natural sugars, the wine can be very neutral, high in acidity and if not pressed with care, can get a rather grassy herbaceous tone. However, it takes to oak-ageing well, is a good foil for lees-ageing and *battonage* and is great for sparkling wine. What's not to like about it one might ask?

Seyval blanc suffers from a bad press and, rather like Meunier in Champagne – it's a useful variety, but don't let's frighten the horses by talking about it too much. Most wine writers and many wine merchants, faced with the word 'hybrid', seem to recoil into their shells a bit, strike an arrogant pose, and declare without a *shred* of evidence, let alone experience in winegrowing or winemaking, that 'of course you cannot make good wine from a *hybrid*'. The truth is of course that you can and people do. Wines made from Seyval win their share of medals and awards: I won the Gore-Browne Trophy with Seyval twice (in 1981 and 1991) and Colin Gillespie at Wootton won it in 1986 with a Seyval blanc. It can still be found in some good sparkling wines (Breaky Bottom, Camel Valley, Denbies, Monnow Valley and Stanlake Park for instance) as well as a lot of good still wine. Many growers like it and although the area fell from a high of 122.7-ha in 1990 to 88.9-ha in 2000, it has now staged a very modest comeback to 92.1-ha in 2013. It is the UK's fourth most widely planted variety. We fought hard for it when the Quality Wine Scheme was put together as I knew the exclusion of hybrids from the scheme would mean the start of their decline. To deny wines made in whole or in part from a vine variety solely on the grounds of its parentage, does seem somewhat perverse, but that's the EU for you.

When I imported my first Seyval, I obtained stock from one of Professor Becker's friends, Ernest Pfrimmer who had a nursery at Hurtigheim near Strasbourg, and the results were always good. When I started importing a lot of Seyval vines from France, I spent a considerable time searching for a good source-block of vines and together with François Morisson (from the Morisson-Couderc Nursery) found an ideal one in Blois on the Loire. From this vineyard he took wood and grafted many thousands of vines for me. Having seen a fair few Seyval vineyards, both in the UK and overseas, I am convinced that there is quite a bit of clonal variation and some of the UK's vineyards are planted with inferior clones. This might account for some of the grassy, herbaceous notes that are sometimes seen, although that could just be harsh pressing. Recently I have seen some Seyval that is plainly another variety altogether – possibly another Seyve-Villard hybrid – and plainly unsuited for UK conditions. In 2013, I travelled to Switzerland to see an excellent mother-block of Seyval and from which wood is being taken for UK plantings.

The slight revival in Seyval's fortunes, and the plantings that I know to be in the pipeline, give me some encouragement that a mini-revival might be on the way. The sight of a heavy crop of Seyval gently turning golden in late October was always a welcome one and it is such an *easy* variety to grow and turn into wine! Too easy – perhaps that's the problem? Having praised Seyval blanc, I feel it only fair to say that in 2013 it thoroughly disgraced itself, with lower sugars, higher acids and more *Botrytis* than I have even known for the variety. My guess is that the combination of a very heavy yield (20 tonnes-ha in some vineyards) proved too much for it in the exceptionally late vintage. Let's hope 2013 was a one-off performance.

## Siegerrebe

Type: *Vinifera*
Colour: White
Area in the UK: 14.3-ha (35.3-acres), 0.9 per cent of the planted area in 2013
Origin: Freely pollinated seedling of Madeleine Angevine

Siegerrebe is another Georg Scheu crossing from Alzey, made in 1929 and released to growers in 1958. In the *Taschenbuch der Rebsorten* (2010 edition) the breeding details are given as follows. It was originally said to be Madeleine Angevine x Gewürztraminer, but it was later revealed by Scheu's son, Heinz, to be a freely pollinated seedling of Madeleine Angevine (which is the same as the UK's Madeleine x Angevine 7672). However, in *Wine Grapes* it is given as Madeleine Angevine x Savagnin Rose. Savagnin Rose (without an é) is a 'non-aromatic version of Gewürztraminer', which, in Germany, is often called Roter Traminer (Red Traminer). In Germany there

were 97-ha in 2012 and the variety reaches very high natural sugar levels and is used for making sweet dessert wines, although the acid levels are often very low. The grapes have a strong Muscat character and when ripe, can be very concentrated and almost overpowering. It is more often used for blending with other, less distinctive varieties.

It has been in the UK since 1957 when Brock was sent cuttings from Alzey. By 1960 he was able to report: *exceptionally early and the grapes have a strong bouquet* and he highly recommended it as suitable for both the table and winemaking. Despite its attributes of early ripening, low acidity and strongly flavoured grapes, it has really failed to be planted in anything like serious amounts and although one or two vineyards do make interesting varietal wines from it, it mainly gets lost in blends. Maybe because it does ripen very early and falls so far outside what most growers consider their normal harvest time, it is rather disruptive? Wasps are a particular problem and good wasp nest control needs to be practised if real damage is to be avoided. Birds likewise, tend to be a nuisance.   The area planted in the UK has risen slightly: 9.30-ha in 1990, 12.8-ha in 2009 and 14.3-ha in 2013, which makes one think that it still has a future. Three Choirs consistently make an interesting semi-sweet wine with the variety (it's usually one of their better wines) and their 2006 Estate Reserve Siegerrebe won the Gore-Browne Trophy in 2008, their 2007 Three Choirs Siegerrebe won a Gold medal in 2009 and their 2010, 2011 and 2012 all won Silver medals. Siegerrebe can add a nice piquancy to an otherwise dull blend and is probably worth considering as a minor variety. The rise in the area would suggest there is some interest in the variety and it will probably hold its own and possibly expand slightly.

## Solaris

Type: *Vinifera* (complex hybrid)
Colour: White
Area in the UK: 16.1-ha (39.9-acres), 1.1 per cent of the planted area in 2013
Origin: Merzling x Gm 6493

Solaris is a Freiburg interspecific-cross, once known as Fr. 240-75, bred by Dr. Norbert Becker in 1975 and released in 2001. In 2012 there were 101-ha planted in Germany, mainly in the south and it is also found in Belgium, Holland and Switzerland, and is by far the most widely planted white variety in Denmark. Its parents are Merzling and Gm 6493. Merzling is a crossing between our old friend Seyval blanc and a (Riesling x Pinot gris) crossing. Gm 6493 is a Geisenheim *Vitis Amurensis* influenced crossing and is Zarya Severa x Muscat Ottonel, Zarya Severa being one of the parents of Rondo! Complicated or what? The *Taschenbuch der Rebsorten* says that it is very vigorous, with very large leaves, and that it ripens early with very high sugars, usually over 100°OE (13.8 per cent potential alcohol) and often nearer 130°OE (18.4 per cent potential alcohol). It also states that the acidity is less than Ruländer (Pinot gris) – which would mean that its acidity is towards the bottom of the acid spectrum, i.e. 5-6 g/l as tartaric acid. Being a hybrid, it has a good resistance against the major diseases, especially *Botrytis* to which high-sugared varieties are usually prone and its loose bunches help in this respect. It sounds very similar in many ways to Reichensteiner, but with better disease resistance.

In the UK it is planted on 16.1-ha (2013) up from 4.7-ha in 2009 and has found favour in vineyards in the more challenged, northerly counties. To date, little single-variety wine has been made from Solaris and the jury is still out over its long-term potential. However, as vineyards spread ever further north in the UK – a vineyard in Scotland can surely only just be round the corner – perhaps Solaris will fill a small, but useful, niche. Early reports suggest a vigorous variety, with loose bunches and good disease resistance. A variety to watch.

## Triomphe

Type: *Hybrid*
Colour: Red
Area in the UK: 14.7 hectares (36.3-acres), 1.0 per cent of the planted area in 2013
Origin: Unknown parentage

Triomphe is an old French–American hybrid bred by Eugène Kuhlmann in Alsace in around 1911 and released in 1921. Its breeding number is Kuhlmann 319-1 (although some references state 319-3) and it was originally known as *Triomphe d'Alsace* and for many years was labelled as such. When, in 1992, the UK tried to register it under that title, the EU Commission objected (because it contained the name of an *appellation contrôlée* region – Alsace) and the name was shortened to Triomphe. Its parentage is slightly uncertain, but would appear to be the rootstock variety 101-14 *Millardet et De Grasset* crossed with Knipperlé, an ancient Gouais blanc x Pinot crossing from Alsace.

Triomphe was first introduced into the UK by Brock at Oxted, quite widely planted by the early growers and together with Cascade, Léon Millot and Maréchal Foch, became one of the most widely planted red varieties. It is a vigorous variety and needs a bit of canopy management to keep it under control. However, disease resistance is fairly good and it has the small berries and dark red skin, red flesh and red juice of the other Kuhlmann hybrids. However, its wine quality is not that good, certainly below that of Dornfelder and Regent, with a slightly non-vinous tone about it. It is probably best blended with other varieties.

Despite the fact that it is an old hybrid and despite the fact there is said to be a lot of clonal variation, the planted area has expanded from 7.5-ha in 1990 to 14.7-ha in 2013, an area which has been much the same since 2002. It is the fifth most widely planted purely red variety – after Rondo, Regent, Pinot noir Précoce and Dornfelder – and I am surprised that it has held up as well as it has. I really do not think it has much of a future in the UK, but someone seems reluctant to pull it up. Must be those northerners again!

## Würzer

Type: *Vinifera*
Colour: White
Area in the UK: 4.5-ha (11.2-acres), 0.3 per cent of the planted area in 2013
Origin: Gewürztraminer x Müller-Thurgau

Würzer is a crossing made by Georg Scheu at Alzey in 1932 and released to growers in 1978. It is another of Scheu's spicy crosses (Scheube, Faberrebe and Huxelrebe being the other ones used in the UK) and in a similar mould. There were 61-ha in Germany in 2012, an area that has fallen from 108-ha in 1999.

For the UK it is really rather too late for most sites, has high acids and does not show any real advantages over several other similarly flavoured varieties (Bacchus for instance) and the decline in the area from 14.3-ha in 1999 to 4.5-ha in 2013 is probably a good indication of its usefulness. Not a variety for the future.

## Clones of Chardonnay, Pinot noir and Meunier for sparkling wines

Until Nyetimber started winning medals and prizes, the question of which clones to plant had never really been much discussed amongst UK growers. In around 1998 I remember planting 1.77-ha (4.37-acres) of Pinot noir when I was at Chapel Down and I selected clones 115, 666, 667 and the *teinturier* clone *Tête du Nègre* as the intention was to produce red wine, not sparkling. This was the first time that I had really given much thought to clones. The next occasion I had to choose some clones was in 2001-2 when I was asked to advise on the planting of the initial vineyards at Hush Heath Estate which were solely for the production of a bottle-fermented rosé sparkling wine, which became *Balfour Brut Rosé*. This time I made sure I had done some homework before I put pen to paper. I therefore did as much investigative work as I could with: (a) the vineyards in the UK then making the best sparkling wine, (b) the CIVC and (c) some of the *pépiniéristes* selling vines to Champagne and other sparkling wine producers.

From UK sparkling wine producers, principally Nyetimber and Ridgeview, I discovered some of the clones they were using, although about others there was a certain amount of secrecy. The CIVC sold me their *Viticulture raisonée guide pratique* which in a separate chapter headed 'Clones' lists all the clones allowed to be used in Champagne: eleven clones of Chardonnay, eighteen clones of Pinot noir, and eleven of Meunier, all listed according to their ability (or otherwise) to crop, produce sugar and succumb to *Botrytis*. From vine nurseries I was able to find out a bit more about other clones, especially ones with lower acid levels and better disease resistance, two attributes I felt important for the UK. As with many other things viticultural, one always has to remember that when taking data from abroad, the UK is different, in some respects very different, from other vine growing regions. Compared to Champagne for instance, our yields are laughably small. The average yield in Champagne since 2000 has been 14,980 kg-ha (6.06 tonnes-acre) whereas in the UK it has been 19.44 hl-ha or around 2,680 kg-ha (1.09 tonnes-acre). Of course the planting density in Champagne of around 8,000 vines-ha (3,238 vines-acre) compared to a typical UK vineyard of around 3,500-4,000 vines-ha (1,416-1,619 vines-acre) and the unprofessional nature of many of the UK's smaller vineyards accounts in part for our low yields, but the truth is that high yields are what the Champenoise want and high yields is what they get. Their selection of clones therefore takes this into account.

In the UK, the natural sugar levels we achieve are, in all but the best of years, towards the lower end of those achieved in other cool climate regions and distinctly off the scale compared to anywhere warmer. Chardonnay and Pinot noir is generally picked at between 8.5 and 10 per cent natural alcohol and in 2013, admittedly a year when sugar levels were at their lowest for many years, most of the harvest of Champagne varieties came in at between 7 and 9 per cent. These are low levels and make many an overseas grower wonder how we manage to make wine so good! Likewise our acidity levels. Even in Germany where Riesling's high acids can test even the best winemakers, the UK's acid levels which, with Chardonnay, can often be around 14-16 g/l as tartaric with pH levels routinely below 3.0, take a bit of getting used to. In Champagne, the average potential alcohol and acid levels (as tartaric) between 2005 and 2012 were: Chardonnay 10.2 per cent and 10.95 g/l; Pinot noir 10.2 per cent and 11.25 g/l; and Meunier 10.1 per cent and 11.40 g/l. Whilst these figures may not seem vastly different from the UK's, you have to bear in mind that the yields in Champagne are many times ours, which makes their acid levels – 11.20 g/l over the three varieties – several notches below those found in the UK. This helps show that the UK is a very different winegrowing region compared to Champagne and clones should be selected with this in mind.[13]

One also has to remember when looking at clones of two of the three Champagne varieties – Chardonnay and Pinot noir – that these are also major varieties for the production of still wines of different qualities: high-volume, entry level quality; mid-range, generally higher volume quality; and low-volume, top-notch quality. Chardonnay and Pinot noir are also varieties found in some of the warmest parts of the winegrowing world – California's Central Valley and some of South Africa's hot regions – as well as some of its coolest, Champagne, Chablis and of course, coolest of all, the UK. Therefore opinions about what clones suit what regions are always coloured by the type, style, and quality of wine being produced, plus the yield levels wished for.

Owing to our historic links with Germany in relation to viticulture, some UK vine suppliers seem keen to recommend and supply German clones grafted on to rootstocks common to German vine nurseries. This practice is something that concerns me. I take the view that if you are trying to produce a top quality sparkling wine, then you have to have a very good reason not to copy what happens in the region that produces, without any argument, the best bottle-fermented sparkling wines in the world: Champagne. Champagne has the advantages of scale – there are 35,000-ha (86,485-acres) of vines in the region –

and of time – they have been growing vines in the region for many centuries. They also have the unique advantage that every individual winegrower, all 15,000 of them, growing vines in 270,000 individual plots, belong to one organisation – the CIVC – whose job it is to oversee every aspect of production, including research into what clones suit the wine being produced. Therefore, my practice since 2002-3 has been to stick very firmly to selecting French clones, mainly, but not only, CIVC recommended clones, for producing UK sparkling wine.

Although I am sure there are very many good German clones of both Chardonnay and Pinot noir, there are several factors which make me wary of using them in the UK. To start with, Chardonnay is still a relatively new variety in Germany, and although they have 1,496-ha (3,697-acres), making it the fifteenth most widely planted variety, most of it is used for making still wines and very little is used to produce sparkling wines. Likewise Pinot noir. Although a much more popular variety than Chardonnay, the 11,769-ha (29,081-acres) make it the most widely grown red variety and third most widely grown variety overall, very little of it goes into bottle-fermented sparkling wines. Although there are some very serious growers of Pinot noir, mainly in the southern growing areas, producing some excellent Burgundy-style red wines, much of the Pinot noir is used for making relatively light-character, fruity wine, which finds favour with the German consumer. An additional factor in Germany is cost of production and yields, both of which are high. For a vine variety and/or clone to be taken up in Germany, it needs to be easy to grow, show good disease resistance and yield well. Low yielding, disease-prone clones are soon weeded out.

Clonal development of Pinot noir in Germany started in the 1930s in three principal institutes: Freiburg, Geisenheim and Weinsburg. To start with, high yields and high natural sugars were the key goals, with disease resistance a distant aspiration. In the second generation of German clones, those with loose bunches were preferred as they had a greater resistance to *Botrytis* and these have found favour with growers. Consequently, most German vine nurseries concentrate on producing these clones, and Freiburg and Geisenheim clones such as Fr 18-01 and Gm 20-13 are the most widely planted. Taking all these factors together, I am not persuaded that German clones are to be preferred for the production of sparkling wines in the UK.

As for recommending which clones to plant, as I have already said above, this is a confusing and unfathomable task. The clones I recommend below are ones used by many of the most important UK sparkling wine producers and all can be planted with confidence on suitable sites. This is not to say that they are the only clones that can be successful in the UK, and I am sure, in time, others will be tried and will prove suitable. My advice would be to plant at least two clones of each of the three varieties and on a vineyard of more than 2-ha (5 acres), you might plant more clones. Around 0.4-ha (1-acre) of each clone makes a good sized block and if you are making your own wine, allows you to make separate *cuvées* of each clone.

As a general rule, clones will, in most instances, vary only a little. Some will be earlier than others, some will have bigger and/or better crops than others, but these differences might well be much less important than the influences of the site, the rootstock, the weather during the year and of the management of the vineyard in all its aspects. Finding 'the' clone for your vineyard, one that will produce you perfect wine, year in and year out, is probably not possible, so play safe, and use a sensible range for the size of vineyard. Over the years, on your site, you will get to notice the differences and when you come to plant more, you can take a more educated decision.

Chardonnay    The following CIVC clones have performed well in UK vineyards for sparkling wine: 75, 76, 78, 95, 96, 118, 121, 124, and 131. I also like these non-CIVC clones: 119, 277 and 548. Clone 809, which has a slight muscat tone, might also add some interest to a blend.

Pinot noir    The following CIVC clones have performed well in UK vineyards for sparkling wine: 292, 375, 386, 521, 779, 792, 870, 871, 872 and 927. I also like non-CIVC clones: 114, 115, and 459.

Meunier    The following CIVC clones have performed well in UK vineyards for sparkling wine: 817, 865, 900, 977 and 978.

**Note:** The best source of information on French varieties, clones and rootstocks is the Pl@ntGrape website: http://plantgrape.plantnet-project.org. The US National Grape Registry, based at the University of California, also has a good website for varieties, although clones have all been given FPS (Foundation Plant Services) numbers http://ngr.ucdavis.edu.

## Rootstocks for the UK

**Note:** The planting of ungrafted 'own-root' vines is covered in *Chapter 16: Pest and disease control* in the section on *Phylloxera* and at the end of *Chapter 17: Trunk diseases.*

The question of which, of the many dozens of rootstocks used around the world, are best for UK vineyards is an interesting one. Like the choice of varieties, this task is made harder by the fact that no rootstock has been developed for UK conditions and that all rootstock recommendations are based upon data derived in climates which are both warmer and drier than the UK's, where yields are typically higher (often much higher) and more regular and in soils which may differ considerably. The behaviour of a rootstock in a lean, dry soil, where there is little summer rainfall, where temperatures are often over 30°C and where yields are both higher and more consistent than in the UK, will not be the same in a deep, fertile soil, well-watered with summer rainfall and where yields might be modest one year, negligible the next and well over average the year after. Likewise, a rootstock in a region where the climate is hot, vines are irrigated and yields are consistently high. Therefore, whenever looking at

recommendations for rootstocks to use in the UK, these differences need to be taken in to account.

Rootstock tables (such as the one at the end of this chapter) will usually give you several recommendations concerning not only their active $CaCO_3$ tolerance and root growth habit, but also their 'vigour' and 'influence upon maturity'. As I have said above, these recommendations for are not based upon UK data (another job for Plumpton perhaps?) and therefore a 'health warning' needs to be issued before relying too much upon the tables you can find on the internet and issued by vine nurseries. In my experience, there are other factors which can also have an influence upon the behaviour of the vine, not only the rootstock. The weather during the season undoubtedly has a huge impact upon the vigour of vines: a cool, wet season will promote growth; a hot, dry season will almost certainly curtail vigour. The other very important factor is yield. A vine bearing 5 tonnes-ha (2 tonnes-acre) is going to be more vigorous than one carrying 10-15 tonnes-ha (4-6 tonnes-acre), especially if this is coupled with a warm, dry year (i.e. the sort of year likely to lead to high yields). In 2013 UK vineyards were subject to very unusual circumstances. We had a very late spring, an ideal flowering period which gave high yields, a warm spell in the middle of the summer, followed by a cooler, wetter, less-sunny October and the latest harvest ever experienced. How could you expect a rootstock to conform to a description based upon completely different circumstances?

In the early days of modern UK viticulture, with the exception of a few growers who obtained their vines from France, the bulk of vines planted up until the early 1990s were German varieties, of German origin and consequently, on German rootstocks. 125AA, 5BB, 5C and SO4 are the four standard German rootstocks with Teleki 8B and Börner bringing up the rear. All of these are classified as 'high' to 'medium-high' in terms of vigour and coupled with already vigorous varieties such as Bacchus, Huxelrebe, Kerner, Müller-Thurgau, Ortega, Reichensteiner and Schönburger, tended to produce, in our cool climate and our fresh, loam-rich, well-watered soils, some exceptionally large, leaf-endowed, canopies which did little to help the problems associated with shading and over-vigorous canopies. Of the 'old' varieties, only Seyval blanc, being a naturally low-vigour variety, did not suffer from over-vigorous canopies, one of the reasons why, of almost all of the varieties popular in the early days, it has maintained its position in the list of UK vine varieties.

The arrival in the UK of the Champagne varieties has somewhat altered the rootstock situation and, in my view, made a significant impact upon the vigour of our canopies. In France, the origin of the majority (but by no means all) of the Chardonnay, Pinot noir and Meunier vines now being grown in the UK, the most popular rootstocks for these varieties are 41B, SO4 and Fercal in high active calcium carbonate ($CaCO_3$) soils (with 161-49 as another option) and 101-14, 3309C and 420A in soils with 20 per cent or less active $CaCO_3$. With the exception of SO4 and Fercal (both classified as having 'medium' vigour) all of the others are classified as 'low' or 'low medium' in terms of vigour. On paper, this may seem a very marginal difference, but it is my experience that these marginal differences, in the vineyard, make an appreciable difference to vigour of shoot-growth and therefore to the density of the canopy. It worries me sometimes that growers prefer to get their Chardonnay and Pinot noir from Germany and on German rootstocks without realising the difference the rootstock can make.

The first thing you need to know before you can select a rootstock is whether you are likely to need lime-tolerant rootstocks. In soils of pH 7 or lower, and without any obvious signs of chalk or limestone, the level of active $CaCO_3$ in your soil is likely to be low. In soils of over pH 7, the best and safest advice is to test for the level of active $CaCO_3$. This is NOT the same as the level of total $CaCO_3$ – they are related, but not in a linear fashion and it is not, in my view, safe to rely on taking 50 per cent of the total level of $CaCO_3$ as being the level of the active $CaCO_3$ (something I have seen suggested is acceptable) as this is not accurate enough. The reason that the level of active $CaCO_3$ is important is that if the rootstock selected does not have the right level of tolerance, the vines will get Chlorosis, a condition where they are unable to access iron in the soil and are therefore unable to produce chlorophyll, necessary for photosynthesis to take place. Vines suffering from Chlorosis will turn light green, then yellow, and then almost white, before starting to die. Vines suffering from Chlorosis can be treated by spraying or soil drenching with chelated iron, iron that has been treated so that it is soluble (Ferleaf and Fersoil are the two best known products) and whilst this may be a temporary solution, it is much better to select the right rootstock in the first place. In France, rootstocks are given an 'IPC' rating (*l'Indice de Pouvoir Clorosant*) which runs from 0-120, with rootstocks at the lower end (0-20) being safe in soils with no or low levels of active $CaCO_3$ and those with higher ratings (30-120) being better in soils with high levels of active $CaCO_3$. I have never used this index myself and in practice find that the active $CaCO_3$ measurement is more than adequate.

When it comes to active $CaCO_3$ levels, I would prefer to err on the side of caution as however well done, sampling a field can only tell you about a small section of the whole field and there may well be patches of ground where levels are higher than shown by sampling.

*Vines with Chlorosis on soil with high active $CaCO_3$*

Therefore, for levels of active $CaCO_3$ of 15 per cent of more, I would only plant on 41B or Fercal. 41B to me is the better rootstock, even though it is listed as having a delaying effect upon maturity. I find it less vigorous than Fercal. Unless you are really sure about the accuracy of your soil sampling I would avoid SO4 at levels of 15 per cent or more, even though the tolerance of SO4 is generally stated to be 20 per cent. 161-49 is also an option, but whilst in some situations I have found this to be an excellent rootstock, producing a low-vigour canopy and good crops, in other situations it has struggled, especially when paired with Chardonnay. With Pinot noir and Meunier it has proved to be better. It suffers from what I call 'tylosis' (and which the French call *thyllose* or sometimes *folletage*) which can result in a higher percentage of early vine deaths than would normally be expected with other rootstocks. I would therefore advise caution with 161-49, especially in situations where the vine might be put under stress in its first two years. Such situations might be poorly drained sites, adverse soil conditions, drought, weed competition, early cropping. If 161-49 is used, I would recommend keeping the young vines as weed-free as possible and cultivating the inter-row areas for the first two full growing seasons before grassing down.

In situations where levels of active $CaCO_3$ are 15 per cent or lower, my first choice would be 101-14, 3309C and 420A, all of which are at the lower end of the spectrum for vigour and have a slight advancing effect upon maturity. If these were not available, I would select 5C, 125AA and SO4, listed in increasing order of vigour with SO4 being the most vigorous. However, in soils with low levels of active $CaCO_3$, there is nothing stopping you using 41B or Fercal and I have planted plenty of vines in soils with pH 6.5 using these rootstocks. For very acid soils i.e. pH 5.5 or below, the only rootstock that appears to be recommended in the literature is Gravesac. In some sources it is suggested that 101-14, 3309C and SO4 might also suitable, although in other sources this is contradicted, and before one embarked on a large scale planting on soils with this level of acidity, some further research on rootstocks would be advised. Luckily there are few soils in UK fruit growing regions with this level of acidity and in any event, soils with pH levels below 6.0-6.5 must be limed in an attempt to bring them up towards neutral (pH 7).

Two other factors must be considered when selecting rootstocks: soil and vine variety. With deep, free-rooting soils, the best rootstocks are going to be ones with lower vigour. This does not mean that more vigorous rootstocks cannot be used, but in order to have an open and airy canopy, you will probably need to do more canopy management (trimming and deleafing) than with lower vigour rootstocks. Likewise with vigorous varieties such as Bacchus, Reichensteiner, Müller-Thurgau and other German varieties, I would always aim for lower vigour rootstocks, although 101-14, 3309C and 420A are seldom available from German nurseries unless custom grafted. Pinot noir can also be quite vigorous and is best on a lower vigour rootstock, although Chardonnay appears to do well on both. Only with Seyval blanc, which is naturally low in vigour, might I look for a rootstock with a slightly higher vigour potential and I have known it do well on SO4 and 5BB. On deep vigorous soils, 420A also suits it.

Apart from those mentioned above, there are many other rootstocks which may be perfectly acceptable in UK vineyards. I have used both Gravesac and Riparia Gloire de Montpelier (RGM) in vineyards and they performed well, although RGM does not appear to be that low in vigour. However, they are not widely used and are not always easy to obtain. Yalumba Nursery has both an excellent *Rootstock Selector* as well as a lot of information about individual rootstocks on its website (www.yalumbanursery.com), although of course aimed at Australian growers. Mercier Nursery also has good information in English on their Californian website (www.mercier-california.com) under 'varieties' and then 'rootstocks'.

A final warning concerns vine nurseries. They are in the business of selling as many vines as possible from the vines they graft and seeing those vines survive and thrive in their client's vineyards. Some rootstocks graft more easily than others, giving a higher percentage of 'take', meaning that once lifted and on the sorting table, far fewer are rejected.

Rootstocks with higher vigour also tend to root more easily giving better roots at lifting from their eight to nine months in the nursery and also tend to put down roots more easily once planted out in the vineyard. Fercal and SO4 are well known to fall into this category and are well-liked by nurseries. However, that does not mean that these vines always produce the best vineyards and the best crops in the long term. Under UK conditions, with most situations and vine varieties, I prefer a rootstock with a slightly lower vigour potential.

| Rootstocks for UK vineyards | | | | | |
|---|---|---|---|---|---|
| Rootstock | Crossing | Active CaCO3 tolerance | Root growth | Vigour | Influence on Maturity |
| Riparia Gloire (RGM) | Riparia | 6% | Shallow | Low | Advances |
| 101-14 | Riparia x Rupestris | 10% | Shallow | Low | Advances |
| 3309C | Riparia x Rupestris | 11% | Semi-deep | Low-Medium | Advances |
| Gravesac | 161-49 x 3309C | 15% | Semi-deep | Medium | Advances |
| Börner | Riparia x Cinerea | 15% | Semi-deep | Medium-High | No effect |
| 125AA | Berlandieri x Riparia | 17% | Deep | Medium-High | No effect |
| 5C | Berlandieri x Riparia | 17% | Deep | Medium-High | Slightly Advances |
| 420A | Berlandieri x Riparia | 20% | Semi-deep | Low-Medium | Slightly Advances |
| SO4 | Berlandieri x Riparia | 20% | Semi-deep | Medium+ | No effect |
| Binova | SO4 Mutation | 20% | Semi-deep | Medium++ | No effect |
| 161-49C | Riparia x Berlandieri | 25% | Semi-deep | Low-Medium | Advances |
| 41B | Chasselas x Berlandieri | 40% | Shallow | Low-Medium | Delays |
| Fercal | Berlandieri x Riparia | 45% | Deep | Medium | Advances |
| Note: Recomendations on root growth, vigour and influence on maturity are based upon non-UK data | | | | | |

1 Under Article 62 of the EU regulation 479/2008, wines made in part or in whole from 'Pinot blanc, Pinot gris, Pinot Meunier or Pinot noir' may substitute the single word 'Pinot' when describing their varietal makeup. In other words, a wine made from 60 per cent Chardonnay, 20 per cent Pinot blanc and 20 per cent Pinot gris, could say: 'this wine is a blend of Chardonnay and Pinot'.

2 I say 'probably' as no official figures are collected for the type of wine produced or sold. My 60 per cent is an educated guess based upon the varieties planted.

3 I say 'seemingly' as in fact Lamberhurst Vineyards at the time was loss-making, something that didn't seem to trouble Kenneth McAlpine too much as he was probably able to write it off against other income. When I took over as winemaker and general manager in 1988, I was given audited accounts which showed annual losses running at around £350,000 pa, which equates to around £775,000 in 2013 prices, and this level of loss had been going on for several years.

4 At the time I owned Tenterden Vineyards (today's Chapel Down) which was only a few miles from Lamberhurst, and I found that this price reduction didn't have quite the effect I feared, mainly because we hand-sold most of our output from the farm-gate. When people said: 'why is your wine more expensive than Lamberhurst's?' we always said: 'our wines are better of course and you get what you pay for'!

5 The Champagne Bureau, sometimes also called the Champagne Information Bureau, is a CIVC financed marketing organisation with twelve offices around the world, including one in London.

6 Wye College, near Ashford in Kent, used to be the University of London's agricultural outpost which, amongst other things, had a Hop Department. Jack Ward, Chairman of the EVA, raised £10,000 from members and supporters and persuaded Wye College to provide some land and look after a vineyard. This was planted in 1973 with vines donated by German wine companies and nurseries and amongst the seventeen varieties – all then new to the UK – planted in the 0.526-ha (1.3-acre) vineyard were Bacchus, Faberrebe, Regner, Würzer and Zweigeltrebe. The grapes from the vineyard were either sold to Merrydown, or sent to Long Ashton Research Station (then the UK's centre for cider research) to be made into wine. The vineyard was grubbed to make way for a new hop garden in 1984.

7 The best UK-grown Huxelrebe I ever tasted was the late Bill Ash's 1982 Staple St James Huxelrebe, one of the very few English wines I have ever bought a case of. The interesting story about this wine is that Bill sold half the grapes to Lamberhurst (he was always strapped for cash) and they made a wine with it, sweetened with some high-strength *Auslese* Gewürztraminer *süss-reserve* that Karl-Heinz Johner had prized out of the local co-op winery where he lived in Baden. This wine won the 1983 Gore-Browne Trophy, largely on account of the great *süss* used, but fell apart after a while and the Staple wine, with as I recall 12 per cent natural alcohol, aged into a really great wine. The *süss* trick was one I remembered and when I was winemaker at Lamberhurst I used the same Gewürztraminer *süss* in the 1988 Schönburger which won the Gore-Browne in 1990! They say all's fair in love, war and winemaking. Pilton Manor also produced a very good late harvest Huxel in 1992. This was a complete accident and the crop had been written off, but then owner Jim Dowling was persuaded by his winemaker, John Worontschak, to pick the crop despite it being completely affected by

*Botrytis*. It was an excellent wine and I recently read a report of a tasting at which it was still showing very well.

8 Madeleine Royale, a table grape vine variety once thought to be a Chasselas seedling, but now shown to be a Pinot x Black Hamburg cross, has been 'outed' by the gene-jockeys as the father of Müller-Thurgau, with Riesling being the mother.

9 See *Appendix III* for the full story of Wrotham Pinot.

10 In the late 1980s, German vine developers, who had bred complex interspecific crosses – now often known as PIWI, standing for *pilzwiderstandfähig* or fungus resistant varieties – were being denied the right to produce quality wines with them. They asked the German *Bundessortenamt* (the regulatory body that grants plant breeder's rights and classifies new cultivars) whether they could tell, from their growth habits, their leaf and fruit shape and the taste of the wine, whether they were *viniferas* or non-*viniferas*. The *Bundessortenamt* decided that as they resembled *viniferas* in every respect – apart from their superior natural disease resistance, then they could be classified as pure viniferas and thus be made into Quality Wine. This judgment was accepted by the EU and German winegrowers were then allowed to make Quality Wines from them. After five years of lobbying by the UKVA and a lot of heel-dragging, MAFF/DEFRA finally agreed that what the Germans had done was legal and the four PIWI varieties then being grown in the UK – Orion, Phoenix, Regent and Rondo – could then be made into English and Welsh Quality Wine.

11 *Selection massale* vines are produced by taking scion wood from (usually old) vineyards which are not planted with clones and contain vines whose ancestry is typically from a local well known and successful vineyard. In this way, clonal variation and local typicity are maintained in new vineyards.

12 Ingelheim, situated on the southern side of the Rhine, about halfway between Mainz and Bingen, is where Charlemagne built a palace (in about 800). According to legend, he noticed that the snows melted first on the south-facing slopes opposite and could see that the area had a unique microclimate. His son, Ludwig the Pious, started growing grapes there and the slopes eventually became the site for what is today Schloss Johannisberg.

13 It is however, worth noting that until the mid-'90s, grapes in Champagne only had to reach a potential alcohol level of 7 per cent before they could be harvested and that today it is only 9 or 9.5 per cent, depending on the vintage.

# Chapter 5
# Pruning and trellising systems for UK vineyards

## A short history of vine training in the UK

There are not only dozens of completely different pruning and trellising systems in use in commercial vineyards throughout the world, but even within a general style of pruning, there are also an infinite number of individual variations based upon personal choice, the equipment used to run the vineyard and the different materials employed to build the trelliswork. Having said that, in certain regions – old world ones such as Bordeaux or Burgundy – there is an almost universal uniformity about how vines are pruned and trained, although row widths and planting densities will still vary. However, drive along the St. Helena Highway, which runs up the centre of the Napa Valley, and you can see almost every system and every vine density known to man being used. Which therefore, is the correct system for UK vineyards?

In the very early days of the revival, most vineyards looked very French. Ray Brock at his Oxted Viticultural Research Station planted most of his vines at 3-feet (0.91 m) between the rows and the vines 4-feet (1.22 m) apart, giving a vine density of 9,007 vines-ha (3,645 vines-acre). The vines were always *Guyot* trained and very low to the ground. Brock remained convinced throughout the life of his Oxted vineyard that close planting encouraged root competition and that vines close to the ground ripened their fruit better as they absorbed heat from the soil.[1]

In 1952, Major-General Sir Guy Salisbury-Jones, who had visited Oxted and knew Brock well, planted his vineyard at Hambledon in a very Burgundian style, with 4' (1.22 m) between the rows and the vines 3' (0.91 m) apart, giving the same densities as Brock was using at Oxted. With such narrow rows, specialist equipment was needed and as the vineyard got bigger and spraying by hand was no longer an option, Salisbury-Jones bought a Jacquet *tracteur-enjambeur* (straddle tractor) to make life easier. As the vineyard expanded, so did the row width and inter-vine spacing. In 1982, an experiment was tried with 8' (2.44 m) wide rows and 4' (1.22 m) between the vines, with the vines trained to a single high trellis – they called it a 'modified Geneva Double Curtain (GDC) system – and eventually, after the Major-General's death in 1985 and in the hands of a new owner, additional vineyards were planted using a full-blown GDC system at 3.5 m row width and 2.0 m between the vines with 1,429 vines-ha

(578 vines-acre). The vineyards stayed that way, being gradually reduced as owners came and went, until by 1999 only around 2-ha (5-acres) remained. Today, it has been replanted and expanded to 18.55-ha (45.8-acres) with most of the vineyards planted at 2.20 m x 1.2 m and 1.1 m.

Jack Ward, who spoke fluent German, started planting vineyards at Horam Manor in 1954 and took a much more Germanic approach to UK viticulture. He visited Geisenheim on at least one occasion where he saw Professor Helmut Becker who introduced him to Geisenheim varieties and growing techniques. Ward, as has already been mentioned, was the Chairman of the EVA, and also ran what was known as the Merrydown Co-operative Scheme which made wine under contract in exchange for a proportion of the grapes which were taken in lieu of payment and used to make a blend of English Wine called 'Anderida'. He always made time for new growers, myself included, tirelessly promoting the cause of English and Welsh wine. Merrydown, the company he co-owned, also imported vines and he was instrumental in popularising varieties such as Bacchus, Reichensteiner and Huxelrebe (amongst others) in the UK.

Ward's initial plantings were with 5' (1.52 m) rows and 4' (1.22 m) between the vines, a density of 5,393 vines-ha (2,182 vines-acre) and his book, *The Complete Book of Vine Growing in the British Isles* (published in 1984) says that for those with specialist 'vineyard tractors' these distances and densities hold good. He also said that farmers who were 'not prepared to invest in a vineyard tractor' would need to plant at 7'6" (2.29 m) row width. On inter-vine distances, he advocated planning according to the vigour of the rootstock, with weaker rootstocks at 4' (1.22 m) and on 'richer soils' and 'strong rootstocks' an inter-vine distance of 6'6" (1.98 m) could be used.[2]

(Ward also employed two people who each in their own way helped change the face of English and Welsh wine: Christopher Lindlar and Greg Williams. Lindlar (usually called Kit) was one of the most experienced winemakers working in the UK in the late 1970s to mid-1990s. After Ward retired and the board of Merrydown decided to end their involvement with English and Welsh wine in 1980, Lindlar ran a contract winemaking business based at Biddenden Vineyards, and then built his own winery, High Weald Winery, at Grafty Green near Maidstone, Kent where he co-made the first three vintages of Nyetimber (1992–1994) as well as a large number of other wines. After that closed, he became winemaker at Denbies for two years before retiring from winemaking to take up Holy Orders. I guess that his experience of praying for good weather and good winemaking conditions gave him something of an advantage at theological college! Williams looked after the selling of vines whilst at Merrydown and after their involvement with English wine ended, he moved to Tenterden and continued to sell vines for a number of years. In 1988 he tragically fell downstairs and was killed.)

### High and wide – the rise and fall of GDC

Jack Ward also favoured Dr Lenz Moser's eponymous system of high training (*Hochkulture*) which was developed in Austria in the 1920s and found favour both there and in Germany in the 1950s, '60s and '70s when the price of wine came under pressure and growers sought ways of lowering input costs.[3] The system was essentially a wide-rowed, single curtain system, very similar to the 'ballerina' variant of the Smart-Dyson system (which was developed in the early 1980s) and based upon a row width of 3.0 m to 3.5 m with a fruiting wire at around 1.2 m to 1.3 m from the ground – hence the name 'high culture'. This spacing enabled growers to convert existing narrow-rowed *Guyot* systems to Lenz Moser by removing every other row and re-training their vines. Nelson Shaulis, Professor of Pomology at Cornell University, Geneva, New York, (and Richard Smart's mentor and PhD supervisor) developed his GDC system in the 1960s[4] borrowing freely from Lenz Moser and the experiences of producers who had used it. GDC was developed for growers of the vigorous *Vitis labrusca* variety 'Concord' which in New York State is mainly grown for making low-value grape juice or grape jelly and high yields, low establishment costs and low running costs (including machine harvesting) were required. It was never envisaged that it would be suitable for growing high-quality *vinifera* wine grapes, although in some countries it is now used for this purpose.

*Ancre Hill Estates in Wales – one of the last UK vineyards to be planted using GDC*

Which vineyard was the first in the UK to be established using GDC is open to question, but the best-known were New Hall, near Maldon in Essex, planted by Bill Greenwood in 1968 and Westbury, near Reading, Berkshire, planted by Bernard Theobald in 1969. These two, together with David Carr Taylor, who planted his

vineyard at Westfield, near Hastings, East Sussex, in 1973 and A. H. Holmes at Wraxall near Shepton Mallet in Somerset, who planted in 1974, were not the only growers using GDC, but certainly amongst the most vocal in their support for the system.

The standard GDC has rows at 12-feet (3.66-m) and vines spaced at 8-feet (2.44-metres) giving a vine density of 1,120 vines-ha (453 vines-acre). Its attractions – on the surface – are obvious: the ability to use standard farm tractors, mowers and sprayers down its wide rows; the low vine density meaning that a GDC vineyard was much cheaper to plant, establish and trellis than a high density *Guyot* vineyard; and its relatively low labour input, once it was established and cropping. These were all attractive attributes, especially to growers with little experience of growing vines on any system. On the downside, GDC vineyards, especially those planted on marginal, windy sites, were often very difficult to establish and the wide rows and sparse vines do not create the site microclimate seen in a more densely planted *Guyot* vineyard. In addition, most GDC vineyards, even well-managed and well-sited ones, take at least five years to come into full cropping and although crops can be good, the vineyards are often not quite so labour-saving as many claimed.

The pro-GDC growers, notably Bernard Theobald and David Carr Taylor, would hear nothing against the system and did a lot to encourage growers to plant what at the time were considered to be huge vineyards, almost all of which eventually disappeared. Karl-Heinz Johner, who ran Lamberhurst from 1976-88, was also attracted to GDC when it came to advising growers, many of whom were under contract to supply grapes to Lamberhurst. Whether this enthusiasm on the part of these people was because they thought it was the best way of growing grapes in the UK, or a way of producing grapes as cheaply as possible so that grape prices were low, I will leave to speculation. However, whatever the reasons, the GDC system was popular with growers who wanted to get into owning a vineyard with (a) the minimum of capital cost and (b) the minimum of effort in growing grapes. The results often showed.

GDC growers often wanted an 'easy-care' system of growing vines – 'ranching' I called it – and were not always really committed to the attention to detail that each individual vine calls for in any climate, let alone a challenging climate like the UK's. Consequently, many GDC vineyards established poorly – if at all – with multiple misses and re-plants and some taking forever to fill out the wires and achieve a full canopy of fruiting wood. With each vine occupying almost nine square metres, one missing or poorly performing GDC vine has four times the impact that a missing or poorly performing *Guyot* vine has. Whether the failure[5] rate of GDC vineyards was any higher than that of high density *Guyot* vineyards it is impossible to tell – so many vineyards from the 1970s and 1980s of both types have disappeared – and the reasons have been varied.

Many of the failed GDC vineyards were quite large and prominent and therefore stood out more than the others perhaps, but either way, there are almost no GDC vineyards left from the 1970s (Carr Taylor being a notable exception). The roll-call of large GDC vineyards that came and went is long and these are only a few of the largest, all in the south-east: Ashburnhams (7-ha), Barkham Manor (14-ha), Chiddingstone (14 ha), Great Shoesmiths (7-ha), Honeybee (11-ha), Lamberhurst (20-ha), Leeford (14-ha). I cannot claim complete immunity from the desire to plant a GDC vineyard and in 1980, whilst at Tenterden Vineyards, having planted around 4-ha (10-acres) of 2.0 m wide *Guyot* vineyards, I did succumb and planted 2-ha (5-acres) of GDC in order to see just how it performed. Sadly it took so long to establish, that I sold up and moved on before I had a chance to make comparisons.

The main problem with GDC, at least as it is practiced in the UK, is that the canopy is very often a tangled mass of shoots and side-shoots and the grapes are often hidden below several layers of foliage and require considerable hand work to expose them. Although the buds for the coming year are produced at the top of the GDC canopy, and therefore exposed to air and light, because most sprayers are not made to spray from the top down and from the bottom up, it is much more difficult to keep disease under control in GDC vineyards. Apart from damage to grapes, the effect of disease – especially *Botrytis* on the fruiting buds for the next year's crop – is also an issue. Although GDC is sold as a 'low input' system, it is my experience that the vines are often just as vigorous as their cane pruned compatriots (so much for the 'big vine' theory which suggests that the bigger the vine the lower will be the vigour) and in order to manage GDC vines well, a considerable amount of shoot positioning, shoot removal and 'combing-out' of shoots between the curtains is required to expose the fruit and buds/canes. Given that some growers only used GDC because they had been advised that it was a 'plant and forget' system, this work often did not get done.

As you can tell from the above, I am not really a fan of GDC trained vines! Having said that, I consult to two (albeit fairly small) vineyards planted on GDC and crops are produced and results are acceptable and sometimes very good, so it is possible to make GDC work in the UK. However, apart from my own small experiment whilst at Tenterden, I have never advised a grower to plant a vineyard using GDC and cannot really see any circumstances in which I would. I am also not aware of any GDC vineyards having been planted in the UK in recent years.

## High density Vertically Shoot Positioned (VSP) training

By the time I came to plant my first vineyards in 1977, having spent almost two years working in German vineyards and studying at Geisenheim, I was firmly of the opinion that a 2.00 m row width was right, with vines spaced at between 1.1 m and 1.3 m in the row – classic cane pruned Vertically Shoot Positioned (VSP) training – and I bought a David Brown 885 Narrow which, at 1.25 m wide, fitted down the rows. At the time, a ferocious GDC vs *Guyot* debate was going on in the EVA and every new edition of the Grape Press seemed to contain a letter or two, usually one from a 'pro' and one from an 'anti'

extolling the virtues of their pet system and spacing. As a newcomer, I held back at first, but it wasn't too long before I waded in on the side of the anti-GDC brigade. It seemed to me that although GDC had some obvious advantages, the results didn't really show it to be a system that could produce the best quality grapes (and therefore wine) and I felt that whatever the savings in establishment and running costs, if the end result was worse wine, I was against it. I have always taken the view that the establishment and running costs of a vineyard must always take second place to the single most important and long-lasting factor: the production of the highest quality wine that any particular site is capable of. Of course establishment costs and running costs have to be taken into account and of course yields are also important, but GDC certainly didn't seem to me to offer enough advantages to outweigh its failings. With grapes worth at least £1,500-£2,000 per tonne and considerably more if you are selling wine, it doesn't take much of an increase in yield (which I believe is possible with cane pruned VSP trained vines) to pay for any additional costs. Add in the unquantifiable bonus of better wines which, in the long-term, has to be every grower's aim, and the question of 'which pruning and trellising system to use' in UK vineyards is, I believe, easily answered. In order to justify why I consider that a high-density *Guyot* system most suits UK vineyards, I offer the following evidence:

• Almost all northern European winegrowing regions – most of Germany, all of the Loire, Champagne, Burgundy and Bordeaux – as well as many other 'cool' winegrowing regions around the world, use high-density *Guyot* cane pruned systems. Yes, there are a few exceptions ('Chablis' cordon pruning on Chardonnay in Champagne) and with winegrowers in some places being free to do exactly what they want, there are bound to be other systems used. But these are very much in the minority. In many cases, narrow rows and cane pruned vines have been the norm for centuries and whilst this is no reason not to innovate, it ought to make one stop and think.

• Narrow rows help create a better vineyard microclimate than you get in low density vineyards. The rows are closer together and, as the fruiting wire is nearer the ground, there is less air movement below the vines. The idea that air movement beneath a vine's canopy is necessary 'to keep disease away' is false and in VSP *Guyot* trained vines with a fruiting wire at say 700 mm, there is very little (and what's more important, should be very little) air movement. The aim is to keep as much heat in the vineyard as possible. If there are disease problems, open up the canopy and spray.

• It is said that having the grapes nearer the ground is beneficial as they get some heat from the soil which is released as the sun goes down. Whilst I am a bit dubious about whether this is really true – it may be just one of those old-wives' tales we have taken as truth from our overseas brethren – I do think that the immediate area beneath the vines should be kept as weed-free as possible. This reduces the amount of moisture below the vines, which will help with disease control, and will help keep the soil temperature as high as possible. Of course, the narrower the rows, the higher will be the percentage of the vineyard which is (in theory) weed-free.

• An individual vine is able to nurture and ripen a smaller quantity of grapes more easily that a larger quantity. A single vine occupying 9 m$^2$ (GDC spacings) needs to ripen 9 kg of grapes at 10 tonnes-ha. A vine occupying 2.4 m$^2$ (standard VSP spacings) carries 2.4 kg of grapes for the same yield per hectare. In addition, a vine in a low-density vineyard has a large amount of permanent wood to support and the grapes are often several metres from the roots.

• The fruit from cane pruned vines in cool climates appears to be intrinsically better than the fruit from trellising systems which are spur pruned. Whether this is because the fruit comes from buds borne on canes or whether it is because the canopy is easier to manage is open to debate. If the rows in a VSP *Guyot* trained vine are orientated north-south, then each side will get sunshine during the day. With GDC trained vines this is not the case as the fruit is on one side of the curtain or the other. Low density GDC trained vines, in order to carry the same weight of grapes for the area they occupy, have to be spur pruned. Vines planted at 2.44 m apart cannot really grow canes long enough to be cane pruned.

• The higher the density of the vines, the greater will be the element of root competition for the available water and nutrients. In cool climates, especially in 'ultra-cool' climates like the UK's, we usually have more than enough water to support vine growth and our soils are typically well supplied with nutrients. Our problems are usually associated with over-vigorous vines which lead to crowded and shaded canopies. Root competition for the available water and nutrients is not something that happens the instant a vine is planted, but after the first few years this kicks in and helps towards overall vigour control. A GDC vine, despite being physically several times larger than a high-density planted vine, has much more soil into which to expand until it meets competition from its neighbours and in my experience may never get to the point where its roots are in competition with other vines. In *The Grapevine* (p.51), the authors state: 'Higher density planting generally results in a reduced root system per vine but a higher density per unit soil volume – this causes more rapid water extraction in the spring. Increased planting density tends to produce deeper roots where soil properties allow this to occur'.

• The leaf-wall and the canopy of a high density, VSP trained vine is relatively thin, hopefully no more than four leaves from one side to the other, so that the grapes can be plainly seen and there are plenty of gaps. A canopy like this allows air and light to reach both the grapes being ripened as well as to the buds being produced for the following year's fruiting. This is probably THE most important factor in canopy quality.

• A relatively thin canopy also enables chemical sprays to penetrate, keeping both grapes and buds healthy. Getting chemicals, especially anti-*Botrytis* chemicals, into the flowers and into the grapes before bunch-close[6], is a <u>major</u> factor in disease control.

• A VSP system also allows you to have a good height of leaf-wall which will help in the battle against high vigour. The higher the leaf-wall, the greater the number of leaves and therefore, the greater the rate of transpiration and of the drain on the available water. (The height of the leaf-wall is discussed in some detail in *Chapter 9: Trellising systems – construction* in the section on *Posts*.)

• It is much easier to carry out the summer canopy management tasks on a relatively thin VSP trained leaf-wall as operations such as deleafing and 'hedging' (trimming top and sides) can be done efficiently with a machine. Deleafing can also be carried out by hand more easily on a VSP than a GDC system. This is not to say it cannot be done with GDC trained vines – it's just more time-consuming and therefore less likely to get done well or even done at all.

• Fruit thinning, whether post-flowering, post-*véraison* or pre-harvest, can really help improve quality, and is much easier on a vertical plane where the fruit faces the operator, than on GDC trained vines where the fruit is all over the place. Again, it's not that it cannot be done, it's just that it's more difficult and more time-consuming.

• A high density VSP *Guyot* pruned system is simple to install and manage and is easy for those looking after the vines to get to grips with and there are no difficult concepts to understand.

*Classic VSP trained vines in a Kent vineyard*

## 'Blondin' training system

In 1998 I was sponsored by the Canterbury Farmer's Club (Canterbury in Kent that is) to travel to New Zealand for three weeks to study their viticultural practices. One of the nuggets I returned with was the idea that a 'high-trained, Sylvoz' training system, such as I had seen at Matt Dicey's vineyard off Felton Road in Central Otago, might suit UK growers for its ease of management and lower costs of production. I had already tried this system with a few rows of Seyval blanc in my Scott's Hall vineyard (planted in 1988) and had found it to be a low input system giving good results with regard to both quantity and quality. This system uses rows at around 2.40 m wide and an inter-vine distance of 1.80 m if spur pruned (giving a density of 2,315 vines-ha or 937 vines-acre) or 1.20 m if cane pruned (giving a density of 3,472 vines-ha or 1,405 vines-acre). I named this the 'Blondin' system after the first person to walk across the Niagara Falls on a (single-wire) tightrope. The single wire needs to be at around 1.50 – 1.80 m off the ground depending on the variety grown and the size of your tractor, although if you have your single wire at 1.80 m (assuming you are not very tall) it also enables you to walk across the vineyard at right angles to the rows, ducking under the wires – very useful for inspecting the vineyard! By planting the vines in pairs, one either side of an intermediate post or planting stake (one vine trained in one direction and one in the other direction), the number of posts and planting stakes can be kept to a minimum. The only problem with this type of irregular planting is that it precludes machine planting.

This system has all the advantages of GDC – lower establishment costs, ease of working, and downward facing canes – without the tangle of shoots and side-shoots and the work involved with GDC canopy management. Pruning, whether spur or cane, is much easier than with VSP as most of the wood to be pruned will be hanging free of the wire and will simply drop to the ground. As the vines are high off the ground, the weed control need not be quite so good and indeed, I have seen vineyards trained like this where 'mow-and-throw' has been used (see *Chapter 14: Weed Control* for an explanation of this technique). Taken together, this is a lower cost system – lower establishment costs and lower annual management costs – which could be useful for growers selling lower-value wines (still wines) or to producers just selling grapes. Bolney Vineyards have several hectares trained to this system and regularly win prizes for their wines, so there don't seem to be any ripening or quality issues. I will not pretend that it suits all varieties and it needs correct management as with any training and trellising system. For some varieties and situations however, it might be worthwhile trying.

*Tracteur-enjambeur (straddle tractor) in a French vineyard*

## Row width

My experience in growing vines in the UK over the last forty years is that rows should be, within reason, as narrow as possible. We do not need the ultra-narrow rows that they have in some European vineyards – 1.0 m wide is not unknown in areas where *tracteur-enjambeur* (straddle

tractors) are used – but in the UK, rows of between 1.75 m and 2.25 m ought to be the aim. In order to have enough space between the tractor wheels and the canopy, allow around 350 mm between the edge of the tractor wheel and the centreline of the row, i.e. add 700 mm to the width of your tractor for a safe working row width. For instance, for rows (accurately) planted at 2.00 m wide, a tractor of no more than 1.30 m overall width ought to be used. When looking for a tractor, always see if the wheels can be moved in (the rims can often be reversed so that they stick in rather than out) and often narrower tyres will shave a few millimetres off the width. Once you have selected a tractor, make sure all other equipment (mowers, sprayers and trailers) are no wider (or very little wider) than the tractor. Having rows with more distance between the outside of the tractor and the vines themselves is just a waste of good vineyard space and, for reasons set out below, will not make for as good a vineyard.

Remember also when choosing a row width that in cane pruned vines, where the fruiting wood is trained along the fruiting wire, the narrower the row, the greater will be the number of fruiting buds and therefore the higher will be the potential yield. In a vineyard with a row width of 1.75 m, there are 5,714 running metres of fruiting wire (and therefore of productive canopy) per hectare. For the sake of the argument, if one says that 90 per cent of the wire can be filled with cane, and say that there is one bud per 100 mm (ten per metre), then the number of buds in the vineyard per hectare is 5,714 x 90 per cent x 10 = 51,426 buds. However, take a vineyard with 2.25 m rows (only 500 mm wider) and the running metres of fruiting wood is 4,444 per hectare. The bud number equation is therefore 4,444 x 90 per cent x 10 = 39,996, over 22 per cent less than in the vineyard with a 1.75 m row width. In other words, if the vines in both vineyards are planted at the same inter-vine distances and both pruned identically to two flat canes, each vine in the wider rowed vineyards has got to work that much harder and carry 22 per cent more crop for the same overall yield. At 10 tonnes per hectare (4-tonnes per acre) in the vineyard with 1.75 m rows, each vine will carry 2.10 kg of grapes; in the vineyard with 2.25 m rows, each vine will have to carry 2.70 kg of grapes to bear the same yield per hectare. This is not likely to happen.

Where are these extra grapes to come from? Are the buds going to be more fruitful because the rows are wider? No. Are the bunches of grapes going to be more plentiful and larger? No. You cannot lay down more canes as you do not have the space along the row. You could adopt an arched cane system – arched *Guyot* or *Pendlebogen* – but for reasons which I will point out later, this is not to be advised except under certain circumstances. You cannot make the vines work any harder than they already are. In addition, the narrower rows will create a better microclimate, there will be more root competition (and it will come sooner) and you will get better vigour control. For these reasons, the vines in the narrower rowed vineyard will be happier and probably more productive than the vines in the wider rowed vineyard. On the downside, the vineyard has more vines and more trellising, so yes, establishment and running costs will be higher, but it is my contention that the benefits of narrower rows far outweigh the negatives and over the 30-40 year life of the vineyard, the additional investment to begin with and the additional running costs should not be an issue.

A row width of 1.75 m is quite narrow for the UK, but I had a small vineyard planted at this width at Scott's Hall near Ashford, Kent which did well (President's Trophy in 1994) and in recent years, Henry Laithwaite planted both the Marlow Estate vineyards at Pump Lane, Marlow, Buckinghamshire in 2010 and the Mezel Hill vineyard in Windsor Great Park in 2011, with 1.80 m wide rows and 800 mm and 1.0 m inter-vine distances. I will be interested to see how these vineyards turn out. For me, 2.00 m is the optimum width for UK vineyards, giving a high enough density of vines, coupled with enough length of fruiting wire to give the crop aimed for and there are plenty of tractors available at or under 1.30 m overall width. Now that the question of row width has been debated, the question of inter-vine distances needs to be resolved.

*Wide rows like this are only viable in hot climates where spur-pruned vines deliver high yields*

## Inter-vine distance

With cane pruning, the question of whether you have one cane (single *Guyot*) or two canes (double *Guyot*) needs to be considered and also, the length of the cane needs to bear some relationship to the length of good quality, fruit-bud bearing cane that can be grown. The canes which are going to become your fruiting wood for the coming year typically stem from a two-bud spur (or 'thumb') that was left at pruning the year before. Alternatively, they come from a suitably positioned point around the 'head' (also sometimes called the 'crown') of the vine. If your vines are spaced at 1.20 m apart, and you propose to leave two horizontal canes, allowing for a handgrip's gap (100 mm) between each vine's canes, then the length that each cane needs to be is around 550 mm. If your vines are spaced at 1.50 m apart (a distance I believe too wide for cane pruning) you need two canes around 700 mm long. Given that your leaf-wall is (hopefully) going to be around 1.00 m to 1.20 m, then this is well over half way up the canopy and into one of the most crowded parts of it. Given that the condition and quality of the buds on the cane is critical in determining yields, it is important to appreciate that the microclimate within the canopy, especially in the first 0-700 mm, is critical to future yield as it is in this area that

the buds on next year's canes are situated. This is also the area where the vine will mostly carry its grapes. Given that both the quality and condition of this year's crop and the quality and condition of next year's fruiting wood – and therefore of the future yield – is contained in the same area, it is critical that this area should receive as much light as possible.

Within the buds that overwinter and which are left to produce fruit in the coming year is all the plant material required to produce everything that the shoot will carry: leaves, inflorescences and tendrils. Before budburst, whilst the vine is still dormant, the question of whether the shoot to emerge from the bud will produce inflorescences or tendrils is not decided and it is only once the bud bursts and the growing shoot emerges that the changes take place. Smart and Robinson, in *Sunlight into Wine* (p.11) put it like this:

*'The buds that contain the shoots and clusters for the following season begin growth early in the spring as shoots develop. Flowering is a critical stage. It is at this stage that the cluster primordia are laid down. Cluster primordia are microscopic pieces of tissue which eventually develop into clusters the following season. Within the young 'compound' bud there are three small shoots which develop – the primary, secondary and tertiary. Whether or not these shoots produce cluster primordia is **very dependent on shade in the canopy**. It is [still] important that shade be minimised on the sections of shoots that will be pruned to in the winter, as the light response is very localized.'*

From the above can be seen that, in relation to yield, a factor which I consider to be of great importance to UK producers, whatever can be done to reduce shade in the critical first half of the canopy should be done.

For *Guyot* pruning, inter-vine spacings as low as 750 mm could be considered (giving a vine density at 2.00 m row width of 6,666 vines-ha or 2,698 vines-acre) in which case single-arm pruning would be appropriate. Much above 1.00 m inter-vine distance though, and two-arm flat *Guyot* would be better. Although I can see the advantages of inter-vine distances of between 750 mm and 1.00 m (higher vine density, less fruit load per vine, greater root competition), the additional cost of setting up and establishing a vineyard with such a high vine density is probably not worth it. For me, the ideal inter-vine distance for two-arm flat *Guyot* is 1.20 m or 1.30 m – no wider.

In the early 1970s and '80s, many growers in the UK, myself included, used arched canes. My first vineyards, planted when I returned from Germany in 1977, were spaced at 2.00 m x 1.10 m to 1.30 m and trained to two-cane *Pendlebogen* (pendulum arch) training which was an exaggerated arch where the cane is arched over one fruiting wire and tied down to a lower one, with the two fruiting wires around 300 mm apart. In Germany, this is a very common pruning system and, in vineyards where a high yield is required, is almost universal. The reason is that, depending on the space between your two fruiting wires, the length of cane, and therefore the number of buds on it, increases by between 10 per cent and 25 per cent, thus potentially giving higher yields. In Germany, high yields are important to many growers, especially those selling lower classification wines and/or belonging to co-operatives where their returns are weight-based. Yields of 100-150 hl-ha (14-21 tonnes-ha – 5.7-8.5 tonnes-acre) are typical and yields 50 per cent higher than this certainly not unknown. In order to get these types of yields, the bud count is critical: narrow rows and arched canes help achieve this. However, in the UK, where this level of yields are the stuff of dreams (except in exceptional years) and where our light levels and temperatures are so much lower, arched canes only aggravate the situation. It is not more buds that are required for higher yields, but fewer, more fruitful, buds – a critical difference.

The length of a single arched cane on a vine planted at an inter-vine distance of 1.30 m and pruned to a two-cane *Pendlebogen* system may well be around 750 mm to 850 mm long which means that the last half of it will have been growing right in the thick of the canopy, well above the region which is typically deleafed (or at least partially deleafed). In addition, they will be growing later in the season when side-shoots may well have started contributing to the canopy mass, when disease pressures will be higher and when crop-load may well be testing the vine's resources. In UK vineyards, where light levels and temperatures are often low, which in itself is reason enough to worry about bud fruitfulness, we just do not need any extra stress placed upon fruiting buds. In addition, as I have pointed out above, arched canes are only necessary where high yields can easily be obtained. In fact, leaving more buds in order to get higher yields in UK vineyards might actually be doing the very opposite. Leaving more buds just places a higher strain upon the winter reserves of the vine and in the spring and early summer, when the vine depends almost entirely upon winter-stored reserves to both grow leaves and canes and – most importantly – to lay down the inflorescences for next year's harvest, the vine will struggle. In *The Grapevine* (p.66) the authors state that: 'yield variation from season to season in a vineyard or region is largely the result of bunch number/vine (60 per cent), followed by number of berries/bunch (30 per cent), followed by berry weight (10 per cent). The variation in bunch number is a consequence of conditions that occurred in the previous growing season'. In other words, it's NOT the number of buds that are left at pruning that determine yields, but the number of bunches per shoot that emanate from those buds. In poor yielding UK vineyards it is common to see many shoots with no, or only one, good bunch. This is a result of low light and temperature levels at the critical time in the preceding year. In high yielding UK vineyards, the difference is that there are less blind canes bearing no bunches and plenty of canes bearing two and even three good bunches. As I have said above, what we actually need is fewer buds producing more and larger bunches of grapes per cane.

Having said that, I do not favour arched canes, in a well sited, sheltered vineyard, perhaps one which had been planted slightly too wide (say over 2.30 m row width) which had already proved itself capable of producing good yields (7.5-10.0 tonnes-ha, 3.0-4.0 tonnes-acre), it might be worth experimenting with a lightly arched cane – say over a second fruiting wire around 200-250 mm above the first fruiting wire – which would increase the bud count by about 10-15 per cent. With a little bit of extra deleafing and careful attention to shoot positioning, a higher yield might be achieved without any problems.

## Other pruning systems for the UK

As for other pruning and trellising systems for UK, there are several that have been tried, but there are none that I consider superior to two-cane flat *Guyot*. Several growers use the Scott Henry system, which has a split canopy with half the leaf-wall growing vertically and (in theory) half growing downwards. Whilst I am sure it can be made to work, I ask myself why we need this in the UK? The system was developed to deal with over-vigorous vines (often on their own roots and usually irrigated) in Oregon, and later in New Zealand, where growing conditions are very different to the UK's. It was developed with the hope that an increase in bud numbers per vine would increase yields and these yield increases would have a devigorating effect upon the vines. The reason I do not favour its use in the UK is that to start with, we are not able, in most years, to get the types of yields that they can achieve in Oregon or New Zealand, and that the levels of yield we do get in the UK has negligible impact upon the vigour of our vines in most years. The choice of a devigorating rootstock has much more effect. Downward facing shoots, even supposing you can achieve the type of downward facing canopy that the textbooks show, also causes problems with late-season weed control and in my experience just leads to a damp jungle of vine foliage and weed growth where there ought to be clean, dry soil. This makes disease control much harder and poor disease control impacts not only upon the current year's crop, but also on the viability of next year's buds. I firmly believe that loading one individual vine with so many buds must place a strain upon that vine which in our cool growing conditions must be a negative. If you are hell-bent upon Scott Henry, my advice would be to visit as many UK growers as you can that use it (Sharpham and Yearlstone in Devon and Kenton and Wodetone in Dorset come to mind) and then just try a few rows to start with.

Of the many other pruning systems used throughout the world, I do not believe there are any that are superior to the ones I have recommended above. Some have been tried – Lyre, Single Pole, and Sylvoz for instance – but have not lasted the course. If cane pruning is what a cool climate needs – which I believe it does – then the options are in any event somewhat limited. The simplicity of *Guyot* systems, from both the installation and management points-of-view make it the de-facto system for most UK growers.

1 In June 1961, Brock had heard from Nelson Shaulis who said that he would be coming to the UK in September and wished to visit Oxted which he duly did. In a letter sent in November that year, Shaulis thanked Brock for his hospitality, saying that the noon meal: "was very delightful, especially the ginger beer shandy". Shaulis also said that he was just concluding the harvest at Geneva and yields had been between 3 and 9 tons per acre. What Brock must have made of Shaulis' views on trellising is not recorded, but it would be interesting to know.

2 A more complete accounts of Ward's involvement with English and Welsh wine can be found in 'Jack Ward, Horam Manor and Merrydown' which is Appendix II of the UK Vineyards Guide 2010.

3 Dr Lenz Moser III (1905-78) came from a long-established family of Austrian winegrowers and developed his system of high training in an effort to reduce both establishment and running costs. He wrote and self-published a book called *Weinbau Einmal Anders* which translates as 'Viticulture with a difference'. Professor Becker used to say the book's title meant 'try the new system, but only try it once' as once you had tried it, you never wanted to use it again!

4 Smart and Robinson in *Sunlight into Wine* say that a paper describing the GDC system was published in 1966 and that it 'was a milestone in the development of canopy management theory, elegantly establishing that shade within the canopy was the principal limit to production of quality grapes'.

5 I use the term 'failure' to mean any vineyard that was grubbed out before the end of its useful life. It could have 'failed' because the vines died, the wine it produced was poor quality, or the producer had problems selling the wine. Either way, the vineyard is no longer.

6 Bunch-close is the point where the immature grapes on a bunch expand so that they start touching each other and make access by fungicides to the interior of the bunch virtually impossible.

# Chapter 6
# Site planning and preparation

## Site planning and preparation

So the site has been chosen, the varieties, clones and rootstocks selected, the row width and inter-vine distances decided upon and now it's time for the next stage: getting the site planned and prepared.

**Note:** See *Appendix VI: Vineyard pre-planting check list*. Also available at: *www.englishwine.com/wgigb*

## Site layout

The first task is to decide how the vineyard should be laid out. For many sites, the decision is an easy one. The shape or the slope of the site dictates that there is an obvious way the rows should run. In the case of sloping sites, the easiest way to work the vineyard will be with the rows following the slope and this will also help with air drainage in case of frost. If there is a gentle slope across the site, then this is not usually a problem. However, a steeper slope across the site could possibly cause tractors and machinery to start 'crabbing' (i.e. sliding) and once you get trapped, it is often very difficult to escape without vines and posts being damaged. Reversing in the row, especially when towing a sprayer or trailer, is usually not an option. A way around a slight slope is to grade the soil so that gentle terraces are created. This needs doing after the site has been planted (assuming machine planting – if hand planting it could be done before) and before the soil firms up and grass starts growing. A few passes along each row with a cultivator fixed at an angle to the slope so that the soil is levelled up will help create a more comfortable working platform. Creating terraces, much as you see in other countries, is not something that has ever been done in the UK, mainly because our sites tend not to be that steep and with relatively wide rows, wider (and more stable) tractors are used which can cope with the slopes that we do have.

The question of row orientation is one that often perplexes those new to the task of laying out a vineyard. The literature will tell you of course, that in order to get the maximum sun exposure and heat on to the vines, the best orientation is north to south or possibly north-east to south-west. Maybe on paper this is the case, but in reality my preference is to orientate the rows so that they run at 90° to the prevailing wind. Why? – because in the UK one must attempt to provide as much shelter in the vineyard as possible and in laying out the rows at right angles to the prevailing wind, the first few rows will act as 'sacrifice' rows, offering shelter to the remainder. Typically in UK vineyards, the prevailing wind comes from the south-west, so the rows would want to run north-west to south-east for maximum shelter. Easterly facing rows will also get the benefit of the morning sunshine and dry out sooner than westerly facing rows.

Of course, on many sites there will be one boundary which will dictate the direction of the rows, otherwise you will end up with too many short rows and awkward corners. Following the line of this boundary will ensure that the rows are as long as possible (although see below about row length) and the number of short rows – and therefore of end-posts and anchors – will be kept to a minimum. What you will need to do, especially if using a GPS planting machine, is to be able to strike a very accurate right angle to the line of your first row. This is discussed in *Chapter 8: Planting your vineyard* in the section on *Machine planting*.

## Measuring the site

After the decision about row orientation has been taken, the next task, before the correct number of vines can be ordered, is to measure the site as accurately as possible, a job that is sometimes easier said than done. If you do not intend to fill the whole field, then the question of how accurate you need to be is less relevant and as long as you don't massively over-order, then the exact number of vines does not matter that much. Either way, you will need to peg out the area to be planted taking into account space for fencing, windbreaks and internal roadways (more about these below). On sites that have good straight sides, no awkward angles or curious corners, a decent tape measure (of at least 30 m or even 50 m length) will suffice. I always use a Leica Disto D5 laser measure. This device needs to be mounted on a camera tripod and measures up to 200 m, quite far enough for most UK vineyards. Unless you are measuring quite short distances and there is some solid object to bounce the laser off, you need special 'bounce plates' that reflect the laser back to the device. I have two of these mounted on metal posts which can be easily pushed into the ground. Take measurements of the sides of the site, plus diagonals across the site. These can then be plotted on to a 1:10,000 OS map of the site and a total number of square metres arrived at. Divide this by the area occupied by each vine and you will have the total number of vines to be planted. For easy to measure sites, Google Earth (not Google Maps) with its line measuring facility is fairly accurate and unless the site is very tight, probably good enough. On the Google Earth Professional site, there is an area measuring facility, but for a one-off measurement this is not really an option.

However, before the planting area can be measured, there are several things to be taken into account. The exact position of rabbit and deer fencing must be settled as this will take up space; if there are to be windbreaks, both external and often internal, then they have to be allowed for; and finally, the area devoted to headlands (the space between the ends of the rows and the fence or windbreak), internal roadways and/or turning spaces have to be factored in. Fencing and windbreaks are discussed later in this chapter, but headlands, internal roadways and turning spaces can be dealt with here.

Most tractors suitable for commercial viticulture, i.e. not garden or hobby tractors, will require at least 6.0 m (and quite often a bit more) of clear headland to get them out of one row and into another. The exact turning circle will be part of the manufacturer's specifications. Some tractors have better turning circles than others – New Holland tractors with 'SuperSteer' for instance – and almost all tractors have independent braking on the rear wheels which allows you to spin round on one wheel, but at the expense of your brake pads and usually with some scuffing of the grass and not easily done if towing a sprayer or trailer. Whether a tractor can turn directly into the next row will depend upon row width and with most tractors and in most vineyards this is not possible without stopping and reversing, something generally to be avoided. It must also be remembered that a tractor seldom works without an implement of some sort mounted behind it, a mower or sprayer or a piece of machinery or trailer being towed behind it, all of which will make the whole unit longer and thus requiring the headland to be wider.

If you are proposing to have a trailed sprayer, use a dung spreader, or tow a trailer or any other long implement, then you will typically need at least 8.0 m of headland for comfortable working. Tractors with a three point linkage and PTO (power take off) at the front which will allow a front-mounted mower to be used whilst spraying at the same time will naturally require even more space. You should also bear in mind that you may one day want to use contractors to spread manure, compost, and fertliser (especially lime which is very bulky) and they generally favour high capacity spreaders that can hold maximum volume, but which are narrow enough to fit down vineyard and fruit orchard rows. These spreaders tend to be much longer than the average. My rule of thumb is therefore to leave 10.0 m between the boundary – fence line or edge of where you expect your windbreak trees to grow to – and the first planted vine. This allows for around 1.40 m to be taken up by the end-post and anchor and 600 mm for the final vine to spread its cane into. This will leave you with a clear 8.0 m of headland. Obviously if your inter-vine distance is greater than 1.20 m then this

distance ought to be slightly larger. You may also need to leave additional space at the bottom of a slope to allow frost to drain away. This is covered in *Chapter 13: Frost protection.*

The question of row length will very much depend on the shape and size of the site. Rows much longer than 150 m can be daunting to work in. Get half way along, and you are 75 m from the end and it's a long walk. It's easier today when almost everyone has a mobile telephone, so none of the shouting 'where are you?' and loud whistling that used to be the case. 150 m is also a long way, when picking, to take out the full bins or boxes of grapes and return with empties. This can take up an awful lot of time and leave the pickers waiting for boxes. If your measurements show you that you have an appreciable number of rows of 150 m long or more, I would advise considering two options: creating a mid-point walkway through which you can walk and/or drive a quad bike or motorcycle, or splitting the block into two with an internal roadway. Creating an internal walkway is simply a question of splitting the row with two extra high posts, typically end-posts as they need to be strong, and tying them together at the top with wire. You need to make sure that the wire is high enough for a person to walk under without decapitating themselves, but not so high that a leaf-trimmer cannot raise itself up to clear them.

If you decide to split the block in two, then of course you will double up the number of end-posts and anchors required, plus lose a fair amount of space. You have to decide whether your internal roadway will be just enough to get a tractor through – around 3-4 m between the anchors ought to be enough for this – or whether it is to be enough to turn a tractor around in – in which case you will need 6.5-8.0 m between the anchors.

*Walkway in the middle of long rows formed from two end-posts joined together at the top with wire. Make sure the posts are tall enough so that the wire doesn't scalp you!*

## Ordering vines

**Note:** The planting of ungrafted 'own-root' vines is covered in *Chapter 16: Pest and disease control* in the section on *Phylloxera* and at the end of *Chapter 17: Trunk diseases*. In *Chapter 17* there is also a full explanation of the process of producing grafted vines.

Almost all vines used in commercial vineyards consist of a scion – the variety to be grown – and a rootstock[1] – the part of the vine in the ground – and these are joined together by the graft. Vines are bench-grafted during dormancy on to rootstocks in the early spring of one year, spend a few weeks in a greenhouse to get the graft calloused (hardened off) and the roots started, and are then planted out in nursery fields for the remainder of that growing season. Once they are dormant in November and December, they are lifted, taken back to the nursery, sorted, cleaned, trimmed, disinfected and placed into a cold store until sold.

*Boxed vines in store waiting for planting. Each box contains around 300 to 350 vines*

Most European growers plant vines in the spring of the year, although winter planting is not unknown. In regions with plenty of winter rainfall and the possibility of both winter and spring frosts – such as the UK – there is absolutely no advantage to winter planting. For one thing, most nurseries will not have stock available and therefore getting hold of vines can be a problem. Secondly, I have known vines planted in March and April which have started to grow and then been hit hard with a spring frost in late April or early May. In some regions, rooted cuttings of rootstocks are planted out into position in the vineyard for a year or two, after which the scion variety is chip-grafted (also known as field grafted), on to the rootstock. This system of planting is usually only found in warm climates and where experienced labour is available to carry out the chip-grafting.

To my way of thinking, the best time to plant vines in the UK is in the first two to three weeks of May. Correctly planted into well prepared sites and looked after properly, there will be absolutely NO difference in the amount of growth by the end of October between vines planted in November, December, March, April or May (and I have known vines planted in June do just as well). In fact, quite the reverse, and I would put money on vines planted in the first half of May being the best of the lot. By then, sites will have started to warm up and root growth will start soon after planting. By the time green shoots first appear (late May to early June) the dangers of spring frost will be over and they can spend the summer putting on weight.

Although vines can be ordered at any time, the 'high season' for ordering vines in Europe is late September to the end of October. This is the time when growers will have a good idea of the size of their harvests and can decide if they are able to afford to plant vines and the nurseries will have a good idea of what sort of 'take' their vines will have had and how many they will have for sale. Not all the vines grafted and placed out into the nursery fields will be saleable and losses from poor graft callusing, poor size matching and disease can be as high as 50 per cent. Some varieties and some rootstocks are particularly prone to losses at this stage, one of the reasons why vine prices vary. My advice to UK growers is to get orders in for vines as early as possible. Ideally vines should be ordered 14-18 months in advance and the nursery can then supply vines to the exact rootstock, variety and clone combination requested. In practice this seldom happens and therefore August or September of the year prior to planting is usually soon enough, although earlier is better. If you leave ordering until later, then some nurseries will start a vine-hunt amongst other nurseries they know to try and source the vines you want. If they do this without telling you, then this is regrettable as they cannot always know the circumstances under which the vines have been produced. Unfortunately it is a fact of life and one of the penalties of later ordering, of ordering from nurseries you perhaps don't deal with very often or nurseries you don't really know at all. Although I have a vested interest in saying this, of course you should always order through a reputable vine supplier.

Most vines these days are prepared for machine planting and their roots will have been cut to the right length. If you propose to hand-plant using a water-lance, you will want to have the roots cut shorter, although this is something that can be done in the field. All vines will normally have their scions and grafts re-waxed before shipping and will be shipped in stout boxes, or sometimes plastic bags. Either way, they ought to be moist, sometimes packed with damp peat to keep them moist and well-wrapped in plastic to stop them drying out. They will be stored in cold storage at the nursery until shipped to the UK and hopefully will not get too warm en-route. Once in the UK, they should go straight back into a cold store, running at about 4-5°C, until just before planting. I always keep vines packed in the boxes or bags in which they have left the nurseries and they stay in those boxes or bags whilst they are delivered out to the vineyard site and until the moment of planting.[2]

One question which new growers always ask is 'how many vines are there in a box?' and 'how big are the boxes?' The answer is that a box of around 650 mm x 500 mm x 300 mm (about the size of a large suitcase) will hold between 300 and 600 vines, depending on how much root they have and how many the nursery needs to pack in. If the vines are in bags, a bag the size of a typical 25 kg fertliser sack will hold around 250-300 vines.

Sometimes when you open the boxes of vines, you will find that they have grown white sprouts, sometimes 25 mm long or even longer. This is usually a result of the vines having been kept at too high a temperature and/or being exposed to light whilst in storage. Whilst this is probably not a good idea, I have planted plenty of vines with white sprouts and – so far – have not experienced problems. The sprouts usually blacken and wither, to be replaced in the normal course of events with fresh shoots.

One other way in which vines are produced is known in Germany as *kartonage-reben* or *topf-reben* and in France as *sept a neuf* (seven by nine – the size of the pots they are planted into). I have also heard them called *vignes Jiffy pots*. These are vines produced in the spring of the year of planting and instead of being placed into nursery fields after grafting and callousing, they are placed, immediately after grafting, into 7 mm x 9 mm fibre pots (Jiffy pots) filled with peat and then rooted in trays and sent out to growers as soon as the grafts have calloused and the roots have started to emerge from the sides of the pots. The advantages of these are that they can be ordered and supplied in the year of planting. The disadvantages are that they are expensive to buy (around twice the cost of a normal vine), difficult and expensive to transport as they take up much more space than bundles of dormant vines, more difficult and expensive to plant and losses will be higher. Because they are typically supplied later in the season, the chances are that the weather will be warmer and drier and therefore these vines may need to be watered after planting. Although I have used them in desperation and known growers who have used them, the results, both short-term and long-term, have never been that satisfactory and my advice is to avoid them.

All plants produced in the EU have to bear 'Plant Passports' and on vines, these are small (70 mm x 110 mm) plastic labels, usually blue (other colours exist for different categories of vine) and usually attached to each

bundle of twenty-five vines or each larger maxi-bundle (as per picture on left). On the passport will be details of the variety and clone, the rootstock and clone, the details of the supplier, lot number and other relevant information. It is your guarantee that the vines are what they say they are and that they have been inspected and are free of viruses and *Phylloxera*. What they do not do is guarantee that they are free of other diseases or that they will necessarily grow. Quite what to do with plant passports after you have planted the vines is open to question. Unless you track every bundle and know

which passport relates to which block of vines I cannot see that they are of any help if you find that some vines – for example – have a virus. For years I had dozens of plant passports hanging on a hook in my workshop gathering dust, but eventually threw them away. I was once told by a WSB inspector that 'one has to keep them for six months' after planting, but I am fairly sure this is not true. (You are meant to register your vineyard with the WSB within six months of planting, but that is a different issue).

## High-graft vines

By far the majority of vines produced in the world are grafted on to 300-400 mm long rootstocks which means that the primary shoot has to grow from just above ground level in order to produce the stem and then the fruiting wood. Nurseries do however produce 'high-graft' vines, called '*hochstammreben*' (high stem vines) in German and '*greffe haute*' (high graft) in French. These are grafted vines with a long rootstock – around 550-600 mm in France and 700-900 mm in Germany – so that at planting, the vine's stem is already grown and all the vine has to do is to grow the fruiting wood. The advantages of these vines are that: you save a year's growth and (in theory) can get the vines to fruit a year early; you can use weedkillers as soon as the vines are planted without the need for spray-guards; you do not need rabbit guards as the young shoots are beyond the reach of rabbits (but not deer); and – most importantly from a cost-saving point-of-view – you do not have the annual spring work of removing shoots from the stems. The disadvantages are that: they are slightly more than twice as expensive to buy; they are more expensive to transport; they can be machine planted, but the work is slightly slower; and you have to have the fruiting wire installed more or less as soon as the vines are planted otherwise the vines will blow about in the wind and the grafts can get damaged. And even though they may have a pre-built stem, the roots of a high-graft vine are no more developed than those of a standard vine.

Whether the advantages of high-graft vines outweigh the disadvantages is still an unanswered question and given that the technique is not that old or widespread, many growers view high-stem vines with some suspicion. The most obvious advantage – that of an earlier crop – is one I feel unhappy about. Given that the vine's root system expands with age, not with the length of the rootstock, even though with high-graft vines you might have grown a fruiting cane at year two, can the root system take the stress of fruiting? Given a dry season and no irrigation, a high-graft vine with a small rootstock might suffer. From what I have seen, high-graft vines do not establish as well or as evenly as low-graft vines, possibly because high-graft vines start off by waving around in the breeze and gain nothing from being close to the ground during their first, all-important, growing season.

And then there is the question of Trunk Diseases (TDs). The classic technique for invigorating a vine infected by *Esca*, one of the oldest and most widespread of the TDs, is to take a water shoot from as low down on the trunk as possible (just above the graft being ideal), cut the old trunk off just above the water shoot and re-grow the trunk[3]. With high-graft vines this is not an option. Some growers also think that having vines with twice as much rootstock is probably best avoided just from the TD aspect. Given that you can (if you really want to), in favourable circumstances, get normal vines to crop at the end of their second summer, I cannot see that high-graft vines offer a real advantage and, with one exception, for the time being I would avoid them. TDs are dealt with in detail in *Chapter 17: Trunk diseases.*

The exception is where you are 'gapping-up', replanting the odd missing vine in and amongst already established vines, in which case high-graft vines are useful. If you plant standard vines when gapping-up, unless you are careful to keep the foliage from neighbouring vines away from them, they often get overshadowed and will take several seasons to grow to full size. High-graft vines start at fruiting wire level and stand a better chance of making it to full fruiting size in a season or two.

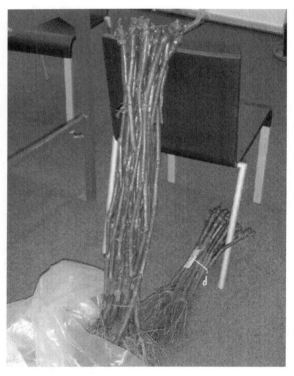

*High-graft vines on the left. Standard vines on the right*

## Site preparation

The aim of site preparation is to get the ground into the best condition possible to take the vines. The task falls into two categories: physical and chemical. On the physical side are the following: earthmoving, water to the site, drainage, green manuring, additions of humus, the actual cultivations which will prepare the soil for planting, fencing and windbreaks. The chemical side involves the addition – if required – of fertilisers and of chalk to correct the pH and this is dealt with in *Chapter 7: Vineyard nutrition.*

## When to prepare a site

The sooner the better is the quick answer and if you have the luxury of two (or more) growing seasons before you plant, so much the better. Having said that, I have seen fields turned from grass, arable, orchards and even hop-gardens, into vineyards in the space of a few days.

Starting early gives you the chance to have a go at reducing the weed spectrum by spraying the site with herbicide, thorough cultivating, perhaps growing a cleaning crop for a season or two, and making sure that the soil has settled well after any earthworks or drainage has been carried out. It also gives you the chance to get windbreak trees planted a season or two before planting, meaning that they will start to provide shelter to the site as soon as the vines are in the ground.

In the normal course of events, most sites will be available in the late summer after the previous crop has been harvested, in which case all major preparatory works – additions of manure, humus and fertilisers, earthmoving, and drainage – can be carried out whilst the land is dry, followed by subsoiling and deep ploughing, after which the land can be left to over-winter before tackling it again in the spring prior to planting. The site may need re-ploughing after the winter, or just disc-harrowing followed by power-harrowing. If you are using a competent agricultural contractor to do the work for you, then he (and I say 'he' because I have never known a female one!) will probably have knowledge of the type of soil you have and advise accordingly. It is important to state that of course, no two sites are the same and therefore how they are handled will vary considerably. One would therefore approach chalk downland, heavy clay and light sandy soils in different ways.

## Earthmoving

Many sites will have features which it is best that a vineyard does not have. Small ponds or low-lying areas, ridges, humps and bumps of all sorts, plus stray pieces of hedgerow, are best removed so that the site is as flat and uniform as possible. Although this question is dealt with later under 'frost prevention', if your site is at all prone to spring frost, then it is best to try and fill in or to re-grade any areas that are low lying, however slightly, as these will hold the frost, even on a gently sloping site. If a substantial area requires filling in, it is best to remove the topsoil first, from both the area to be filled and the area from which the 'fill' is to come, so that subsoil is placed upon subsoil and the topsoil upon topsoil. Always leave the filled area a bit proud to allow for settling.

Whilst trees in the middle of a site can be a lovely feature, they take up a considerable amount of space with both the area they actually occupy, plus the area they shade, and to my way of thinking, are best removed. Before doing so however, it is always best to make sure there is no TPO (Tree Preservation Order) on them. You will also need to think about access roads to the site, car parking for visitor's and picker's cars and possibly an area of hard-standing for both storing picking boxes and bins and for loading them on to a lorry.

## Water to the site

A supply of water will be required in, or near to, the vineyard for pesticide spraying, as well as for chemical weed control with herbicides. Spraying is not a task that most people want to spend any more time doing than is absolutely necessary and the nearer the water supply is to the point of use, the quicker you will be able to fill up the tank and get back to spraying. In order to make tank-filling as quick as possible, it is best to have the water supply as near to the vines as possible and, to make filling up even quicker, erect a supply tank connected to the mains with a ball-cock and valve. This tank, which needs to be bigger than your sprayer's capacity, should be placed on a suitable platform so that it can empty under gravity into your sprayer. Make sure that the outlet from the supply tank is fairly big – at least 37 mm or 50 mm – with a ball-valve to control the supply. In that way you can fill up your spray tank in one quick dump of water and get back to spraying. Don't forget to drain down the tank and turn off the water supply after the end of the spraying season and before the winter frosts arrive.

*Tanks for quick filling of vineyard sprayers*

## Drainage

The question of drainage – does a site need it or not – is often a difficult one to answer but there are three big things we know: most sites are probably better drained than not drained; drainage is relatively easy before planting and relatively difficult after planting; and drainage is expensive (although the value of the land will definitely be enhanced). Therefore the question of whether to drain or not must not be lightly dismissed.

When I am looking at a new site, almost the first thing I am asking myself is whether any of it needs drainage. There are obvious tell-tale signs: visibly damp areas, rutting where tractors and machinery have been; areas where grazing animals have 'poached' the land; and the presence of rushes and other moisture-loving plants. Asking the landowner, unless they have farmed the land commercially over a period of years, I have found to be almost worse than useless. The stock answer to my question: 'does this field drain well' is 'yes, this field is never wet and always dries out in the summer' and the merest hint of a gradient will cause them to add 'it's on a slope you know' as if land on a slope always drained well. Sloping land certainly does NOT always drain well and can often contain springs and wet areas which need to be dealt with.

*Field drainage machine at work in a new vineyard site*

Before field drainage is considered, one ought to appreciate the benefits of drained land for vines. The benefits of drained land are that:
• Vines will get a much better start in life, allowing them to establish quickly and evenly and get into cropping by year three or four. This will help reduce stress and lessen the incidence of TDs.
• The soil will dry out faster and more completely and force the vine's roots to dig deeper. Deep rooting is beneficial for many different reasons and it makes for a more stable environment for the vine. Is also allows oxygen to penetrate deeper, encouraging earthworm and microbial activity at deeper levels.
• Roots that are drying out will produce more abscisic acid (ABA) which the vine needs to both produce and ripen its grapes.
• The soil will warm up more quickly in the spring and the vine's fine root-hairs, which actually do all the work of transferring water and nutrients from the soil to the plant, will begin to grow earlier. The earlier the budburst, the longer the growing season.
• The vine will develop a larger root system which will help reduce stress in dry seasons, something often given as one of the contributory factors leading to TDs.
• The land will be accessible to machinery sooner in the spring and will be less likely to rut, compact and suffer long-term damage. This can be important in the early weeks of growth when spring and early summer rainfall is most likely, and when the vine needs maximum protection

against mildews and other diseases. It is also important at the end of the season at harvest time for the same reasons.

• The land will be more valuable than un-drained land because, for many crops and for livestock, it is more productive and therefore more profitable.

The best way of telling whether land needs draining is to call in the experts. A reputable drainage contractor or soil consultant will carry out a survey of the land and draw up a proposed plan. Costs will vary according to many factors such as drainage layout, distance between laterals (10 m is usual for vines and fruit), whether you have gravel backfill or not (usually recommended) and the overall size of the scheme. The John Nix *Farm Management Pocketbook Edition 44, 2014* gives £2,400-£3,500-ha (£971-£1,416-acre) for an arable scheme with laterals spaced at 20 m apart and using permeable backfill, but on a vineyard, where closer spacing would normally be required, costs would be considerably higher. The latest site I have been involved with where a full drainage system was installed was in August 2014. In a field of 4.57-ha (11.29-acres) which will be planted with 3.30-ha (8.15-acres) of vines, the cost per planted hectare, for a 10 m spaced system using permeable backfill, came to £4,944-ha (£2,001-acre)[4]. Whether this cost can be justified or not is for each grower to decide. Given that land and vineyard establishment costs might easily come to £50,000-ha, and stock costs another £50,000-£100,000-ha (depending on whether you are producing still or sparkling wines) a sum of £5,000-ha added on to a total investment in the enterprise of £100,000-£150,000-ha doesn't seem like much of an additional expense in order to have a well-drained vineyard, given that bad drainage often lies at the heart of a poorly performing winegrowing enterprise. It is also possible to do a percolation test on a site using nothing more than a spade and water. See *Soil drainage* document at www.englishwine.com/wgigb.htm.

The drainage work itself should take place ideally when the soil is dry and as far before planting as possible. Although I have known planting take place within days of the drainage being finished, it is better to get all the drainage done in the late-summer or early autumn, followed by subsoiling and ploughing, after which the soil will have a chance to settle over the winter. This will allow the slots where the drains have been laid, especially the larger main drains, to close up.

After the drainage is finished, your contractor will provide you with a detailed plan showing you where all the drains are laid and to what depth. These days, plans are drawn up using GPS so ought to be very accurate. Knowing where the drains are is important for any subsequent work involving digging down – laying water mains for instance – but for vineyards it is especially important as it would be better not to have one's line of end-posts directly over a drain run for obvious reasons. Drains are seldom laid deeper than 800-900 mm and end-posts can sometimes be in the ground to this depth (or even deeper than this). In addition, all posts depend on their stability by being in undisturbed ground and if they are sited in the immediate area where a drain has been laid, they will lose much of their strength. The Land Drainage Contractors Association (www.ldca.org) has a list of members and some good information on drainage.

## Green manuring

If you have the luxury of six months or more between taking possession of the site and planting a vineyard, then you should consider growing a 'green manure' crop which will clean up the soil, add humus and help reduce weeds. If you can get any major site operations – earthmoving, drainage and subsoiling – carried out early enough, then a green manure crop can be planted into cultivated land, left to grow, mown (or grazed) off, and then incorporated into the soil the following spring, prior to planting, but always allowing enough time for the green matter to rot down. The species of plant (or more probably plants) to be used will depend on the timing of sowing and the exact task you want it to perform. Green manuring is discussed in more detail in *Chapter 7: Vineyard nutrition* in the section on *Green manuring*.

## Humus additions

Additions of humus (organic matter) in the shape of FYM, green waste compost, chicken manure, mushroom compost, hop waste or some other source of organic matter should ideally go on to the site whilst the ground is firm and dry to avoid compaction and wheel ruts. It is also best put on before the ground is cultivated so that tractors and spreaders are not shaken to bits. The amount of organic matter that you put on a site will (almost) entirely depend on how much you are prepared to spend. You could easily put 50 tonnes per hectare (20 tonnes-acre) of FYM on a site as a pre-planting dressing without it being excessive. With chicken manure there are rules about the amount that can be applied as the nitrogen content is high. Whatever product you apply, an allowance for the amount of nitrogen (N), phosphate (P) and potassium (K) contained in the compost/manure will have to be made when it comes to working out the amount of chemical fertliser to apply. The DEFRA 'Fertliser Manual' (RB209) has a whole section (Section 2) on 'Organic manures'.

If you are in a nitrogen Vulnerable Zone (NVZ) – and much of the UK now is – there are restrictions on how much N you can put on your land and, at the time of writing, the limit is 250 kg-ha in a rolling 12 month period which equates to 33-tonnes per hectare of BSI PAS 100 green waste compost.[5] The rules for perennial fruit crops (such as vines) are changing to allow 1,000 kg-ha over a four year period. Further information is available in a DEFRA leaflet 'Guidance for farmers in nitrate vulnerable zones' (PB1273c April 2009).

## Cultivations

The extent to which any individual site requires cultivations will depend upon its previous crops and/or current state. Obviously a field that has been under arable cultivation for many years and is say in arable stubble prior to planting with vines, will need cultivating differently to one which has been unimproved grassland for decades. In general though, most sites will benefit from

*The best type of machine for subsoiling*

having any weeds present sprayed off with something like Roundup Biactive (glyphosate) prior to any work on the site. If the vegetation on the site is not killed off prior to cultivations, not only will the work be harder (especially if the site is old pasture) but also, when the site is ploughed, the old grass will form a rotting layer just where the vine's roots will end up. The next task, apart from any of the other operations already mentioned, is subsoiling.

There appears to be reluctance on the part of some people to accept that deep subsoiling – and when I say deep I mean at least 600 mm and possibly even deeper – is an essential part of preparing a site for planting vines. In France, Germany, Italy etc, it is quite common to subsoil down to 900 mm prior to planting vines, especially if the site has been a vineyard for many years so that all old roots are disturbed. The reason that vineyard sites need subsoiling is that it is generally the only chance you have of loosening the soil at the depth where the vines will be putting most of their roots. Once the vines are planted, it is much more difficult to get a tractor of sufficient size and power to carry a subsoiler down the narrow rows. Subsoiling will aid drainage at these levels and will clear the site of any plough-pan[6] or impermeable rock layers. If the site has had trees on it at some stage, it will also help clear the site of any old roots that are still there.

The action of subsoiling is to drag an implement fitted with at least one, and usually two or more, long blades, called 'tines', which usually have a 'wing' at the end to help shatter and loosen the soil, through the ground. The depth to which a tine will go and the number of tines that can be dragged at any one time will depend upon two things: the soil condition and the type of vehicle pulling the subsoiler. Obviously a site with tough, heavy soil, with a plough-pan, stones or rock layers and which has not been cultivated for many years will take more work and require more effort than one which has been in arable cultivation for several years and which may already have been subsoiled at some time in the recent past. It is usual to subsoil across the site from both corners and then up and down the site in the direction of planting. In this way, the whole site is thoroughly dealt with.

The best vehicle to pull a multi-tined subsoiler to the right depth will almost always be a tracked vehicle – a bulldozer or tractor – which has enough power and traction to pull the implement through the soil at the correct depth. The problem with using a wheeled tractor, with four-wheel drive or without and of whatever horsepower, is that most tractors are fitted with sensors so that when the resistance from the implement being towed becomes too great, they automatically lift up the implement in order not to damage or slow down the tractor or the implement. This means that when the subsoiler hits the toughest ground, i.e. the ground that really needs subsoiling, the tractor automatically raises the tines up to jump over the very problem it is there to alleviate! Although a tracked vehicle will cost more to hire – it cannot be driven on the roads so will usually have to delivered to the site on the back of a low-loader – the job it does is so much better that it really is worth the cost. One Kent contractor charges £40 per hour for a Caterpillar D6D with haulage to and from site at £500 and in one day, could easily subsoil 5 ha, therefore a cost of around £180-ha (£73-acre). The average contractor's rate for subsoiling is currently £57-ha (£23-acre), but this is for relatively shallow subsoiling (400-500 mm) and is for a 'one-pass' operation.

As an alternative to a fixed-tine subsoiler, the *McConnel Grassland Shakaerator* is an implement worth considering. This is a subsoiler which is powered via the PTO and vibrates as it passes through the soil, both making the passage of the tines easier and achieving a more thorough 'shatter' effect at the ends of the tines. A 2.0 m wide version is available which can carry two to three 750 mm tines, but requires a 35-55 kw (50-75 hp) tractor to pull it. In fruit growing areas of the UK this type of machine is often available for hire.

The other specific reason why vineyards which are to be machine planted – and that is the majority of commercial vineyards these days – need subsoiling, is that the planting machine works by opening up a deep and wide slot in the soil, into which is placed the vine to be planted. As the planter moves along, the slot is opened up, the vine goes in, and the machine moves on. What happens next is of the utmost importance if the vine is to settle well and root properly. Once the machine has passed on, the soil must fall back into the slot and around the roots of the vine. This would typically be at a depth of 250-300 mm. Although the soil at the very surface will invariably fall back around the stem of the vine and visually the vine will appear to be settled, it is what happens below the surface level that is critical. Vines planted in sites where subsoiling has not taken place and where cultivations have only been at a relatively shallow depth, may well suffer from having their roots waving around in the air, some way below surface level and out of sight.

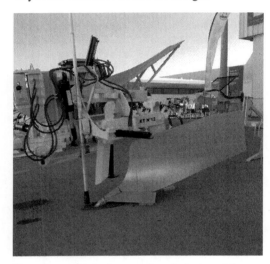

*Very deep, single-furrow plough designed for preparing vineyards, but not used in the UK*

After subsoiling, the site will probably look very cut up and raised in places and there may well be tree roots, slabs of rock or stone, or other previously buried debris that is best removed prior to the next activity, which is ploughing. The aim of ploughing is to turn over and bury whatever is on the surface: any manure, humus or fertilisers applied, plus any vegetation that is (or was) growing there. The depth of ploughing will depend upon the plough used and in European vineyard areas it is common to use a very deep single or two furrow plough specifically for this purpose. These ploughs, although slow to cover the ground, will turn the soil over to a depth of at least 300 mm, and often more, leaving the soil in loose, broad furrows which, if left to over-winter, especially if there is enough frosty weather, will break down naturally so that spring cultivations are made easier. This will also allow winter rains to penetrate deeper into the soil. If the vines are to be hand planted, then really deep ploughing is a great advantage. Most UK agricultural contractors will not have this type of deep plough and will typically use six, seven or eight-furrow reversible ploughs, ideal for fast ploughing for arable farming. If this is the only type of plough available, then it is not the end of the world. Ideally all this heavy work should be carried out in the autumn when the land is fairly dry. The site can then be left for the winter to 'weather'.

The next set of cultivations will typically take place in the spring, perhaps a month or so prior to planting. Assuming that planting takes place in late-April or early-May, then mid-March is soon enough to get on to the site with machinery, although this will depend on the weather at the time and the state of the site. Most sites, if they have been sprayed-off and deeply ploughed, will be carrying

very little in the way of vegetation at this stage, so a pass with a disc-harrow, followed by a power-harrow will leave a typical 'seed-bed' finish which is what the planting machine requires. On occasions, especially if heavy rain falls after the power-harrowing and the soil caps over, a second pass with the power-harrow immediately prior to planting may be required. Prior to these pre-planting cultivations, the second half of the fertilisers should go on to the site. The aim must be to get a completely clean, level and even site ready for planting.

As far as is possible, all cultivations should be carried out in direction of the planting line, especially the final disc and power-harrowing, otherwise ridges will tend to form across the planting line which means that the planting machine will have difficulty in keeping its planting level accurate, with the result that some vines will be deeper in the ground than others.

## Fencing

Most vineyards will be prone to attack from a range of four-footed predators – rabbits and deer being the most common – but hares, badgers and even wild boar not being that uncommon. In the establishment phase, when the vine's foliage is at, or near, ground level, rabbits can be a real menace and very easily prevent young vines getting away. Whilst rabbits and hares can be excluded by using individual guards around each vine (fully covered in *Chapter 11: Management – establishment phase* in the section on *Protection against predators* and in *Chapter 14: Weed Control)*, perimeter fencing is far more effective. The reason I advise against individual guards is that to get good protection against rabbits you need guards of at least 750 mm high and the type mostly used are the small diameter 'tree guard' type (as manufactured by Tubex and others). The reason these are typically used is that they are the least expensive: larger diameter guards cost considerably more. Inside these guards, which are sold as creating 'an improved micro-climate' for the vine, it tends to get very hot and humid and it is impossible to control weeds inside the guard other than to pull them up by hand. In this humid atmosphere, slugs and snails will also often have a field-day and you may find it necessary to sprinkle slug pellets into each guard. I am also concerned that this hot and humid atmosphere around the graft might be a contributory factor in the development of TDs. These guards also tend to make the young shoot grow faster, with longer internodes[7] than would be the case if they were growing in the open air or in larger diameter guards and I am not sure this is wholly good for the long-term health of the vine. There is also the initial cost of buying them. A Tubex 750 mm high, 71-86 mm diameter Ecovine costs around 36 p per guard (for 5,000+) plus the cost of removing or undoing them every time you need to gain access to the vine (which in the establishment phase can be several times a year). True, there may be a small residual value in the used guards after they have been removed – this will be once the vines have developed a trunk robust enough to take herbicides – but what then to do about the rabbits and hares who will, believe me, start gnawing at the vines? As will be seen in *Chapter 14: Weed Control*, I am not totally against using individual vine guards, but these are 600 mm high, 125 mm diameter ventilated 'spray-guards' whose sole purpose is to protect the vine in its first year or two against herbicide damage.

There are also rabbit guards made of plastic netting which, although used widely in mainland European vineyards, have proved themselves inadequate when faced with sturdy British rabbits and, except in situations where rabbit damage is slight and perhaps localised, cannot to be recommended. They also of course, do not offer any protection against weedkillers. Electric rabbit fencing can also be used and whilst this might be fine as a short-term measure, perhaps whilst permanent fencing is being erected, it is not a long-term solution to rabbits. In established vineyards, where protection is required against rabbits and hares gnawing the trunk down to bare wood, rabbit guards made of galvanised chicken-wire netting can be used. These can be bought from suppliers used to dealing with top-fruit growers who often have the same problem, especially in hard winters when there is snow on the ground and the soft bark of apple and pear trees makes for a tasty meal.

*Vine trunks badly gnawed by rabbits*

Rabbit fencing, on the other hand, is a one-off remedy and if done correctly, is almost 100 per cent fool-proof (or perhaps that ought to be rabbit-proof) and with luck will keep out badgers and hares as well. Agreed, it needs monitoring on a regular basis to make sure nothing is trying to get underneath it and you must keep the ground at the base sprayed off with herbicide so that you can see what's happening there. The netting used, generally known as chicken-wire, must have a tight enough mesh size (don't be a cheapskate and use any that has an aperture greater than 31 mm between diagonals), and make sure the wire used is strong enough – 18 gauge (1.2 mm) is required – as rabbits can bite through 19 gauge (1 mm) netting. The fencing should ideally be buried in the soil – 150 mm vertically down and 150 mm horizontally out, away from the vines – so that rabbits attempting to dig in from outside will meet the netting on the way down. Laying 300 mm of fencing on the ground and pegging it

down and/or placing turves on top is often advocated as a way of keeping rabbits out, but it is a short term measure. Even if rabbits don't work out what to do, badgers, foxes

and dogs soon will and allow the rabbits to get in. The top of the fencing should be at least 900 mm above ground-level and fixed to a line wire with an additional top wire (plain wire will do, but barbed wire is better if you also want to discourage people from climbing over your fences) at around 100 mm above the netting. This will also discourage animals attempting to jump over or pushing the netting down with their bodies. I have known rabbits and hares jump fencing of over 1 m high, especially if there is high ground adjacent to the fence, but this is rare and they seldom are able to jump out, so can be hunted down and shot. All gateways need to be properly rabbit-proofed with railway sleepers or poured-concrete thresholds. Also make sure that all diagonal fencing support struts (on corners or on long runs of fencing) are inside the fence as, if they are on the outside, rabbits have been known to run up these and get over the fence.

The cost of rabbit fencing will depend on the size and shape of the site, but assuming a 2 ha (5-acre) rectangular site with one gateway, with fencing erected to Forestry Commission[8] standards costing £5 per metre, and with vines planted at 2.00 x 1.20 m (4,166 vines-ha) then the cost would be around £4,000 or 48p per vine. As I have already pointed out, the cheapest individual guard, something like the Tubex Ecovine, costs 36 p, plus there is the cost of putting it on and securing it to the fruiting wire, plus the cost of undoing it for access, plus the cost of removing it and storing it or disposing of it. I accept that there may be a residual value in a used guard, but not very much. Even if there were a cost saving by using individual guards (which I doubt there is), as I have pointed out above, they don't do as good a job as perimeter fencing and may even contribute to problems with the vine in later years. I accept that perimeter rabbit fencing is not completely a one-off cost and it will require inspection as holes can be made by a variety of animals (man included) and in time, it will start corroding at ground level. Usually by this time though, the vines' trunks are sufficiently robust not to be troubled by a little bit of winter rabbit damage, although hares can be a bigger problem, and if they are, wire netting guards should be used.

If deer are a problem, and this is not the case on every site, then perimeter fencing is the only real solution. Deer fencing needs to be erected to the correct standards for the type of deer to be excluded. Unless you are growing vines where there are larger red deer, the most likely deer to cause damage are roe, fallow, muntjac and sika and these can be excluded with a 1.80-2.00 m high fence. Obviously if you are erecting deer fencing, the addition of dug-in rabbit netting at the base makes sense. Because deer damage tends to be when the plants are in their first two to three years and not quite so much when they are established, in situations where deer pressure is light, one could consider a temporary electric deer fence around the site. I have known this to be effective, but I have also known it to be totally ineffective. Electric fencing needs to be switched on to work and if the battery loses its charge or the power goes off or something lands on the fence (a branch perhaps) and shorts it out, deer will soon discover a way over. I have also known growers to erect deer fencing only on the perimeters facing the woodland where the deer appear to come from. This is also generally ineffective as they find their way round the edges. The Forestry Commission and the British Deer Society both have very good advice on deer fencing.

*Steel deer fencing with rabbit proofing at the bottom*

As for other predators, badgers and wild boar for instance, these tend to go for the grapes rather than the young plants, and therefore are typically a problem in established vineyards, not new ones. Apart from the legal issues surrounding badgers, they are exceptionally difficult to exclude from a vineyard – they seem to see a fence as a challenge rather than a barrier – although two strands of electric fencing at around 100-150 mm off the ground at snout-level will often deter them. One can also install 'badger gates' in rabbit proof fencing and Natural England[9] has leaflets on these and on electric fencing against badgers. Wild boar are luckily not (at least not yet) a feature in most parts of the UK, although they are found now in parts of East Sussex and Kent and will eat ripe grapes.

## Windbreaks

As was pointed out in the section about site selection, wind is undoubtedly the curse of the vinegrowing classes and almost all sites will benefit from additional shelter. In top-fruit orchards, hop gardens and in soft-fruit plantations, windbreaks have always been a common site and certainly in Kent and East Sussex, counties that once had many more hop gardens and orchards than they do today, you can still tell where they used to be by the rows of tall poplars and willows that border fields. It always surprises

me therefore that today's vineyard owners don't follow the example of their fruit-growing forebears and plant as many windbreaks as I believe they should. The aim of a windbreak is not to stop the wind completely – an impervious barrier would just cause the wind to eddy and jump over the obstacle – but to cause the wind to be raised up to the height of the windbreak and continue on its way above the crop. Windbreaks, if planted on the vineyard side of a watercourse (although not if conifers are used), can also be used to reduce your spraying buffer zones. See *Chapter 16: Pest and disease control* in the section on *Buffer zones* for more details.

Windbreaks can be sited both on the windward boundary (or boundaries) of a site – normally in the south of the UK this will be the south-western side – as well as internally. A good, well-established windbreak will protect land up to ten times its height. Therefore a 7.5 m tall windbreak will protect 75 m of vineyard. The height of a windbreak will generally be limited by the machine that trims it, so if you intend to allow a windbreak to grow to more than say 3 m, make sure your local hedge trimming contractor has a machine that can trim to the height you require. In certain areas, where there are plenty of orchards and plantations with tall hedges, then extra high-reach flail trimmers may well be available which can reach up to 4.5 m high. Alternatively, you can allow the tress to grow to whatever height you like, but know that once they get above a height which can be reached by a trimmer, then cutting them back to around 1 m above ground level and allowing them to re-generate, is the only viable way of keeping the trees from completely shading your site. If the cutting back is limited to say every other tree or one in three and spaced over several years, then a useful degree of wind cover can still be maintained whilst the windbreak is brought back under control.

The other limit on height is that of shade. Given that most windbreaks will be to the south or south-west of vineyards, its stands to reason that they will, at certain times of the day, shade the vines growing in their lee. Apart from the fact that growing vines too near to trees is to be avoided – the trees will take both water and nutrients from the vines well outside their canopy spread – the shade will lower the vine's fruiting potential and undoubtedly any fruit on them will be more difficult to ripen. However, space is not to be wasted unnecessarily and although the first row or two of vines adjacent to a windbreak may not be as good as the rest of the vineyard, a few 'sacrifice' rows can be tolerated if the vines in their lee are protected.

My preferred windbreak trees are Italian Alder (*Alnus cordata*). They have several attributes: they are not expensive trees, especially if bought as bare-rooted 600-900 mm 'whips'; they grow quickly, attaining a height of 3 m or more after three to four years; they perform very well as windbreaks, being permeable enough to allow some wind through, but dense enough to raise the wind over them; they are not attractive to birds as nesting sites; they leaf up before the vine does and keep their leaves until well after harvest; they do not spread very wide and even when 20+ years old, spread no more than 1-1.5 m either side of the planting line; they can be trimmed mercilessly without being harmed, can be cut back to a low level to regenerate and are more-or-less indestructible; they do not seem to suffer from canker or other diseases and do not harbour harmful pests; and lastly, they are attractive trees with small, mid-green leaves and carry dark green 'cones' in the autumn. After all these attributes there is one thing they do not do well: burn – so do not expect to get much firewood from them. The Italian Alder that I planted in 1977 at Tenterden Vineyards (today's Chapel Down) are still there and still performing well. Other members of the alder family, Common Alder (*Alnus glutinosa*) and Grey Alder (*Alnus incana*) are also suitable, although to my mind not quite as good.

*Alnus cordata (Italian Alder) make an excellent windbreak for vines*

There are of course plenty of other trees which will work well as windbreaks, and even a hedge of mixed native hedging, which I accept has a more natural look than a windbreak all of one species, will work, but will take many more years to reach the desired height and will be much denser, and harbour many more birds and their nests, than a windbreak of specialist trees. Poplars and willows used to be common in windbreaks, but one does not see them quite so often these days. Conifers have also been used, but for vineyards and orchards are not to be recommended. They are too dense, causing the wind to eddy and jump over the hedge, harbour all kinds of birds, pests and diseases and suffer from die-back and are not acceptable if you want to reduce your buffer zone. They are also very ugly. Whatever species of tree you use, make sure they keep their leaves until after the UK grape harvest, which can be as late as early November.

Windbreaks are best planted as far in advance of the vineyard as possible so that they protect the vines as they establish. If this is not possible, then they should go in at the same time as the vines. If the trees are planted into well prepared ground, looked after, staked and kept weed-free, then by the time the vines start cropping in their third or fourth year, they should be 3-4 m high and starting to provide some protection. The spacing of windbreak trees will depend to a certain extent upon the species of tree selected and your budget. A row of Italian Alder planted at 1.0 m apart will give you a good windbreak, although if you have the space, a double staggered row with the trees planted at 1.50 m apart with the rows 1.50 m apart will give you an even better windbreak. The overall width of the double row will be up to 5-6 m if left untrimmed, but if trimmed can be kept down to 3.5-4.0 m.

I have always used the smallest (and cheapest) trees available which are always bare-rooted and therefore very easy to plant. A slit cut with a good spade in most soils will normally allow the tree to be pushed in and the ground firmed up afterwards with a boot. These 'whips' are usually no more than 1 m high when planted. They will require staking just to keep them upright as they develop, but a stout bamboo or small tree stake will suffice. It is only larger, pot-grown trees that require properly dug holes, decent stakes and proper tree-ties, a good reason not to use them. Whatever trees are used, they must not be neglected and require protecting from deer and rabbits – so better inside the vineyard fence than outside – and must be kept weed-free. In other words, they need just as much care and attention as your vines. They also shouldn't be forgotten when it comes to fertliser additions. Also note that if you are machine planting your vines, then the same machine can also plant windbreak trees (assuming they are not too big).

If your vineyard is sufficiently exposed and sufficiently wide enough, then the site ought to be divided into blocks with internal windbreaks. How wide each block will be, will depend upon the height you propose to allow the row of trees on the windward side to grow to and how wide your site is. If you allow your first row of windbreak trees to reach say 10 m, then you don't really want any one block wider than 100 m. You also have to factor into your calculations the space that an internal windbreak will take up both with the spread of its foliage and with the shade it will cast. Because of this it may well be worth while keeping internal windbreaks to single rows of trees, topping them at 5-6 m and keeping them sided up so that they are kept thin. Although at least one row of vines and possibly two will be shade affected, the benefit of the shelter will far outweigh this slight disadvantage.

If you have the luxury of sufficient space to the windward side of your site to plant a small barrier of woodland which can be allowed to grow to its natural full height and provide shelter, then this is ideal. Bear in mind however, that this may also be a place where birds can nest and roost and hide up prior to launching themselves upon your grapes.

If space really is at a premium, and you don't mind the expense, there are various types of synthetic netting and webbing that can be used. The expense is of both the netting itself, plus the structure needed to hold it up, even in the strongest winds. When Lamberhurst Vineyards were trying to improve fruit-set and ripening across one windy site, they erected what was then called Paraweb (and is today called Parafence) on every fifth row which appeared to help slightly. There is no doubt that synthetic windbreaks work – greenhouse owners use them all the time – but they are both expensive and unsightly so not the first choice to my mind. I note from Rathfinny's website that they are erecting multiple 'temporary' 4 m high netting windbreaks to protect their windbreak trees (which are meant to be protecting their vines), which are not growing fast enough. As owner Mark Driver admits on his website blog: 'wind is the main enemy of vines' and that 'we have come to the realisation that we do indeed have a windy site'. It will be interesting to see how successful these windbreaks, said to have cost £250,000, will be.

*4 m high Parafence*

---

1 Whilst in some countries vines are grown on their own roots, in most parts of the world Phylloxera makes this impossible (and is often illegal). In the UK, there have been many outbreaks of Phylloxera (at least two reported to DEFRA in 2012) and you would only plant ungrafted vines in exceptional circumstances.

2 As I only use nurseries whose packing and storage methods I am happy with, I feel quite comfortable leaving all boxes sealed until the moment of planting.

3 A water shoot is a shoot that seemingly comes from nowhere, i.e. directly from the trunk and not from a piece of one year old wood such as the spur (thumb) left to provide replacement canes. Water shoots seldom produce viable inflorescences.

4 The reason for the large difference between the field size and the planted area is that the field was a difficult shape. The vines are to be planted in three blocks, with internal roads and headlands, plus space left against one side where there is a wood which shades one edge and space left at the bottom of the slope for frost drainage. Whilst this loss of space is quite high – 28 per cent of the total field area – it is not unusual to lose 15-20 per cent of a field.

5 Detail of NVZs can be obtained from DEFRA www.gov.uk/nitrate-vulnerable-zones. Details of PAS 100 can be obtained from www.wrap.org.uk

6 A 'plough-pan' is a layer of hard soil just below the level at which normal arable cultivations – ploughing and power harrowing – take place.

7 The internode is the distance between two buds. A cane with long internodes will have less buds per metre length of cane and therefore with cane pruned systems, be less productive.

8 *The Forestry Commission Bulletin 102 'Forest fencing'* is available at www.forestry.gov.uk.

9 Natural England Technical Note TIN 026 for Badger Gates and TIN 027 for Electric Fencing. www.naturalengland.org.uk

# Chapter 7

# Vineyard nutrition

## Vineyard nutrition

The amount of information available about how to address fertliser requirements in vineyards is vast and, at least to the newcomer, very confusing. In the days when ADAS (the Agricultural Development and Advisory Service) was part of MAFF and offered free advice to farmers and growers, most people just accepted the advice that they gave. Today, when competing advisory firms, farm consultants, fertliser and other agricultural supply companies are all vying for your business, sometimes selling you product as well, there is almost an information overload. There are also FACTS – Fertiliser Advisers Certification and Training Scheme – advisers who are trained to offer impartial advice on farm nutrition although unlike BASIS advisors for pesticide advice, they are not required by law. However, by taking the task one step at a time, working out what nutrients your vineyard needs can be made less daunting.

As my general guide – at least to start with and in the absence of any problems or special situations which might need a different approach – DEFRA's *Fertliser Manual RB209* is my starting point.[1] This covers every aspect of fertliser and manure use and application and over the years, I have found its 'Section 6: Fruit, Vines and Hops' very useful and have in general followed its recommendations. However, as with many things, 'junk in – junk out' and therefore before any manures or fertilisers are applied, you will need to have a good idea of the nutrient status of the site. This involves taking samples. For vines, there are two basic systems of sampling: soil sampling which can be done both pre-planting and in an established vineyard; and what is often referred to as 'petiole sampling' or 'sap analysis' or even 'tissue analysis' which (in vines) involves taking the stalk of the leaf (the petiole) which connects the blade of the leaf to the shoot. Petiole sampling can of course only take place in growing vines and how and when to do this is discussed later in this chapter.

## Soil sampling prior to planting

Until relatively recently, the only way to take soil samples was by manually digging holes with a spade or an augur. The accuracy of this type of sampling to tell you about the whole site was limited by two main factors: the number of different soil samples you were prepared to take across a section of a site which could then be amalgamated to be tested as one sample; and the number of different samples so amalgamated that you were prepared to pay for to be analysed. Standard instructions about how to sample a site will tell you to take multiple samples, following a broad W pattern across the site, making sure that you avoid any obvious areas that have been cropped differently, show abnormalities or are obviously of different soil types. RB209 suggest taking '25 individual sub-samples' which will then be amalgamated to form one sample for testing. They also state that: 'the soil sample must be representative of the area sampled. Areas of land known to differ in some important respects (e.g. soil type, previous cropping, and applications of manure, fertiliser or lime) should be sampled separately. Small areas known to differ from the majority of a field should be excluded from the sample'. They also suggest for vines that samples at two different depths should be taken: 0-150 mm and 150-300 mm. This is all a lot easier said than done.

In my experience, this level of sampling is seldom done (I was going to write 'never done' but thought better of it) as the sheer time and manpower required to dig or augur this number of holes to take the samples, plus the lugging of buckets across a muddy field, plus the homogenising of the 25 sub-samples and placing into individual bags, plus the labelling, let alone if you are proposing to take samples at the two different levels, is just too great. One might perhaps, assuming the site looks relatively even and there is nothing to indicate great differences in soil type, divide the field up into four quarters, or perhaps on a sloping site take top, middle and bottom, and then for each sub-area take around 10 samples at 150-300 mm, which would then be homogenised to form one sample for testing.

On a small site – say under 1-ha (2.5-acres) – where there were no obvious peculiarities or problems, I would still advise this type of sampling as, whilst of course there may well be different soil types in even this small area, the variation is not likely to be huge and over the years there will be plenty of time to fine-tune the fertliser requirements and carry out both soil and petiole analyses once the vines are established. Make sure you know how you are going to sample the site beforehand, take plastic bags capable of holding around 500-gm of soil (a medium freezer bag is ideal) and a bucket, a spade or augur, and some gloves – earth can be very sticky stuff. Then having taken the samples, send them off to a laboratory having first made sure they can handle the type of tests you want. Lancrop[2], the laboratory I normally use, currently (2014) charge £30 + VAT for what they call a 'Broad Spectrum' analysis which covers the basics: phosphorous (P), potash (K), magnesium (Mg), pH, and 'Lime Requirement' (for soils that require a lime addition) plus the minor and trace elements: calcium (Ca), sulphur (S), sodium (Na), manganese (Mn), copper (Cu), iron (Fe), zinc (Zn), molybdenum (Mo), boron (B), and the CEC (Cation Exchange Capacity).[3] Nitrogen (N) is not normally tested as this element will have been used up by the crop on the land or will have leached out into the subsoil. They can also carry out test for active $CaCO_3$ which, on high-pH soils (above pH 7.00), will be required so that you can see whether you need a chalk-tolerant rootstock and if so, just how tolerant it needs to be. Just getting total $CaCO_3$ levels is not enough as although there is a relationship between the two, it is not linear. This test costs £6.95 + VAT (2014 price).

## Soil mapping with Electrical Conductivity (EC) prior to planting

In the last decade, soil mapping using EC has become commonplace in large-scale agriculture as more and more tractors, seed drills, fertiliser spreaders and harvesting equipment is connected to GPS and can be programmed to farm more efficiently.

EC systems work by scanning the field with a GPS connected, vehicle-towed, set of coulters (metal discs) which send an electrical current down into the soil to two depths: 300 mm and 900 mm. By measuring the differences in response to the current, caused by differing levels of moisture in the soil, a picture of the different soil types can be constructed, based upon the fact that the water holding capacity of the soil is closely correlated to its CEC, its clay content and its porosity. In this way, maps can be drawn up showing the conductivity at both 300 mm and 900 mm which gives you a view of the relative depths of the soil layers, which is also tied in to any slope across the site. The site can then be split into different areas by virtue of the varying percentages of clay, sand and silt which are then amalgamated to give you a map of the different soil types running from sand via sandy loam and clay loam to clay, sandy clay and silty clay (there are eleven separate soil grades in total). Then, having divided the site up into these soil sectors, samples can be taken by soil type for analysis using a quad-bike which is GPS guided and takes multiple mini samples (up to 123 per ha) from each soil-type area. In this way a much more detailed, soil-type specific, view of the nutrient status can be arrived at. On one 23.4-ha (58-acre) site that I recently had surveyed in this way, we ended up with eleven separate areas spread across the field and took samples from the six that showed the most variation.

In addition, the maps of soil types give you some very good information about the areas which are likely to require draining, which are likely to be the most vigorous

and which could do with a heavier dressing of compost prior to planting. They also of course give you valuable information about which areas might require a stronger (or more likely) a weaker rootstock and which areas might suit more or less vigorous varieties.

Of course, EC mapping and sampling is going to more expensive than hand sampling, but then the information derived is so much more complete. The cost will depend upon the size of the site, the number of different soil types and the number and nature of the analyses required but for a 20-ha (50-acre) site I have been quoted £600 + VAT for EC mapping and sampling. However, given that a hectare of land, plus a hectare of established vineyard on it, can cost anything from £50,000-ha (£20,000-acre), this seems a relatively small sum to get some detailed data about the site, something which, when the vines are planted, would be much more difficult and costly to do. My only concern with this type of sampling is that the samples may not be taken from deep enough in some soil types and additional hand sampling may be needed to augment the standard EC samples. This is something you would need to speak to the contractor about.

## Petiole analysis in established vineyards

In taking soil samples, the aim is to discover what's in the soil. But, however good your soil sampling, analysis and interpretation, it tells you nothing about what is getting from the soil, via the roots, into the plant. Petiole analysis (also known as 'sap' or 'tissue' analysis), whereby the sap in the petioles (leaf stalks) is extracted and analysed, tells you exactly, at the time you take the samples, what nutrients are in the vine. The leaf stalk is used as this connects the leaf, the part of the vine where the miracle of photosynthesis is taking place, with the rest of the plant. The stalk is relatively narrow and therefore the nutrients running to and from the leaf to the roots via the stem are fairly concentrated. Petiole analysis is not something you would carry out until the vines have started cropping and had an established root structure, but then it should be carried out regularly. Some growers take petiole samples every year, although with a large vineyard and multiple blocks, this can be an expensive process. Lancrop's current price (2014) for petiole analysis, which covers nitrogen, phosphorous, potassium, magnesium, calcium, sulphur, manganese, copper, iron, zinc, molybdenum and boron, is £25 + VAT per sample.

In order to get an accurate snapshot which can be compared over time to previous snapshots of the vine's nutritional status, it is important to take petiole samples from the same part of the plant at the same time of the year. Depending on what you are trying to show, you need to select a block of vines that is as uniform as possible, i.e. same variety, same clone, same rootstock, same vineyard management. Of course you might have one block of vines of the same variety, clone and rootstock, but where you had say mulched half and not the other half, or where one half had been treated one way and the other half another; in which case, take samples from each half. Petiole analysis is also valuable when you have one section of what is otherwise a homogenous block of vines showing symptoms of something being not quite right. In this situation you could sample the healthy versus the unhealthy section and can either pinpoint or eliminate a nutritional reason as being the source of the problem.

In vines, samples are taken from the leaf opposite the first flower or bunch of grapes either when flowering is almost over – 80 per cent capfall as it is known – or at *véraison*, both dates which can be seen visually and at a time when the vine is under a certain amount of stress. Sampling at flowering will give you a chance to address any deficiencies sooner in the growing season rather than later when any adjustments you make might not have that much effect upon the vines. Make sure your hands are clean and then pick around 75 leaves, remove the blade and place the stalks into a clean paper envelope (and not in a plastic bag as they will sweat). Ideally you should take these before it gets too hot (although I am not sure it ever gets THAT hot in UK vineyards in July). You must also make sure that you take leaves across the block, no more than two per vine and select leaves that are well exposed to the light. Avoid taking leaves from vines at the ends of the rows as these are generally not very representative of the rest of the row (as they have less competition from neighbouring vines and are often sprayed more and fertilised more as the tractor starts off down the row) and avoid any vines that are obviously sick, unhealthy or showing signs of stress. You should also avoid vines that have been recently sprayed (especially if using copper or sulphur sprays) as this might distort the results. Once collected, the petioles should be kept as cool as possible and sent off to a laboratory without delay. If you cannot send them off at once, keep them cool and dry until you can send them off. Obviously they do not want to dry out completely as otherwise there will be no sap left!

The results from petiole sampling will show the various elements as being 'very low, low, normal, high, or very high' and should be used as a guide to additions of fertilisers and foliar feeds. They should also show nitrogen (N) status, something that soil samples generally do not, and this can be used to see whether a judicious amount of nitrogen ought to be applied, although often a slight leaf yellowing will have told you this already. Fairly small foliar applications of nitrogen are often the best way of perking up vines that are showing signs of N deficiency, but tread carefully as an excess will only result in too much soft growth.

## Fertliser additions prior to planting

Having got your soil sample results, you will see that each of the major nutrients will have been assigned a nutrient index number from 0 to 5 (or sometimes 0 to >4) and for each nutrient there is an amount to be applied, depending on the starting index level. Page 158 of RB209 has a table showing the different amounts to be applied in order to bring the level up to index level 2 to 3 which is considered ideal. As to the type of fertliser to be used (as there are for most nutrients several different materials containing the same element) RB209 again has guidance on this or your local supplier will certainly be able to help, especially if they are used to dealing with fruit growers. Fertilisers

come in what are known as 'compounds' or 'straights'. Compounds are named after their constituent nutrients and in the order: nitrogen (N), phosphorous (P) and potassium (K).[4] Thus a 20-20-20 will have 20 per cent of each of N, $P_2O_5$ and $K_2O$. There are also compounds with no nitrogen such as a 0-20-20. Often there will be additional elements present such as magnesium and sulphur, in which case the name of the compound might be 9-4-10-5MgO-22.5SO$_3$ which would have 9 per cent N, 4 per cent $P_2O_5$, 10 per cent $K_2O$, 5 per cent MgO and 22.5 per cent $SO_3$. Straights on the other hand are made of one element and would contain a known amount of nutrient. Thus triple superphosphate (TSP) contains 47 per cent $P_2O_5$ and muriate of potash (MOP – also known as potassium chloride) contains 60 per cent $K_2O$. Appendix 7 of RB209 has a full list of most of the common materials and a conversion table to convert element to oxide & vice versa.

For vines, because they are a very long-lived and deep-rooted crop, considerably higher levels of fertilisers can be applied prior to planting. RB209[5] suggests that the site be sampled at 0-150 mm and 150-300 mm and assuming the results of the 150-300 mm show index levels of 0 to 1, then the amount shown on the tables to bring them up to index level 2 should be applied before planting and ploughed down as deeply as possible, ideally the winter before planting. Then, in the spring prior to planting, the amounts shown by the 0-150 mm level results can be applied as a top dressing prior to final cultivations. If only 0-150 mm samples have been taken, then assuming again that the index levels are 0-1, then the amounts required should be applied before deep ploughing, again preferably in the autumn, and the same amount applied prior to final cultivations before planting. If you are also applying compost or manure, the manurial value of these must be known and deducted from the amounts to be applied as fertliser. Depending on the level of nitrogen already in the soil and on whether any manures or compost containing nitrogen are used, you might consider applying a small amount of nitrogen prior to planting to help the vines establish. Unless the vines were showing symptoms of nitrogen deficiency, I would not apply any more until they were fully cropping. If you are in an NVZ (Nitrogen Vulnerable Zone), also be aware of restrictions on amounts of N that can be applied.

When working out amounts of material to be spread, note that all recommendations are given in kilogrammes per hectare of the oxide – $P_2O_5$, $K_2O$, MgO etc – and the actual weight of material to be applied must be adjusted according to the 'strength' of the product. Thus, for example, to add 100 kg of $K_2O$-ha using muriate of potash, which contains 60 per cent of $K_2O$, one would need 167 kg-ha of product to be applied. Appendices 7 and 8 of RP209 have percentages and conversion rates for all the common materials.

## Soils with low pH levels

Soils with pH levels of below 6.0 will require some additions of lime to bring the levels up to 6.5 and maybe a little higher (but certainly not over 7.0) and this is much more easily applied before planting than afterwards. Vines growing in soils of pH 6.0 or less may well have problems in accessing a wide range of nutrients, so if your soil tends towards acidity, then this is something to be aware of. Improving the humus content of the soil and raising the CEC will also raise pH levels. Rates of the material to be applied will vary according to the indices, but between 4.0-7.5 tonnes-ha (1.6-3.0 tonnes-acre) is typical. Where amounts are greater than this (indicating a very acidic soil) it may be better to apply about three-quarters of the total required before deep ploughing and the remainder after ploughing and before cultivations. With soils that tend towards acidity, additional applications may be required after say 4-5 years.

Lime suppliers will advise on the best materials to use and if your soil is also deficient in magnesium, magnesian limestone should be used (which contains around 15 per cent MgO) and the appropriate adjustment made to the amount of magnesium containing fertliser that is then applied. Lime is a very bulky, messy product and is best applied by specialist contractors using their own equipment to both load and spread the product. Some lime suppliers now have spreaders that can be tied in via GPS to EC soil maps, so that different rates are applied to different areas. Lime should be applied as early as possible in the land preparation process as it is slow to act and needs to be worked well down into the soil. Therefore lime should be applied to the site as early as possible, ideally before subsoiling and definitely before deep ploughing, preferably in the winter prior to planting, as you are aiming to get the lime down to 400 mm deep. Once the vines are established you will not be able to get the large equipment typically used by liming contractors down the rows and if at a later stage your soil does need any lime, you will have to use a 'prilled', i.e. a granulated product, such as Calciprill or Magprill, which are considerably more expensive than basic lime, although the manufacturers claim they work much faster than lime (which I can believe).

## Soils with high pH levels

Soils with pH levels above 7.0 are termed alkaline and pose additional problems to vines growing in them and trace element deficiencies, especially of iron, manganese and boron, are much more likely to occur. As has been already pointed out, it is important that the level of active $CaCO_3$ is tested so that the correct rootstock can be chosen, otherwise the vines will succumb to Chlorosis. Many high pH soils will also be deficient in humus.

## Fertliser additions to established vineyards

Once your vines are established, and as long as they are not showing any signs of mineral deficiencies, then the next time to take soil samples will be after their first or second cropping, i.e. after year three or four. The guidelines in RB209 suggest soil sampling every '3-5 years' but I would be guided by how the vines look, in particular how the leaves look, and what stresses they are under and probably stick to soil sampling every three years. Heavy yields and adverse weather conditions (such

as the heat in 2003 or the cold and damp in 2012) can tax a vine's reserves and might mean taking soil samples sooner rather than later. In established vines, take soil samples from near to the vines in the area where the vine's roots are most likely to be feeding and not from the middle of the grass strip. If your site has been previously EC mapped, then samples can be taken from areas which are homogenous from the point of view of soil type and compared to previous soil samples to see what effect the fertilisers and manures being applied are having. Otherwise, samples are probably taken on the basis of blocks of the same variety-clone-rootstock. As with taking pre-planting samples, you need to take a number of small samples in a broad W pattern across the area and then amalgamate them into one sample for testing. Given that you cannot usually walk across a vineyard from one row to another (although if the fruiting wire is high enough you can duck underneath it) getting a really good soil sample consisting of say twenty sub-samples can be time consuming and involve quite a bit of walking. A recent development in soil sampling in crops planted in rows is to use the same sampling quad-bike used for EC mapping which can drive up every row in a vineyard, taking multiple samples. This gives you a much more accurate map, at least going from one end of the site to the other.

Having taken soil samples and had them analysed, your laboratory will have made recommendations for fertliser applications to be applied. The aim should be to keep the major nutrients (P, K and Mg) at the index level 2 and the trace elements at the appropriate level, the precise level and nature of which your soil analysis will show. Nitrogen should be applied to vines very conservatively, if at all, and it may well be better to use foliar urea in small amounts. RB209 suggests annual application rates for P, K and Mg which depend on the Index levels. Trace element deficiencies can often be seen by the way the vine's leaves grow and can be dealt with via foliar feeds (or occasionally soil drenches). Levels of boron, manganese and zinc should be kept up to guidelines. Sulphur and copper levels should not be overlooked and even though nearly all vines in the UK are sprayed with sprays containing these elements, additional applications may be necessary. As has been already pointed out, iron may be an issue in soils with high active $CaCO_3$ levels and if the correct rootstock has not been selected, or if the vines are showing signs of Chlorosis, then even though an iron-containing foliar feed has been used (Ferleaf), a soil-applied drench of chelated iron (Fersoil) will help stabilise the vine and get down to the roots. Molybdenum is a trace element which I believe may be more important in UK vineyards than some people realise. In other countries, when vines have low molybdenum levels, they can suffer from poor pollen tube growth and therefore poor fruitset (particularly Merlot) and I see no harm in applying some in UK vineyards to keep levels up. It is quite normal to include foliar feeds in the regular spray mixtures, typically both pre- and post-flowering, together with a general plant tonic made from plant extracts and seaweed, Maxicrop being one of the best known and longest established.

If a fertliser spreader which can strip-spread is available, then the fertliser can be spread in bands about

500 mm either side of the vine and the rate of fertliser adjusted pro rata to the amount suggested. Therefore, in a vineyard with 2.0 m wide rows, the fertliser rate could be adjusted to 50 per cent of the specified amount. In my experience, even when using maximum recommended fertliser inputs pre-planting, the first post-planting soil tests reveal that very little has changed and it takes up to ten years before much change takes place in the potassium, phosphate and magnesium levels. Trace element levels, which can be dealt with via foliar feeds, can usually be moved more easily.

I have also seen fertliser spreaders that can 'inject' fertliser into the soil at a depth of around 500 mm, although not in the UK. Given that many of a vine's roots are at this sort of depth, this might be an interesting technique to use.

## Green manuring

Green manuring, the planting of a crop specifically to serve a specific nutritional or functional purpose, is a valuable tool in the vineyard owner's armoury. Whether you are looking at a site before planting, in its establishment phase, or when a vineyard is into its cropping years, the planting of a green manure can help in several areas, the main one of which is the addition of humus to the soil. Growing your own organic matter *in situ* will also have the additional benefit of improving the soil structure and drainage of the site – chicory (*Cichorium intybus*) for instance has roots that can penetrate to over 1 m – and will also provide nutrients to help increase the soil's microbial activity. Depending on the timing of sowing and the species sown, green manures can also provide some nitrogen – either for short term or long term use – although in general terms the addition of extra nitrogen in UK vineyards must be treated with care. Late autumn short-term plantings will seldom produce much nitrogen as this does not happen if the soil temperature is below 8°C. Some species of legumes – lucerne, sweet clover and fenugreek – which may have been selected to fix nitrogen, will not do this unless the bacteria *Rhizobium meliloti* is present and this will need to be added to the seed prior to planting. Green manures can also help clean up the soil by suppressing weeds and reducing the incidence of certain pests including nematodes and Mustard has been shown to act as a biofumigant. See *Chapter 17: Trunk diseases* for more details.

As has been discussed in *Chapter 6: Site planning and preparation*, if there is enough time, even if it is only six months, the sowing of green manure before planting, is a valuable extra treatment which will really help get your vines established. Once your vines have been planted, unless there is a really pressing reason why you specifically wanted to sow a green manure crop straight away, I would hold back until the vines were established and entering their cropping phase before doing so. Perhaps if you had a drainage problem that required some very deep-rooting species, or wanted to stabilise a site that was perhaps on a side-slope, then I can see the wisdom of using a green-manure at an early stage. In an established vineyard, you could consider planting every other row with a green manure mixture say on a two to three year cycle. In this way you would always have a firm surface to run on for many tractor operations and allow the sown rows to produce the maximum amount of organic matter.

The actual choice of species to plant will depend on different factors and there are several good seed companies which can provide advice and seed to suit your exact requirements. Cotswold Seeds is one such company which I can recommend and they also publish a very good booklet called 'Sort out your soils. A practical guide to green manures'.[6] The HDRA (Henry Doubleday Research Association) has also produced a very good leaflet called 'Green manures' which is obtainable from the Institute of Organic Training and Advice.[7] The cost of the seeds for green manuring will vary according to the species to be planted and will range from £55-£250 per hectare (£22-£101 per acre) plus the cost of the land preparation and seeding.

How to plant the seed will depend on exactly when, in the lifecycle of the vineyard, the green manure is to be sown. If it is prior to planting, then it can be either drilled, or broadcast using a fertliser spinner (depending on the seed size) and this is something that the contractor preparing the site will handle. A green manure crop is probably best established after all the 'heavy' site preparation operations such as earthmoving, drainage and subsoiling, have been carried out and drilled into a well cultivated seed bed. If you are considering planting a green manure crop following vine planting, whether it is directly after planting or once the vineyard has started cropping, then you have two options. If it is immediately after planting and the soil is bare and weed-free, then you will need to obtain a narrow seed drill (they can be hired) and which can plant the area between the weed-free strips or use a fertliser spreader which has been fitted with side-baffles to restrict the throw of the spreader. The one thing you really want to avoid is getting seed on to the 600-750 mm weed-free area beneath the vines. After planting, the land will probably benefit from a light harrowing and consolidating with a roller.

If you are considering planting into a cropping vineyard, where a grass sward has already been established in the alleyways, you will first need to get rid of this by burning it off with herbicide and then cultivating the area to be seeded. If you don't use herbicide and just cultivate, then the grass species already growing will quite quickly re-establish and you will find that some of the benefits of the green manure will be lost. Finding a narrow cultivator may well be a challenge, although as with a seed drill, they can be hired, and after planting the land is again, probably best lightly harrowed and rolled, assuming you can find the right sized equipment.

Once the seed has germinated and started to grow, when you start topping and how hard you top will depend on what you are trying to achieve and the species being grown. Some species take to early topping; others do not. If you are trying to grow the maximum amount of green matter possible, then later topping will help achieve this, although some plants, if you allow them to grow until they have produced ripe seed heads, may well grow to over 1 m tall (in the case of chicory, a really good pan-busting plant, it can be nearer 2 m) and you will need a powerful flail mower in order to reduce the growth down to a manageable height.

Whatever species of green manure you plant, the crop should be seen as a relatively short-term one as the likelihood is that within two years, certain species, especially grasses including any in the seed mix planted, as well as those native to your soil, will start to dominate and eventually will take over. This is especially the case if you start to mow before the green manure plants have had a chance to flower and seed.

In many oversees vineyard regions, some form of green manuring is commonly practiced and one often sees vineyards either completely sown or with every other row sown, whether on a short term or a longer term basis, with green manures. One of the problems in the UK – and the reason that I suspect green manuring is not more widely practiced – is that most vineyards do not have access to the tools required to do a good job. Ideally one needs to have access to a cultivator, seed drill, harrow, roller and flail mower, all narrow enough to fit down a vineyard row and not trespass on to the undervine weed-free strip. Together these might cost £15,000, (although some of them can be hired) and this type of capital expense, plus the cost of the seed, the cost of planting and establishing the seed and the extra work involved with the proper management of a green manure crop, is seen as an additional expense with an uncertain payback. However, I believe that many poorly performing vineyards would be greatly helped by the beneficial effects of green manuring, especially in the area of improved drainage, improved soil fertility and increased soil microflora activity.

---

1  www.defra.gov.uk/food-farm/land-manage/nutrients

2  www.lancrop.com

3 The CEC relates to the nutrient holding capacity of the soil and relates to the soil's clay and/or organic matter content.

4 Potassium is sometimes called potash and always referred to as 'K' after the German for potash which is Kalium.

5 Pages 154-8 of RB209 June 2010 edition.

6 www.cotswoldseeds.com/seed-info/sort-out-your-soil-practical-guide-green-manures

7  www.organicadvice.org.uk/soil_papers/green_manures.pdf

Chapter 8
# Planting your vineyard

## Planting techniques

The site has been chosen, the vines ordered and the site prepared. The next task facing the vinegrower is planting. As has already been discussed in *Chapter 6: Site planning and preparation*, the best time to plant vines in the UK is in the first three weeks of May. What follows is based upon this assumption.

By now you will have decided upon the layout of your vineyard, the orientation of the rows, the size of the individual blocks, the row length, the space required for headlands, internal roadways, internal walkways, windbreaks, and parking and loading areas, and these will have been allowed for in your overall planting plan.

The first decision to take about planting, one that needs taking well in advance of the actual operation, is whether to plant by hand or by machine. Until Denbies planted their first vines in 1986, all vines in the UK (that is ignoring the efforts of the owner of Barnsgate Manor Vineyard at Crowborough who in 1975 used, with very mixed results, a cabbage planter) had been hand planted. Hand planting, using a variety of implements, can be very successful. With correctly prepared soil, correctly prepared vines and enough people, vines can be hand-planted quite easily, the rate of planting depending on the soil conditions, the ease of making holes and the implement used. The drawbacks of hand-planting are the time it takes and the problems associated with accurately marking out the row positions and the individual vine positions in the row, and therefore the cost. Although hand-planting will probably cost less than machine planting, it is by no means a cheap option. The cost of machine planting will vary according to the number of vines to be planted and what sort of deal you can organise with the contractor (and also the rate of the Euro as most planting contractors working in the UK come from France, Germany or Luxembourg), but you can budget on between £0.40 and £0.65 per vine. On a small scale, say less than 5,000 vines, you may have difficulty persuading a planting contractor to turn up for this number, or he may want to charge you such a high price that it is uneconomical. In that instance, hand-planting is your only option. Having been involved with planting hundreds of thousands of vines over the past forty years, both by hand and by machine, I would never now

voluntarily opt for hand-planting. The time taken in marking out, the difficulty in getting the vines in the right positions, when compared to the ease of machine planting makes the decision – as they say – a 'no brainer'. It has been suggested that machine planting might make TDs worse, but in my experience this is not the case. Sure, if you machine plant into badly prepared ground, then vines may not establish properly and TDs might be worse. But, prepare the soil correctly and plant the vines correctly, and it is my experience that TDs will be no better or worse for the method of planting.

## Hand planting

If you propose to hand-plant, then the first task is marking out. You will need to decide which is your 'reference' row – the one from which all other measurements are taken – and after that it is just a matter of striking a right-angle to this row and making sure all other measurements are taken from it.[1] If the headland where you start planting is not at

right-angles to your reference row, then you have the job of deciding whether the vines should be in line with your headland or at right-angles to your reference row. If you decide the former, then remember that the distance between rows must be measured at right-angles to your reference row, not in line with the headland. Although the difference is not great, over many rows it will show. Personally I always favour planting at right-angles to the reference row, but this is mainly because almost all planting I am involved with is by machine. Either way, your end-posts ought to be installed in a straight line whichever way you decide to plant. Once you have staked out your reference line and struck your right-angle, the rest of the rows can be measured out.

The tools required for hand planting are some good narrow bladed planting spades, string, marker pegs and a decent tape measure, the longer the better. Depending very much on the soil conditions and the organisation of the job, one good hole-digger can keep one planting-person busy and one such 'team' ought to be able to plant up to 300-400 vines a day. Ideally you will want several teams in order to get the job done quickly. This number of vines may not be planted on day one, but once a rhythm is established, in well-prepared and easy to dig soil, this number of vines ought to be achievable. The vines for hand-planting need to be trimmed so that their roots are slightly shorter than you need them for machine planting – 75-100 mm is more than long enough – and each planter should have a wooden box or a bucket in which their vines are kept as they plant. Ideally the vines should be kept under a piece of damp sacking so that they do not dry out. This is especially important if the weather is bright and breezy and doubly important to cover the vines up when your planting teams take a break. It is important for the holes to be dug with a flat bottom of the right size – the hole should be square with one side dug in line with the row – and the vine should be placed against the side of the hole, in line with the string marking out the row, with the roots spread out in the bottom of the hole. If the hole is too deep, then some of the soil from the hole needs putting in the bottom so that the vine sits at the right height. After the hole has been filled in (each planter might like to have a small trowel about their person for this task) the vine should be tweaked upwards if needs be, to bring it up to the right level and finally the soil around the vine should be pressed down with a firm heel to finish it off.

In addition to the digging-planting teams, you will want a team of at least two people marking out the ends of the rows, putting out taught strings to mark every row and pegging out every vine position. Although you can attempt to do this by taking a starting point and measuring the distance between each vine using a piece of wood the same length as the inter-vine distance, it is almost impossible, except on a very small area, to keep the vines in the correct position. Not only do you need to worry about the vine's positions at right-angles to each other, but it is also good practice to get the diagonals in line. Apart from the visual pleasure of having all the vines in the right place, when it comes to installing the stakes in the vineyard, having the vines in the right place is a great help.

Although planting vines using just a spade is a viable option, I have also very successfully used a water lance. This is a hand-held device which, when attached to a sprayer full of clean water, 'digs' a hole into which the vine can be placed. In this way, one lance-person, plus one person driving the tractor, can dig holes at fairly high speed, the only problem being that you do not want the holes to dry out before the vine is inserted, so you do need a gang of two planters per hole-digger. In this way a three-person team might plant 600-700 vines in a day. The vine roots should be trimmed back to less than 50 mm – although this looks quite brutal, don't worry, the vine will survive – and as soon as the hole has been drilled, the vine should be placed into the wet mud-slurry that fills the hole. As the water drains away, the mud will solidify enough to

hold on to the vine which can be tweaked upwards to the right planting level. If I was using a synthetic mulch such as black plastic film or a woven material (see *Chapter 14: Weed Control* for more about mulching) then I would always lay the film or material first and plant with a water lance through it. The lance can also be used for inserting intermediate posts if not all the way, then at least to give them a start. Successful hand-planting depends on getting the soil conditions right before planting. Well-subsoiled, well-cultivated, dry soil is ideal and digging a hole with a spade or water lance will be a simple task. Tough, heavy, waterlogged clay is another matter.

As for the cost of hand planting, I have known contractors quote around 35-40 p per vine, to which would have to be added the cost of marking out and organising the supply of vines to the planting teams. However, in my experience, contractors working on piece-work tend to rush the job and just get the vines into the ground in any way they can and it is better to employ your own labour on an hourly basis.

*GPS guided planting machine*

## Machine planting

Machine planting on the other hand is, given correctly prepared soil, comparatively easy. There are essentially two types of planting machine: laser-guided and GPS-guided. Until about five years ago, the GPS machines were not totally reliable and not to be recommended. Today however, with improved machines and better GPS connections, they are (almost) foolproof. Laser guided machines work by following a laser which gives them a straight planting line (although it depends on the tractor driver to follow the laser) and the inter-vine distance is set by the machine which is guided by a steel guide-wire which is played out from a fixed point as the machine progresses along the row being planted. When the machine gets to the end of the row, the laser is moved by hand to the line of the next row to be planted and the stake holding the end of the steel guide-wire is likewise moved the correct distance at the other end (the starting end) of the vineyard. Laser guided machines can normally only plant from one end of the field and usually plant best driving down a slope. The rate of planting will depend upon several factors, but I would expect a laser-guided machine to plant 1,000-1,500 per hour and a GPS-guided machine nearer to 2,000 per hour. Obviously row length will be a factor in planting speed, with lots of short rows taking longer than a smaller number of longer rows.

The accuracy of planting with a laser-guided machine depends on three people: the tractor driver, the person moving the laser and the person moving the stake holding the guide-wire. Whilst in my experience mistakes seldom happen, it is always possible and my advice is always to be on hand when a vineyard is being machine planted (laser or GPS) and have a tape measure (or two) about your person to make frequent checks on both row width and inter-vine distances. It also helps to have a bamboo cane marked with the correct row width so that each time a row is started, the bamboo can be moved across the site as a final check that the row width is correct. Finding that you have one row which is slightly narrower or wider than all the others is not ideal. As with any type of vineyard planting, a nice square site without undulations or strange angles will always be easier to plant accurately than one where the headland runs out at an alarming angle to the reference row and you cannot see the far end of the row from the beginning.

With GPS guided planting machines on the other hand, after the GPS receiver has been set up and locked on to the satellites and the planting machine has 'shaken hands' with the receiver, all you need to do is decide where the very first vine is to be planted – this becomes your reference vine against which all others will be aligned – and the direction of your first row. Go to where you want your first row to end, mark it and the GPS machine will drive to it, take a reference position and this will then locate the line of your reference row. All other rows will then be parallel to this row. The only caveat to this apparent planting perfection is if the vineyard site is in a valley or there are a lot of tall trees close to where vines are being planted. In these situations, I have known GPS machines to lose their satellite connectivity and whilst they have eventually got it back (as different satellites come over the horizon) it did result in delays in planting. On an open, non-valley, tree-free site however, they work exceptionally well.

Because GPS machines work with total accuracy, if you have a straight headland to which you would like your rows to be at right-angles, it is important to make sure that your reference row is exactly at right-angles to the line of the headland. To do this, the Pythagorean '3-4-5' system (see footnote for more details) using three pegs and a tape measure is not usually accurate enough and the right-angle needs setting out using a theodolite or other measuring device. Having inputted the row width and inter-vine distance into the computer, there is little else to do apart from keep the machine fed with vines and occasionally make sure everything is in line. The accuracy of a GPS planter is down to 15 mm and apart from where soil conditions disturb the planter as it travels across the field, the accuracy of planting, both in-line and across the diagonal, is astounding. Although a GPS machine can plant from both directions, it is generally easier for it to always start from one end, the end where you have your stock of vines. Again, as with laser planting, you will need to peg out the line of the headland at the far end so that the machine operators know where to stop feeding the

machine with vines. In truth, it is easier for them to overplant a vine or two if they are unsure, as immediately after planting, any extra vines can be easily uprooted and placed back on the machine for re-planting. It is also wise to have two spades to hand – one at each end of the vineyard – in case you need to hand plant the odd vine. Occasionally the machine operators will miss a vine or the vine they put into the planting jaws will fall out and hopefully they will tell you this as it happens so that you can walk down the offending row with your spade, find the missing vine and replant it.

Both types of planting machine operate in the same way. A large double blade is dragged through the ground and the vines to be planted are placed into the gap created by the double blade by a wheel which has a gripper system which holds on to the vine until the moment of planting. The machine travels forwards, opens up the slot, the vine is planted and two blades and two wheels follow behind, moving and firming the soil around the vine. The planting height is set by the operator, but depends upon two large wheels upon which the machine runs. See *Wagner Pflanzen-Technik* website for details and a video of their 'IPS-Drive' planting machine.

Although I pointed this out in my section in *Chapter 6: Site planning and preparation* in the section on *Cultivations*, it is worth repeating what I wrote:

*Once the [planting] machine has passed on, the soil must fall back into the slot and around the roots of the vine. This would typically be at a depth of 250-300 mm. Although the soil at the very surface will invariably fall back around the stem of the vine and visually the vine will appear to be settled, it is what happens below the surface level that is critical. Vines planted in sites where subsoiling has not taken place and where cultivations have only been at a relatively shallow depth, may well suffer from having their roots waving around in the air, some way below surface level and out of sight.*

After planting, especially if the soil is wet at the time of planting, the planting machine or any machinery you have had on the vineyard during planting, may have left wheel marks in the rows. Depending on the severity of these, and assuming that you will eventually be mowing in the alleyways, it is sometimes necessary to cultivate the rows immediately after planting, to even things out and level the soil. If of course you propose to cultivate your vineyard during the establishment phase, then this will happen anyway. It is also sometimes necessary to press down the soil either side of the line of planted vines if the soil hasn't properly closed up around the roots of the vine. A quick 'waggle' test can establish if this happened. Grab the newly planted vine by the top and see if you can wave it backwards and forwards in the direction of the planting line or pull it up and see if it moves. If you can, then this means that there is little soil around the roots. With well-loosened soil and perhaps some rain soon after planting, the soil may well firm up around the roots on its own, but if it looks like it is not going to, it may be necessary to run a tractor wheel as near to the vines as possible in order to try and press the soil down into the area where the vine's roots are. It's not ideal, but it's better than letting the roots dry out.

Although you will often read in the literature and sometimes even upon the sides and tops of the boxes containing the vines that they should be 'rehydrated by soaking in water for 24-48 hours prior to planting', I have never done this and have never had a problem with vines suffering from lack of water. I suspect that nurseries state this because: (a) almost all their customers are in warmer climates than the UK's; (b) they are not sure how the vines are stored once they leave their premises; and (c) they are covering their backs. In *Chapter 17: Trunk diseases* you will see reference to a document written by three of the foremost researchers into the subject who conclude: 'Vines, particularly the roots, should not be allowed to dry out during planting. However, standing vines with freshly trimmed roots in a bucket of water is detrimental, spreads disease and should be avoided. It is better to cover bundles with a clean damp cloth.' I have never had to water vines after planting although in dry years I do know growers who have. If the ground is correctly prepared and the vines correctly planted, then at root level, the vine's roots should be firmly surrounded by moist soil and should not suffer from a lack of moisture. To see if your vines have enough water, dig down 200-300 mm to the level where the vine's roots are and see if you can 'ball' the soil in your hand. If you can, then there is enough moisture. If the soil will not ball and collapses into dust, then you might need to water. The other pointer is the weeds: if they are happily growing, then there is almost certainly enough moisture for your vines.

In recent years there have been experiments in planting a wide variety of hardwood plants, including vines, using mycorrhizal fungi dips on the roots just prior to planting. As was pointed out in the *Chapter 3: Site selection* in the section on *Soil type*, mycorrhizal fungi are necessary for plants to access the nutrients contained in the soil, and in soils deficient in these fungi, the growth and development of plants may be slowed. Whilst I have seen experiments using these fungi on hedging plants and fruit trees, showing much better growth and establishment, my experience with vines is not that positive. Unless vines are to be planted in very humus-deficient soil and a soil that has perhaps been poorly farmed, I doubt whether it is worth the expense and, more importantly, the extra time taken to dip the vines at an already very busy time – immediately pre-planting – and I would not recommend the use of mycorrhizal fungi. However, if you feel you need or would like to use them and it makes you feel better, I do not believe there are any disadvantages.

Products based upon *Trichoderma* fungi, which are naturally occurring beneficial soil fungi, are sold on the basis that they can protect roots from many damaging pathogens present in soil. Products such as 'RootShield' are sold in several different forms – as granules and as dips – and offer such benefits as 'forming a shield around' and 'preventing pathogens from damaging' the roots. Again, as with mycorrhizal fungi dips, I am unsure as to how much benefit these products offer to vines planted into well prepared soils.

*Roots coming from above the graft. Make sure your vines are not planted too deeply*

---

1 Striking a right-angle using just a tape measure and three canes is relatively easy using the Pythagorean 3-4-5 technique. A triangle with the dimensions 3-4-5 (or 6-8-10 or even 12-16-20) will have a right-angle between the 3 and 4 edges. It is easier doing this with 2 people or with strings cut to the right length. Whilst it is not easy to get 100 per cent accuracy this way, especially when the right-angle is extended by eye over a hundred metres or more, it is good enough for most hand-planted vineyards. For GPS planting, a more accurate method is required.

# Chapter 9

# Trellising systems – construction

## Introduction[1]

The aim of all trellising systems in viticulture is to secure the fruiting wood and to allow the annual canes and foliage that comes from that fruiting wood to be contained so that operations, both manual and mechanical, can take place with ease and without damaging the vine and its fruit. Trelliswork has to be constructed with materials and methods that are cost-effective and durable and last as long as possible. What is not required is a trellis that is cheap to install which, although it may perform well initially, requires costly maintenance and/or replacement. Good trelliswork will last the lifetime of the vineyard and its cost must be spread over that lifetime.

Of course, not all vines require trellising systems, but these, typically bush-trained vines, are only grown in warm to hot climates where growing-season rainfall is low and, because sunshine and heat levels are high, less foliage is required to produce the sugar levels required. This is not the situation in the UK. In the UK, as in almost all cool growing regions, vines require more foliage in order for there to be sufficient leaf area for enough photosynthesis to take place to ripen grapes to the right sugar level. Although it is not a straight-line equation, in a cool climate, the more foliage your vines have (within reason), the higher the sugar levels and the better the wine. In addition to requiring more leaf area, vines growing in cooler climates, where there is typically more growing-season rainfall, will suffer from more fungal disease and require more canopy management and pesticide spraying (especially fungicides) to keep them healthy and their fruit in good condition.

In the UK, the coolest of all regions where vines are grown on anything approaching a world-scale[2], the problems faced are those of over-vigorous vines which shade both the canes bearing the buds for the following year's fruiting, as well as the buds, flowers and eventually grapes, whose production is the purpose of the vineyard. Although I have already reproduced this excerpt from Smart and Robinson's *Sunlight into Wine* it bears repeating:

*'The buds that contain the shoots and clusters for the following season begin growth early in the spring as shoots develop. Flowering is a critical stage. It is at this stage that the cluster primordia are laid down. Cluster primordia are microscopic pieces of tissue which eventually develop into clusters the following season. Within the young 'compound' bud there are three small shoots which develop – the primary, secondary and tertiary. Whether or not these shoots produce cluster primordia is **very dependent on shade in the canopy**. It is [still] important that shade be minimised on the sections of shoots that will be pruned to in the winter, as the light response is very localized.'*

The trellising therefore, must do all it can to help growers achieve an open, airy, light-inviting canopy which will play its part in the battle to achieve sustainable yield levels and ripe fruit. In *Chapter 5: Pruning and trellising systems for UK vineyards*, I explained why I feel that a two-arm flat *Guyot* system is the most appropriate for the UK and therefore it is the construction of this system that I propose mainly to discuss in this chapter.

## Materials

The basic materials for a trellis system are posts, both end-posts and intermediate posts, wire, anchors and the fittings and attachments that aid various operations in the vineyard. A visit to a viticulture equipment show such as Intervitis (in Stuttgart), Vinitech (in Bordeaux) or Sitevi (in Montpelier) is littered with companies showing a very wide range of different materials and different fittings and attachments for growing vines and it is soon obvious that there is no ultimate right or wrong way, or right or wrong materials, used in vineyard trellis construction. Personal opinion, custom and practice, and availability of machinery and labour will all play their part in how any trellis is constructed and used.

The main thing to understand about a vineyard trellis is that each component plays its part in the construction of the whole. The aim of the trellis is to hold the wires that carry both the vine's canes[3] and the vine's fruit with the minimum of sag. The fruiting (i.e. lowest) wire carries most of the direct weight of the vine's canes and the fruit and this therefore must have as little sag and be as taut as possible. To do this it needs to be attached to two solid end-posts each attached to an immovable anchor. The fruiting wire is supported by the intermediate posts and it is important to appreciate that the load on these anchors is largely dictated by the distance between the intermediate posts. In any trellis that I am involved with, the fruiting wire is also supported by the individual planting stakes to which each vine is trained, and which must be firmly attached to the fruiting wire. If vines have no individual planting stakes then these can play no part in the overall strength of the trellis. The other thing to appreciate is that a row of vines in full leaf and carrying a decent crop will, if exposed to a side-wind, exert a considerable sideways breaking force on the posts. This is particularly so on the outside few rows of the vineyard, especially in the UK on the south-west side, and will cause weak posts to bend or break and strong posts to lean if they are not adequately tensioned by the end-post assembly: end-post, anchor wire and anchor. Once posts start leaning, it is very difficult to stop them leaning even further.

## Posts

The choice of materials for posts – end-posts, intermediates and planting stakes – is wide and includes timber of many different types, steel, reinforced concrete and several different types of plastic and composite materials. Until about ten years ago, almost all UK vineyards were trellised using timber posts. Pressure treated softwood was mainly used, although various hardwoods and semi-hardwoods – oak, acacia, sweet chestnut – have all been used, both with and without some treatment, either completely treated or just to their bases. For decades, the pressure-treatment of softwood was carried out with what was known as CCA (Copper Chrome Arsenate[4]) preservatives, but between 2003 and 2006 these were banned. Today, new materials are used such as Tanalith E, based upon copper triazole technology (no – I don't know what it means either) for both construction and fencing timber and does much the same job as CCA. In some countries however, the burning of treated timber of all sorts has been banned and this has hastened the use of other materials for vineyard trellising, mainly steel.

The main determinant of post material will be cost. Depending on the length, diameter, actual material and treatment, a softwood post suitable for the intermediates for a vineyard – say 60-75 mm diameter tops,[5] 2.50 m long and pressure treated, can cost from as little as £2.50 + VAT each to well over double that. Jacksons Fencing, who use what they call their 'Jakcured' process, will charge you nearer £6.00 + VAT each, but they do come with a 25 year guarantee. In my experience, buying softwood posts is a complete lottery. Whatever the manufacturers of posts tell you and (almost) whatever guarantees they give you, there are too many variables in the production of softwood posts for any to last longer than 10-15 years (and often a lot less). The origin of the timber, the exact type of tree (redwood or whitewood), the time the trees have taken to grow, whether they have been naturally or kiln-dried (and for how long and to what moisture content), how long after cutting the posts have been treated, and lastly, how well they have been treated, are all factors outside of your control. Even if you can afford posts produced to the Highways Agency's (HA) specification,[6] most guarantees that I have seen only cover the replacement of the actual post and not the cost of removing the old one and replacing it – and heaven help you if you have so much as

touched the post with a tractor or implement. Some suppliers treat their posts to British Standard 8417 (2011) but you need to be careful as there are five classes of treatment and three levels of Desired Service Life (DSL) – 15, 30 and 60 years – which are not guaranteed periods of use and each class and each level has different specifications. The most commonly found for exterior timber posts in contact with the ground is what is known as UC4 (Use Class 4) but typically only to the 15 year DSL which is too short a time for vineyard use. If they will (and you will undoubtedly have to pay for it) get your supplier to treat posts to UC4 and DSL of 30 years. Also get them to confirm in writing that this is the specification they are using. Given that timber is such an unpredictable medium for long-term use, my advice is: use steel posts.

Having said 'use steel', if you really have your heart set on timber for aesthetic or other reasons, then I would advise using posts pressure treated with creosote rather than other materials. Softwood pressure treated with creosote was always the timber of choice for railway sleepers and telegraph and electricity poles and many of these are still in use after decades. In Kent, and I am sure in many other fruit-growing counties, pressure treated creosote softwood posts are used for supporting apple trees and work very well. They can be messy to work with when they are new and operators must always wear gloves when handling and installing them. They also tend to exude creosote from time to time, especially in warm weather, and it's best not to run your hands up and down them without protection. However, they are not as brittle as posts treated with other types of material and my experience is that they last longer and if anything, are a bit cheaper. This means that you can afford to get larger diameter posts for the same money. Despite recent restrictions on the use of creosote for treating timber[7], as far as I am aware, it is still permitted to use them in orchards and vineyards.

There is also a relatively new way of protecting the bottom ends of timber posts using a polythene and bitumen sleeve called a 'Postsaver' which is heat-shrunk on to the post. To fit a 100 mm diameter post, these cost around £1.00 each, and for a 150 mm post, £1.75, plus the cost of fitting.

If you do decide to use timber posts, then apart from the obvious of finding a supplier who you can trust and who will give you some sort of reassurance that their posts have not just been recently hauled out of some Russian forest and dunked in a tank of preservative, the main recommendation is not to skimp on diameter at the base. For intermediates you ought to have posts with a base diameter of at least 75 mm with 100 mm being better and for end-posts I would recommend a base diameter of at least 150 mm with 200 mm being better. The breaking force of a 75-100 mm treated timber post is roughly twice that of a 50-75 mm one. Also, the ratio of the surface area of a post to its internal volume decreases as the diameter increases, meaning that the amount of area where the wood preservative is held, increases with the diameter of the post. A 100 mm diameter post has approximately twice the volume of treated timber protecting it when compared to a 75 mm post. Larger diameter posts will also displace more soil and have a greater surface area in contact with the soil, thus making them firmer and stronger. In most soils, timber posts with pointed ends are preferable and are easier to drive in straight and upright.

With timber (as with all posts) it's what's in the ground that counts – not what is showing – and my advice is to have at least 750 mm in the ground for intermediate posts and nearer 900 mm for end-posts, although this will depend on the type of soil you have and how the posts are installed. Ideally posts want to go into undisturbed ground as far as is possible and be hammered, punched or shaken into the ground. Steel posts displace very little soil when they go into the ground, which makes them easier to install, but it is doubly important that they go into undisturbed soil and not into pre-augured holes. Digging or auguring holes prior to putting the post in, except in exceptional circumstances, is to be avoided as this will weaken the post's resistance to both pulling out of the ground and of leaning. As has already been said, once a post starts leaning, it is difficult to get it to stop. Although I prefer buried anchors (see section on *Anchors* later in this chapter), if you are using timber end-posts, there is one end-post assembly you could use. This is the 'horizontal stay' assembly beloved of Australians and New Zealanders (who use it for all their long rabbit and deer fences) and if correctly installed, is immensely strong and gives a nice vertical finish to the ends of the rows without anchor wires which are asking to be snagged.

*Horizontal stay end post structure in a new vineyard*

With treated softwood posts, you will be very lucky if you don't get any breakages (from rot) within 10-15 years of them being installed (and often sooner). Over the lifetime of a vineyard (30-40 years), you must expect to replace softwood posts at least twice, and some of them probably three times. Timber posts tend to break at the worst possible time – just before harvest when there is a full crop and you get an autumn gale blow through the vineyard – and replacing posts, especially end-posts, is not just a question of 'slipping a new one in' as someone hopefully described this task to me – it's a hateful job and one that can be avoided – by using steel posts. When a timber post breaks, it is always at ground level and the

base of the post is usually still sound and impossible to remove without digging a huge hole to extract it. The replacement post therefore has to go into the ground next to the base of the old one and (annoyingly) slightly out of line with all the others. If using timber posts, you also need to make sure that the nails and staples used are the right ones (the ones with barbs) and that the staples are installed at an angle across the grain so that they will not pull out as the timber dries and shrinks.

*End-post assemblies at Bolney Wine Estate, West Sussex*

Having re-read the last few paragraphs, readers will probably be thinking I work for the Steel Vineyard Post Council or whatever such a body for the promotion of steel posts might be called – far from it – I speak from the experience of having used local-sourced coppiced sweet chestnut posts, hot-dipped them myself (all of them for 5 acres of vines) and seen them start to fail after ten years.

Like timber, steel posts come in a fair few variants (and even colours) and, like timber, you tend to get what you pay for. There are several factors that account for differences in price. Apart from the most obvious ones – length and type – the thickness of the steel and how they are galvanised account for quite large differences.[8] The thickness of the steel is one factor in a post's strength, the other being the exact shape (the profile) and manner of its construction[9] and you need to make sure you are happy with the manufacturer's recommendations and guarantees. The most telling recommendation is how far apart the posts can be placed as this has a direct effect on the cost per hectare. I always aim to use posts that can be placed at 6 m apart (i.e. every five vines @ 1.20 m apart) which gives you approximately 800 posts-ha (324 posts-acre) in a vineyard with 2 m wide rows. Given the cost of installing them and the other costs associated with having more posts per hectare, it is better to pay a bit more for posts that can be installed every five vines, than to have weaker ones that have to be installed every four vines, giving you 990 posts-ha (401 posts-acre). I would not recommend that intermediate posts be more than 7 m apart, whatever they are made of, although I do know of one vineyard that spaces them at 10 m for the establishment years and then in-fills so that they end up at every 5 m. If they are wider apart than this, the strain placed upon the wire in an effort to get them tight and sag-free will cause the wires to be tightened beyond their point of elasticity and they will start to elongate and weaken. I accept that with really good anchors, so that forward movement of the end-posts is kept to a minimum, you might be able to stretch the intermediate post interval, but I think it better to be safe than sorry and keep them to around 6 m, depending on your vine spacing.

The other major factor in steel posts is how they have been galvanised. Cheaper ones tend to be 'pre-galvanised' or 'strip galvanised', i.e. the sheets of steel from which they are cut and formed are galvanised before they are cut into post-sized pieces. The more expensive posts are always 'post-galvanised' or 'hot-dip galvanised', i.e. the sheets of steel are cut and formed into posts and their notches and/or clips are pressed/cut out before the posts are then galvanised. In this way all the cut edges and stress edges where the steel sheet has been bent are fully galvanized. Whilst there is undoubtedly a saving to be made by using pre-galvanised posts, they will not last as long and in certain aggressive soils, especially where they are stressed by say side-winds or have been spaced too far apart, some of them may well fail. Even if they do not fail, pre-galvanised posts will start to rust along the edges and where the hooks have been formed quite quickly. However, if you don't mind this, then save some money and use them.

Another difference with steel posts is whether the hooks are 'internal' or 'external' and this will depend on such things as whether you propose to use a harvesting machine (which can damage external hooks), whether your vineyard has a dip in it (which causes the foliage wires to jump out of the hooks) and various other related matters. Most growers in the UK do not have harvesting machines and find external hooks easier to use when manually moving wires up during canopy management. Each manufacturer has their own design differences, most of which are claimed to be 'superior' to other types and it is worth speaking to other growers with similar vineyards to your own before making a final decision.

The final factor in the cost of posts – whether end or intermediate – is how long do they need to be? This decision depends on three factors: how high you want your leaf-wall to be; how wide your rows are; and how low are you prepared to bend down?

Leaf-wall height is the distance from the fruiting wire to the top of the foliage which is typically around 100-200 mm higher than the top of your posts and/or the top wire (which ought to be almost the same height). The height of leaf-wall is actually a very important factor in UK vineyards and I fear not one greatly appreciated by all growers. Although I hadn't realised why, I seemed to know that higher was better than lower and it was only when I heard a talk by Cornelis van Leeuwen[10] (known as Kees van Leeuwen) who is a Professor of Viticulture at Bordeaux Sciences Agro School, part of the *Institut des Sciences de la Vigne et du Vin* (ISVV) based in Bordeaux, that I realised why. In cooler climates, excess vigour is often a problem and whilst soil type and depth and rootstock play their part, the availability of nitrogen and water are of greater importance. Nitrogen can be managed by depriving the vine of access to it and by growing cover crops in the vineyard alleyways which will compete for it.

Water, on the other hand, in an un-irrigated vineyard, cannot be controlled: when it rains, it rains. Good drainage can help get rid of water and again, alleyway management – growing competing plants – will help absorb some of the available water. The vine, however, also uses water and the greater the number of leaves, the greater will be the amount of transpiration and water use. This is just one other factor in your fight against over-vigorous vines.

Of course one has to be realistic about leaf-wall height and there are other factors to consider, but in the UK a leaf-wall height of at least 1.00 m must be the aim, with 1.25 m or 1.35 m better. The height of your trellis must also be related to the width of your rows and the overall height does not want to be much more than the row is wide, otherwise shading of the fruiting zone will occur. Therefore, with a 2.00 m row width you might have posts of 2.50 m long with 750 mm in the ground, 1.75 m out of the ground with the vine's foliage sticking above the top of the posts by around 200 mm. Your fruiting wire could then be at around 600-700 mm from the ground, giving you a leaf-wall of 1.25-1.35 m. If you didn't mind your fruiting wire being at say 300 mm (which would be far too low for most people's comfort) and you decided that a 1.00-1.20 m leaf-wall was adequate – neither of which I would recommend – then you could use posts of around 2.25 m long with say 650 mm in the ground, bringing the overall height of your trelliswork down to 1.75 m. This would also allow you to have narrower rows, say down to 1.65 m wide.

The reason I do not recommend having a fruiting wire at 300 mm is (a) because it's a back-breaking height to prune at, work at and pick at and (b) it's too near the ground for the fruit with regard to: weed control in our often-damp climate; water-splash from the soil on to the fruit which adds to the disease problems; and too near the ground for predators to eat and/or damage the fruit. However, with shorter posts the canopy offers less wind resistance and therefore posts can be made from smaller material, do not have to go so far in the ground and are therefore cheaper.

## End-posts

For end-posts, the same holds good as for intermediates except that they need to be made of stouter stuff and be longer. This ensures that there is more material in contact with the soil and that the soil they are in contact with is more compact. Together these make for greater strength and stability. Don't think you can get away with using intermediates as end-posts. All steel post manufacturers make end-posts with a different set up of hooks and holes from those in their intermediate posts. According to the boffins, a sloping end-post offers no greater resistance than an upright one, but in my experience, all end-posts tend to move forwards a little bit over time, so it's best to start with a slight backwards tilt. Therefore, insert end-posts at a slight angle to the vertical – 10-15° is about right – and to a depth where the top is level with the top of (or very slightly above) the intermediates.[11] If you are using 2.50 m intermediates, then 2.75 m end-posts with about 900 mm in the ground is about right. For extra stability, a 3.0 m post with 1.0 m in the ground is even better. The end-post wants to be installed with its base about 600-700 mm from the last vine, i.e. about half the inter-vine distance, with the anchor installed so that the angle between its wire and the post is 25°. This will give you a distance from the last vine to the anchor wire of about 1.50 m (the exact distance will depend upon post height) and this must be allowed for when setting out the vineyard. The top of the end-post must be attached to a wire which is attached to a ground anchor. Whilst I have seen plenty of end-posts installed without anchors, this is most definitely not to be recommended. Over time, the end-posts will start to lean inwards, wires will slacken and as they are tightened, the posts will be drawn ever-inwards.

## Coloured steel posts

Coloured steel posts are available and several UK growers have used them, although why you would want to is beyond me. The reason always given is that the galvanised posts do not look 'natural' and that green, or brown, or black posts will somehow look better. Given that planting thousands of vines and stakes in dead-straight rows and stringing hundreds of kilometres of wire along the rows isn't very natural, I fail to see how colouring some of those posts alleviates this situation. But, if coloured posts are what you want, then they are available. Made from post-galvanised steel and powder coated in the shade of your choice, they naturally costs more than non-coloured. Hadley Group, probably the only UK vineyard post manufacturers, charge £5.55 for a 2.50 m intermediate post, non-coloured and £6.25 for the same post, coloured. For end-posts cost £11.55 for a 2.75 m non-coloured and £12.38 for the same post coloured. All prices + VAT.

## Individual planting stakes

In my view, every vine should have an individual planting stake against which it can grow, up which it is trained and to which it will become permanently tied. In this way, the trunk of the vine will be straight so that in the event of mechanical weed control or trunk shoot removal, the vines will not be harmed. It is my experience that vines that are tied to a planting stake during their establishment phase develop a better structure and start cropping sooner than ones that are left to their own devices. In some countries (Australia especially) vines are trained up a string tied around the vine and attached to the fruiting wire. Whilst this may be a cheap form of 'support', to me it is barely better than no support at all.

Again, as with the other posts in the vineyard, there are a multitude of materials available. Timber of all sorts, plastic, fibreglass, and steel and again, cost may dictate the final choice. One other factor to bear in mind is that the thicker the planting stake, the more tying material – longer ties or more tape or cord – will be required to go around the stake and secure the vine's stem. With 4,000+ vines per hectare and three to four ties per vine, this can add up to a lot of extra material and cost. Another consideration is the ease (or difficulty) of getting them into the ground and the length of time they will last.

*A 'tuteur trombone' to prevent damage by automatic weed hoes*

Probably the cheapest planting stake and one that is relatively easy to knock into most soils is a 1.2 m (4') bamboo cane. Whilst you can get canes from 8 mm diameter, those at 12-14 mm diameter will last longer. However, no bamboo will last indefinitely and after 5-8 years, the end in the ground will probably have rotted and the cane can either be removed (as hopefully the trunk will be strong enough and straight enough to stand up on its own) or they can be pushed back into the ground again for another few years' service. The Chinese size their bamboo canes according to their weight per 100 canes in pounds (i.e. lbs), so the thinner ones are known as '10-12s', slightly thicker ones as '18-20s' and even thicker ones as '24-26s'. Confusing, but it works for millions of Chinese! Bamboos are also packed in different bundle sizes. A bundle of the thinner ones usually contains 500; the thicker ones hold 250. A 1.2 m, 18-20 lbs (i.e. 12-14 mm) bamboo will cost around 8-10p + VAT each, depending on the numbers involved. Pushing bamboos into the ground by hand can be very wearing on gloves (don't attempt to do too many using bare hands) and hands and wrists will take a battering. Make yourself a 'knocker-in' using a short length of iron pipe with one end closed off. This you can slip over the end of the bamboo and work it up and down to knock the cane in.

The best (but one of the most expensive) planting stakes is made from 6 mm 'wavy' steel rod (ArcelorMittal sell them and call them 'undulated support') which are usually 1.2 m long (although shorter and longer ones are available). These are easy to push into the ground, will last forever and are thin so that they do not consume huge quantities of tying material. In addition, the 'waves' mean that the ties around the vine do not slip down and the stakes can be secured to the fruiting wire with either permanent ties or detachable clips so that the fruiting wire itself will not slip down. However, at around 35 p + VAT each they are three times the price of bamboo. Personally I would always use them as, when secured to the fruiting wire, they become an integral part of the whole structure. There are also similar stakes made from 6 mm galvanised rod which have grooves on them to stop the ties slipping. At the Sitevi vineyard show in Montpellier in 2013, I saw for the first time what ArcelorMittal call a *tuteur trombone* and Ancrest call a *tuteur a décavaillonner*, both of which consist of a hoop of the same 6 mm wavy steel rod as described above, which can be put in the ground over the vine with its 'legs' placed on either side of a vine. In this way, the vine is guarded from the hydraulic arm of an automatic hoe if one is being used. These cost around £0.85 each, so not cheap, but better than causing damage to a young vine each time an automatic hoe is used.

If you are using individual spray guards or rabbit guards around each vine, then you will probably need to remove the guard in order to attend to the vine – shoot selection and side-shooting – so you will need to attach the planting stake with a removable clip. These are made of sprung stainless-steel and can be clipped on and off as required. Do not use the ones made from plastic as they become brittle after a few years and fail. Otherwise, the easiest and cheapest way of permanently securing the planting stake to the fruiting wire is with a ratchet-tied 'bag-tie' which can be made of stainless steel or of plastic-covered wire. Both will last a very long time.

## Anchors

For anchors there are, again, a very wide variety of methods and products. If you are using timber end-posts, then there are several end-post anchors which can be used which are not available to those using steel end-posts. The horizontal stay end assembly already mentioned, works well if properly installed and looks neat. The diagonal stay end assembly, where an inward facing strut rests on a buried stay block is to be avoided as over time it will force the end-post out of the ground. For my money, for both steel and timber end-posts, a decent buried anchor attached to the top of the end-post is the surest solution. When I first installed vineyards, I always used what hop growers call 'dead-men' which are baulks of oak – normally a 3' long piece of 6" x 4" sawn green oak with a hole through the middle. A long slot (the grave) was then dug in the headland on the outside of where the end-post was to go and a long connecting rod, with a loop or hook on the top and a short section of thread on the bottom end, was hammered through the undisturbed soil at an angle, so that it appeared in the slot and could be pushed through the hole in the deadman and finished off with a large washer and nut. The hole in which the dead-man lay was then filled in and the anchor wire, attached to the top of the end-post, was connected to the loop on the top of the connecting rod and strained up. Dead-men, correctly installed and tensioned, are impossible to move – the anchor wire will break first. However, the materials are expensive and they are costly to install and unless the rows were exceptionally long I probably wouldn't use them again.

The most commonly used anchors in UK vineyards are the screw-in disc and the driven-in anchor of which there are two types. The screw-in disc is usually attached to a fixed anchor rod with a hook or a loop at the end – all completely hot-dip galvanised – and the diameters of the disc and the length of the rod vary. The larger the disc and the longer the rod, the better will be the hold in the soil, and it is not worth economising on these as they are relatively cheap. I would not use anything less than a 150 mm disc and an 850 mm to 900 mm rod which will cost around £3.00-£3.50. An anchor with a 200 mm disc and a 1.0 m or 1.2 m rod would be advisable on rows over 150 m long or in soft soil. These anchor rods can be wound into the ground by hand, with a hand-held hydraulic driver, or with a hydraulic winding device on the end of a mini-digger. For maximum anchorage, screw-in anchors must be wound in until the hook or loop at the end is barely visible so that you know the disc is firmly embedded in undisturbed soil. Ideally, the anchor should go in at an angle so that there is a straight line between it and the top of the end-post, but if you are using a mini-digger this is not always possible, but a slight angle helps. If you drive the anchor disc in vertically, it will start to pull straight as you tension up the trelliswork and your end-post may move forwards very slightly. A screw-in anchor combined with a correctly sized and installed end-post makes a very good end-post assembly and only in really hard stony and/or chalky soil will you have a problem getting them in.

If your ground is very hard or stony, then drive-in anchors such as those made by Platipus Earth Anchoring Systems[12] and Fenox[13] are better. Platipus offer a complete 'end-post kit' which contains both the anchor (made of aluminium) and the anchor wire (made of stainless steel). These anchors can be driven into the hardest, toughest soil, using the appropriate drive-rod and can be hand-installed with a sledge hammer or a mechanical driver or with a hydraulic driver. There are three sizes of anchor available, S4, S6 and S8, which cost £4.95, £6.95 and a massive £19.95 each, but only the two smaller ones – S4 and S6 – are really cost-effective for vineyards. Whilst Platipus are happy to recommend the smallest one, the S4, for use in vineyards, the S6 (for only £2 extra) will give you a much better hold.

The other type of drive-in anchor is made by Fenox and again, can be driven in by hand or by machine and will work in the hardest soil. They operate on a very different principal and act rather like an umbrella being opened up in the ground after the anchor has been driven in to the correct depth. They come in several sizes: 500 mm, 600 mm and 1.0 m long. The smaller one is probably best avoided, but the 600 mm one works well and costs around £8-9, depending on the number bought. The 1.0 m Fenox at £24.90 is so extraordinarily expensive that it rules itself out. Gripple, who make wire connectors and associated products, produce something called a GPAK (Gripple Plus Anchoring Kit) which contains the wire and the Gripple joiner required for each end-post. Gripple have also started making an anchor very similar to the Platipus (although subtly different I suspect for patent infringement reasons) which they claim works just as well, although I have no experience of them.

*Forget the anchors and after a few years your end-posts will look like this*

If your vineyard has undulations in it, you may need to anchor some of your intermediate stakes to stop them rising up out of the ground when you tension the wires (this may not happen immediately, but will occur over time). The Platipus S4 and Fenox 500 mm are ideal for this as they can be driven in very close to the post with the a wire then being secured to the post to hold it down.

## Wire – and other similar materials

There are several different types of material which can be used in vineyard trellising, the most common being purpose-made vineyard wire which has a mild steel core and is galvanised with a zinc and aluminium (and sometimes magnesium) mixture. This is made by several manufacturers: ArcelorMittal with their unfortunately named 'Crapal' range and Bekaert with their 'Bezinal' range being the best known. This wire is lighter than plain galvanised wire so that it gives you more metres per kilo and puts less weight upon your trellis, has a much better resistance to corrosion with its superior galvanising (important when the wire is subjected to sulphur and other corrosive sprays) and, when tightened, will elongate (stretch) by 10 per cent, compared to 20 per cent for plain galvanised wire. This means less work at both installation and later on in the lifetime of the vineyard. If you are using this wire, then 2.5 mm wire for the fruiting wire(s) and 2.0 mm for the training wires and top wire is adequate. This is based upon having your intermediate posts at around 6.0 m apart with each individual planting stake secured to the fruiting wire. For joining wires, Gripple connectors are now used very widely and work well. Plain galvanised

wire, such as you will find for sale at most agricultural merchants, is to be avoided as much of it is cheaply made and apart from the other disadvantages listed above, the galvanising will not always last the life of the vineyard. Vineyard wire is also available plastic-coated in different colours – ideal if you want it to match the colour of your posts – but otherwise I cannot see any advantages.

Other types of wire – high tensile steel wire, spring steel wire and stainless steel wire for instance – are available and sometimes used, but are more difficult to work with, more expensive and don't offer any significant advantage that I can see over the vineyard wire mentioned above. At one time a 'wire' made from nylon and called Bayco was touted as the best thing since sliced bread for vineyard trellising but although it is still available, it is seldom seen in UK vineyards. There is also a similar product called Deltex which is made in France. Whilst these are rust-proof, light-resistant, light in weight and retain their elasticity once stretched, they are a challenge to install, cut very easily with secateurs or leaf-trimmers and, in my experience, because they constantly exert a pull on the end-posts, are prone to pull the end-posts and anchors up (unless they are exceptionally good) over time. However, I do know growers who use this type of 'wire' and manage to get along with it perfectly well. This type of product is sold with two other benefits: it does not conduct electricity and is lightning-proof. If these two are what you are looking for in a vineyard wire, here is the solution! If you do use it, I would only use it for the training wires and never for the fruiting wire as it will almost certainly get cut at pruning.

## Trellis fittings – spreaders, chains, end-hooks and other items

There is a huge range of fittings used in vineyards and here is not the place to go into all the different options. There are two areas however, which are worth mentioning in some detail.

The training wires (or 'catch' wires) are the two (and sometimes three) pairs of wires whose function is to catch the vine's canes and foliage as it grows up from the fruiting wire towards the top of the trelliswork. There are two main options as to how these are to be managed.

Many growers attach these wires to the end-posts by means of chains and hooks. The chains are fastened on to the ends of the wires and the hooks to hold the chains are on the end-posts. I usually specify two chains for the end of each wire – giving a greater length of play – and for each pair of wires you require one hook assembly for steel posts or two square-headed nails if using timber posts. The chains are there so that the wires can be tightened or loosened according to the state of the foliage in the leaf-wall. The intermediate posts, if they are steel, will already have hooks on them (another advantage of steel posts) and for those using timber posts, hook nails will have been driven in at the appropriate spacing according to the pruning system, height of leaf-wall and even vine variety. Although these wires are moveable, many growers, especially ones with smaller vineyards, will leave them *in situ* for the whole year, not moving them up or down and merely using them as static wires. Some will even dispense with the hooks in their posts and permanently staple them to the posts.

The 'correct' way of managing these wires is to start the year off with the wires at the bottom of the posts, usually in hook nails provided for this purpose or in the lowest set of hooks on steel posts or sometimes just laid on the ground. Then, as the shoots start growing and turn into canes with foliage, the first pair of wires is moved up to catch as much of the canopy as possible. Then, as the canes grow, the second pair of wires is brought up from the bottom of the posts and placed in a position above the already positioned first pair. Depending on the height of the leaf-wall, these two 'liftings' may be enough, but with some canopies, a third lifting is required, in which case the first pair is detached from where they were initially placed and raised above the second pair. It is for this reason that some growers install a third pair of catch wires although if you move the first pair, this is not really necessary. If you are using an arched-cane pruning system, where the shoots extend over a larger vertical area, then this may also be a reason for a third set of catch wires.

*Wire spreaders attached to metal posts*

A refinement to this process is to install wire 'spreaders', made from sprung stainless steel, on every other intermediate post at an appropriate position which carry the pairs of catch wires. These spreaders hold the wires away from the centre line of the canopy and allow (most of) the shoots to grow up between them before you come along and close the spreaders up and hook them together. In this way, the foliage is more firmly trapped and directed into the right line and it makes the whole job of 'tucking-in' that much easier. You do need to get the positions of the spreaders correct and this will depend on your pruning system and the variety being grown. These spreaders are available for most makes of steel post (and it is important to get the correct one for the exact post you are using) and are also available as nail-on for timber posts. They are however quite expensive. The current price per spreader is around £0.55 which will add about £500 per hectare (£200-acre)[14] to your material's costs, plus the installation. Over the years however, they will repay themselves in the saving in annual work in the vineyard.

They can also be tried out on a few rows and then easily retro-fitted, especially with steel posts.

A slight variation on the above is to fit on to each (or every other) intermediate post two permanent cross-bar spreaders which carry the catch wires. These can be made of aluminium, coated steel or plastic and vary in width from around 200 mm to 350 mm. Most are centre-mounted using a hexagon-headed screw or coach-bolt. Some growers use them to keep the wires apart permanently, in which case they can be tightly fixed to the post to stop them rotating; others use them to keep the wires apart initially, then bring the wires together and hook them on to the post, turning the spreader from the horizontal to the vertical so that they are 'hidden' by the post; there are also spreaders that have fold-up arms for much the same purpose. My preference is for the fixed type. Before you fit spreaders like these, you need to make sure they are compatible with any deleafing machine you might use.

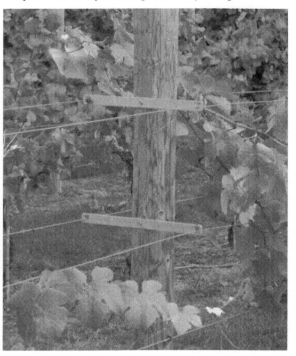

*Aluminium spreaders attached to wooden posts*

The benefit of using fixed spreaders is that they give the leaf-wall more width and more volume, allowing air and light to penetrate, drying out both fruit and leaves, and making sure that sprays reach their target. With fixed spreaders (as opposed to the ones that you close up when tucking-in) you will also find that the bunches have much more space to hang in and, except in years when crops are very large and the leaf-wall is crowded with bunches (not often seen in the UK, but it does happen sometimes), most of the bunches will hang down in their own space, not touching other bunches. Again, this helps with both ripening and disease control.

Getting good at using spreaders of whichever type makes canopy management much easier and certainly helps in achieving a quality canopy.

## Marking the ends of rows

Marking the end of rows, whilst not of course essential, is one of those things that make life a little bit easier. Whether it's spraying, weed control, taking samples or just telling the pickers which row to start on, having a number on every end-post (or every other if you want to save a few pounds), makes a lot of sense. Over the years I have probably seen every method going, but by far the most effective is to use animal ear-tags which can be obtained in a multitude of colours and printed with additional information such as variety, clone and rootstock – really useful if you are trying to spot the subtle differences between say 41B and 3309C. There are several manufacturers, but I have always used Dalton's Supertags Size 4 which work out at about 45-50p each, including printing. You need to order the female half only (the one with the hole in it). They fade over time, especially on the ends facing south, but will last a good decade or more.

*Daltons Supertags used for marking end-posts*

One of the questions I get asked most often by non-wine people is: 'why do some vineyards have roses at the ends of their rows?', to which I go through the story of how, in the past (I say 'in the past' as most roses are now resistant to mildew) roses would get mildew before the vines succumbed to mildew (not the same one, but similar) and acted as an early warning system. Today, you will still find roses planted at the ends of rows, purely decorative of course, and if this pleases you, plant away. In my experience they look nice for a while, but once they get large and start scratching you as you drive by on the tractor, the bushes get trimmed cut back.

## Cost of establishing a vineyard

As stated in *Chapter 2: Why plant a vineyard in the UK?* in the section on *Establishing a vineyard*, the cost of putting in and establishing a vineyard, i.e. to the end of

year two, can vary widely, and each vineyard needs to be costed up individually. However, it would be unwise to budget for less than £25,000-ha (£10,000-acre), to which you would have to add such things as perimeter fencing and land drainage.

---

1 The best book on trellising I have found is *Practical Aspects of Grapevine Trellising* by Mahabubur Mollah. There is also a good section on *Constructing Trellis Systems* at the end of *Sunlight into Wine* (p70-84). See Bibliography for full details. I would also recommend the Fencing Contractors Association New Zealand www.fencingcontractors.co.nz for excellent advice on fencing in general.

2 My apologies to all those growers in Belgium, Denmark, Eire, Holland, Sweden and any other 'cool' regions who feel they are also growing vines on a 'world-scale', but with 1,500+ ha, the UK is several times bigger than any of the above.

3 I am only discussing VSP cane pruned vines here. For cordon trained and spur pruned vines, other criteria will apply.

4 Also known in some countries as Chromated Copper Arsenate – the initials are the same.

5 Beware the difference between the diameter at the top and at the bottom. Most suppliers will quote you the top diameter which is almost always smaller than the bottom diameter. Some posts have been machined so that they are parallel but I cannot see the point in paying extra for these for vineyard use.

6 Department of Transport's Specification for Highway Works No: 0300.

7 The Creosote (Prohibition on Use and Marketing) (No. 2) Regulations 2003.

8 Whilst I have seen untreated bare steel posts in vineyards, they have always been in drier climates than the UK's and seldom in European vineyards. The only exception to this is bare steel planting stakes made from 6mm 're-bar' (reinforcing rod) which I have seen and which doesn't appear to harm the vine, although I personally wouldn't recommend it.

9 See Hadley Group's 'Ultra-Steel' process for instance: www.hadleygroup.com/vineposts

10 www-ecole.enitab.fr/people/kees.vanleeuwen/english_index.htm

11 According to *Practical Aspects of Grapevine Trellising* (p. 21) end-posts are no stronger when they lean backwards and there is no advantage in them being installed so that their tops are shorter than the intermediates – both things one often sees.

12 www.platipus-anchors.com

13 www.faynot.com. They are sold in the UK by Holtwood Marketing: www.holtwood.co.uk

14 Based upon a 2 m row width and a 1.2 m inter-vine spacing with intermediate posts every five vines and two spreaders on every other intermediate post.

# Chapter 10
# Machinery and equipment

## Machinery and equipment

The basic machinery requirements to run a commercial vineyard, ignoring small items and machinery and equipment of a more general nature, are a tractor, mower, pesticide sprayer, weed control equipment and pruning tools. These will be dealt with first. Other viticultural equipment, which falls into the 'optional' category and will probably only definitely be required by larger growers, will then be covered and will consist of: pre-pruning machine, prunings pulveriser, leaf-trimmer, deleafer, cane tying equipment, stem-cleaner and tucking-in machine. Miscellaneous items such as trailers, lifting forks and three-point linkage mounted fork-lifts, all of which would be useful in vineyards, especially at picking time, have not been detailed.

## Basic equipment

- **Tractor**
- Whatever tractor you have, the trellising system needs to be matched to the tractor. If the tractor is too wide, the vines will be damaged; if it's too narrow, then space is being wasted.
- For a double *Guyot* VSP system, the tractor must be able to fit down the rows with at least 350 mm clearance between the outside of the tractor and the centre line of the row. Therefore a 2.0 m row width requires a tractor that is no more than 1.3 m wide. Other systems such as Scott Henry will require more space for the vine's foliage. Wide systems such as GDC can be managed with much wider tractors.
- It must have a standard 3-point linkage to mount implements and machinery and a PTO to power any machinery that might be mounted or towed behind it.
- It must have sufficient power to be able to run a suitably sized air-blast sprayer up any gradients you have in the vineyard and sufficient oil flow and hydraulic take-off points to power any machinery you might think of mounting on the tractor and which require oil pressure to work them: leaf-trimmers, deleafers, inter-vine weeders and some weed sprayers.
- The tractor should ideally have a 'Q-cab' (quiet cab) for protection against sprays when spraying. Most cabs also

have air conditioning, radios etc. Cabs should also have a HEPA-carbon[1] filter to prevent sprays entering the cab. These filters should be renewed annually.
- Tractors are also available with a front-mounted 3-point linkage and PTO which can be used for mounting a mower so that operations such as spraying and mowing can be carried out in one pass. A front-mounted mower will increase the overall length of the tractor and may require additional headland space. Your mower must be a suitable model for front-mounting as the blades need to run the opposite way to a rear-mounted mower.

- **Mower**
- It is a good idea to have a mower around the same width as the tractor so you know that if the tractor fits, then so will the mower. Do not have it much narrower than the tractor as then you will be running on earth rather than grass, or you will have to make two passes for each row.
- For inter-row grass cutting, a single or twin bladed rotary mower is best. These are typically mounted on the 3-point linkage and powered by the PTO via a gearbox and belts, although some are direct driven.
- Mowers either rest on four wheels (or sometimes only two) or are carried on the 3-point linkage with a roller or skids at the rear. The choice depends on various factors, but almost any mower suitable for orchards will work in vineyards.
- There are also mowers which can be rear mounted, but which have a through-PTO so that a sprayer can be towed behind. This will not only require additional power, but also lengthen the tractor and possibly increase the headland required. They will of course halve the time taken to spray and mow the vineyard.
- Mowers are also available with swing-arms which mow right up to and around the stem of the vine, but these are not generally suitable for use in UK vineyards. It is important to maintain a completely weed-free strip beneath the vines and this type of mower cannot do this. It is also not advisable to use these mowers, especially on young vines (under 5 years old) as the mower (or to be more accurate, the hydraulic arm) will hit the vine in exactly the same place each time which will cause lesions and is a possible entry point for TDs.
- A flail mower, whilst it will tackle tougher conditions and heavier material than a rotary mower, is not as suitable for

inter-row mowing as it will not cut the grass as short. This is important as, at certain times of the year, really short grass in the vineyard will help keep moisture levels low.

- A flail mower is suitable for pulverising prunings although in smaller vineyards or where there are concerns about diseases in the vineyard, many growers will remove and burn prunings.

• **Sprayer**

- Your pesticide sprayer is the most important tool in your vineyard and will help you win the battle to keep your vines and your crop clean and pest and disease free. Do not try and economise on it.
- Go to a dealer who is experienced in selling sprayers suitable for fruit trees and who can specify the right nozzles for your row width and cover requirements.
- The best type of sprayer for vines is an air-blast sprayer which has an axial fan at the back to direct the spray on to the crop either directly or via 'snakes'. I prefer a sprayer without snakes.
- Sprayers come in various shapes and sizes. There are mounted ones carried on the 3-point linkage which, depending on the lift capacity of your tractor's arms, will contain up to 600 litres of liquid. There are also trailed ones which, for a larger vineyard, would have a capacity of around 1,000-1,500 litres.
- There are also so-called 'tunnel' (or 'recovery') sprayers, with and without fans, which have shields either side of the row (or rows) of vines so that as they are sprayed, any spray passing through the canopy does not go to waste by falling on the ground, but is caught by the shields and returned, via a filter, to the tank containing the spray. Reports suggest that between 35 per cent and 50 per cent of material can be saved.
- Different types of sprayer are discussed in *Chapter 16: Pest and disease control* in the section on *Machinery requirements.*

• **Weed control equipment**

- Depending on what weed control system you propose to adopt, you will require one or more of the following:
  - Herbicide sprayer
  - Under-vine cultivation equipment
  - Mulching equipment
- The question of weed control is dealt with fully in *Chapter 14: Weed control*

• **Pruning equipment**

- Whilst many vineyards will be pruned using hand-held and hand-powered secateurs (Felco No. 2 are the best), one increasingly sees powered secateurs in use. Whilst their power and the ease with which they slice through almost anything put in their way is something to be wary of, there is no doubt that once you have got used to them, they make life a lot easier.
- At one time both air assisted and hydraulic secateurs were quite widely seen (both of which required a compressor or hydraulic pump), but today, battery powered secateurs are almost universal. These are light, completely portable with a belt-type battery pack and whilst not cheap, have got cheaper over the years.

- Powered secateurs also probably help prevent the spread of some TDs as cuts can be made cleanly and evenly in exactly the place where you want them to be and at exactly the right angle. In this way, the cut will drain easily and the surface of the wound can be painted with wound protectant, should this be required.

## Optional equipment

• **Pre-pruning machine**

- Pre-pruning machines, although they are generally only used in spur pruned vines, can be used in cane pruned vineyards to cut up some of the unwanted wood at the top of the leaf-wall, making the job of 'pulling out' that much easier. ('Pulling out' is the task of removing, from the wires, the unwanted canes that are usually tightly held there with tendrils). Owing to their cost, they are in reality only suited to large vineyards or to vineyard contractors, and to date, there are only a handful being used in UK vineyards.

• **Prunings pulveriser**

- Whilst a rotary mower (discussed above) will deal with small amounts of pruning wood, especially if it is cut into short lengths and anything large pushed under the vines out of the way of the mower, the full amount of pruning wood from an established vineyard, especially if the wood from two rows is piled into one row (which is the normal practice) will be too much for one. A prunings pulveriser, usually known as a 'flail mower', is required. These mowers are driven via a gearbox and belts and work in the horizontal. The powerful flails cut the prunings into small pieces and they come out of the back as a mulch which soon disappears into the grass and over time this is incorporated into the soil. These mowers are expensive considering one only uses them once a year (on the vines) and it might be better to hire one, given that the timing is not critical.
- Other ways of dealing with prunings, burning *in situ* with a *chariot de feu*, and removal and burning off-site are dealt with in *Chapter 12: Management – cropping years* at the end of the section on *Pruning, training and tying down – first cropping year.*

• **Leaf-trimmer**

- One of the most important summer tasks is leaf trimming. This is also known as hedging or summer pruning. Whilst this can be done by hand with secateurs, shears, or powered hedge-trimmers, on anything other than a small scale, this is a backbreaking task, especially with tall trellising where the tops of the vines might be 2.0 m or more above ground level. In a typical growing year, vines in the UK would be trimmed at least twice and with some varieties and in wet seasons, three or even four times. Keeping the leaf-wall tight and trimmed is an essential part of canopy management and will help with disease control and improve ripening.
- There are several different types of leaf trimmer but the main two are the reciprocating blade type and the rotating multi-blade type. Both types are usually driven by

hydraulic motors although at least one manufacturer is offering one driven by electric motors which has a tractor-mounted generator to run it. Some of the multi-blade type have two-armed blades; some of the newer ones have four-armed blades which work a bit like helicopter blades, creating suction which sucks the cut leaves away from the leaf-wall.

- All machines have height and lateral adjustment allowing you to lower and raise them (for different trellis heights and where there are tall posts and other obstructions to be overcome) and to angle the trimmer to cut the leaf-wall in a gentle pyramid, wider at the base (where the grapes are) than at the top.

- Whilst there are leaf-trimmers which will cut both sides of a row in one pass and even trimmers which will cut two rows at once, most UK vineyards are not large enough to warrant these and prefer to use a machine which cuts one side and the top in one pass. Whilst this may be slower, it is much easier to manage and avoid knocking into things and damaging both posts and vines and cutting wires.

*Double-sided leaf trimmer*

• **Deleafer**
- Together with leaf trimming, deleafing is an essential part of canopy management in a UK vineyard. Whilst, like many tasks in the vineyard, this can be done my hand (and often is), a machine that removes the leaves makes it much more likely that it will be done at the right time and done quickly and effectively. In recent years, when poor flowering conditions have led to low cropping levels, I am convinced that a partial deleafing just after flowering, when the bunches are still open and bunch-close has not happened (and well before *véraison* which is often given as the time for first deleafing), helps open up the canopy for light, air and fungicide sprays, keeping this year's crop clean and next year's buds healthy.
- There are several types of machine: some suck the leaves into a void where they are sliced off; others that work with rollers that do much the same thing; and the (slightly old-fashioned) 'Collard' type that destroy the leaves with blasts of compressed air. Some users report that this last type blows shards of leaf into the centre of the bunch. There are also types that use gas jets that singe the leaves so that they desiccate and drop off, but these are not often

seen, although pre-harvest might be of interest.
- Whilst no machine is as accurate or as discriminating as a person, the quickness and ease with which leaves can be removed by machine make this an important piece of equipment for any serious vineyard.

*Deleafer of the 'suck and slice' variety*

• **Tying down of annual canes**
- Tying down of annual canes is a task that many growers will carry out by hand using paper or plastic covered wire ties and the size of their vineyard will not really warrant automatic vine tying equipment. However, in larger UK vineyards one is starting to see these machines (such as the Pellenc[2] AP25) which all operate in a similar way with wire, covered or uncovered, being dispensed from a roll or cartridge. Whilst they are not suitable for tying up young vines (the wires tend to cut through the canes) for the post-pruning tying down of canes they are ideal.
- For tying canes to the planting stake during the establishment phase the Max Tapener machine is the best device.
- There is more on this topic in *Chapter 11: Management – establishment phase* in the section on *Side-shooting and tying up*.

• **Shoot removal - trunks**
- Most UK growers will be removing unwanted shoots from the vine's trunk just after bud-burst by hand or with simple hand-held tools. Some use an approved chemical defoliant called Shark which works well although doesn't always completely remove all of the larger shoots or the higher up shoots, requiring some hand-work as well.
- Tractor-mounted powered stem brushers are widely used in large overseas vineyards and work simply by brushing the stem from both sides at once with stiff 'road-sweeper' type brushes powered by the tractor's hydraulics. Again, like some of the other 'minor' pieces of machinery listed above, a stem cleaner is not an essential 'must-have' item, but as agricultural wages rise and labour gets both more expensive and difficult to obtain, I expect to see larger vineyards investing in them.

• **Tucking-in machines**
- In many vineyards around the world, tractor-mounted

tucking-in machines are widely used, although none, so far, in the UK. There are two basic types: ones that work with the existing foliage wires, lifting the canes and trapping them with the wires; and ones that work by lifting the canes and trapping them with thin plastic twine 9similar to baler twine) that requires removing at the end of the season. These would only be affordable for a vineyard of considerable size, at least 20-ha (50-acres) or perhaps for a contractor.

- **Subsoiler**
- A subsoiler is probably unnecessary except for the larger vineyards as they can be hired, although having one to hand when the soil conditions are right and you have time to carry out the work is always better. As has already been discussed in *Chapter 6: Site planning and preparation* in the section on *Cultivations*, there are several different types available and tractor power will be an important factor in which type suits a particular vineyard.

*Subsoiling pre-harvest when the soil is at its driest can pay dividends over the winter*

---

1 HEPA stands for 'high-efficiency particulate absorption'.

2 The French firm, Pellenc, is one of the largest manufacturers of viticultural equipment in the world and their website is well worth a look at. www.pellenc.com/agriculture/en.

# Chapter 11

# Management – establishment phase

## Caring for vines after planting

After planting, your vines will sit for a while and take stock of their new surroundings before they wake up and decide to start growing, so don't worry if you don't see any signs of life for two to three weeks. The exact time of budburst will depend on the date of planting, the soil temperature and various other factors. However, once they have started to shoot, your work of training them can begin.

## Protection against predators – rabbits, hares, deer, badgers, wild boar

If you have not fenced the site against deer and rabbits, you will need to have decided how you are going to protect your vines against these predators. Whilst perimeter fencing is to my mind the best way of doing this, against rabbits there are various types of individual guard that can be employed. There are the tree-guard 'grow-tube' type which come in a wide variety of shapes, sizes, colours and materials. As has already been discussed in *Chapter 6: Site planning and preparation* in the section on *Fencing*, I am against the small diameter guards (75 mm to 95 mm) for a number of reasons, mainly the long-term health of the vines. Larger diameter round guards (150 mm diameter) or square guards (125 x 125 mm) can be used, but they need to be 750 mm high and will be expensive, probably around £0.85 each. However, they should be large enough to get your hand down without having to remove them each time you wish to weed the vine, but they will still have to be opened up or removed in order to carry out shoot selection, side-shooting and tying up the stems if this is to be done properly. Once the vines are established and have grown trunks robust enough to take herbicide spray, the guards can come off, although in vineyards where rabbits are a real menace, such as where they are planted near woodland or scrub land, then it may well be necessary to provide protection even after the vines have developed trunks. In the absence of perimeter fencing, this is best done with individual guards made of chicken wire which must be at least 600 mm high and 125 mm in diameter. These are typically used by apple and pear growers to protect established trees against 'barking'. There are also flimsy (and therefore cheap) individual rabbit guards made of plastic mesh, usually coloured blue (don't rabbits like blue?) which are slightly better than no guard at all, but only just. I wouldn't use them unless your rabbits are extremely timid or it was a temporary arrangement until your fencing was installed. Electric fencing can be effective in the short term against rabbits, but not as a long-term solution. As for various preparations that can be painted or sprayed on to the stems, these are totally ineffective against rabbits eating the shoots, leaves and canes of a young vine, although might work against winter bark nibbling by rabbits and hares.

Whichever route you choose to protect your vines against rabbits, it needs to be effective as otherwise you will never get them properly and evenly established.

*Individual rabbit guards around newly planted vines*

## Training young vines – year one

There are, dear reader, you will not by now be surprised to hear, several different theories about training vines in their youth and, much like child-rearing, theories come and theories go and the world moves on. Like much of this book, I can only speak from my practical experience of growing and advising people how to grow vines in the UK over 40 years and the methods and techniques I will set out here are the ones that I find work best.

## Shoot selection

When most of your vines have started to shoot, the time has come to select a single shoot that will grow away from the ground and encourage the vine to put down as big a root system as it can in its establishment phase. To do this you must select the most central and most upright of the several shoots that have probably come out of each vine – NOT the strongest shoot – and rub all the others off with finger and thumb. If this task has been left too late and some of the shoots have already started to turn woody, then you must use sharp secateurs to take these off. Ragged wounds where shoots have been torn off are not a good idea so close to the graft and might possibly be an entry point for various diseases. Get used to making pruning cuts at an angle so that any sap that seeps from the cut drains downwards and seals the wound and any rain drains away. Make sure when you cut any piece of wood, you cut fairly near to the cane so that a long piece of dead wood isn't left behind. Also, when cutting near a bud, make sure you angle the cut away from the bud, otherwise this too will become covered in sap. Whilst some of this is just viticultural housekeeping, it pays to get into good habits.

The reason for selecting the most central shoot and not the strongest is simple. The main reason that vines fail, apart from physical damage and disease, is graft failure and at this stage of the vine's development, when the graft is only just over twelve months old, it is important not to place any additional strain on it. The idea is to create as straight and as true a path from the vine's roots, up through the rootstock and graft and upwards into the shoot that is starting to grow. In this way, there are no kinks and chicanes within the graft which, as the vine expands over the next forty years, could give rise to too much twisting and tension. The aim is a straight sap line from earth to heaven. Once the vine has been 'singled out' and you have a stem, the vine will put all its energies into growing away and climbing its planting stake. Depending on how many of your vines have developed shoots when you first carry this task out, you may need to go through the vineyard one more time to get all of the vines dealt with.

## Side-shooting and tying up

As the vine climbs upwards, it will naturally try and grasp on to the planting stake with its tendrils, but these are not strong enough at this stage to support the vine's weight and in addition, the task of side-shooting – taking out the vine's side-shoots – must take place. Side-shoots are the shoots that will grow out of the angle between every leaf and the stem and, if left to their own devices, will continue to grow and take away energy and vigour from the main shoot. In some cases, side-shoots actually think they are the main stem and attempt a takeover coup. This must not be allowed to happen and early side-shooting is both easy and essential.

In addition to side-shooting the young vine, the growing shoot needs to be tied to the planting stake using something that will hold it in position, but only loosely. The best device for this is a Max Tapener machine which is a self-contained tying and cutting device with a roll of tape in its base and sharp blade and stapler at the other end. Whilst some people seem to take a while to get the hang of them (and some never do) I have always found them a pleasure to use. The tape comes in different colours and different strengths. For vines, the lighter-weight white or green are quite adequate (40 m per roll) whilst the medium-weight blue and green (26 m per roll) and the heavy-weight in red and green (16 m per roll) are too heavy and a waste of money. What you do not want to use for tying up the vines at this stage is anything that has a solid core, such as a plastic or paper covered wire tie, as this will resist the vine's stem as it expands and if put on too tight, will cut right through the stem. If you do use this type of tie, make sure you put it on loosely and hope it gets taken off before the stem expands into it.

*Max Tapener machine for tying up young vines*

Side-shooting and tying up must continue for as long as the vine is growing which, in a good season, might be until the end of September and even into October. By then, vines planted in a well prepared site and correctly looked after, should have grown at least 1.0 m and very often twice that. This is the reason that ideally the full trelliswork wants to be installed in the first summer as otherwise your young vines will be flapping about in the breeze and some will, in all probability, break off at the top of the planting stake (which will be at about 1.0 m out of the ground). If the trellising is up, then you will have some wires to tie the canes to for support and some catch wires to hold the canes. If you do not put up your trellising in the first summer, then you will need longer planting stakes for the vines to grow up and these need to be stuck in the ground fairly well, otherwise with the first autumn gale in September, when the vine has its maximum complement of leaves, many will get blown over. As a temporary measure, if you are not installing the full trelliswork in the first year, consider installing the end-posts and a few intermediates and stretching one wire along every row in order to secure the planting stakes to something.

The end of the first growing season is also the time to walk through the whole vineyard and take stock of the number of vines that didn't grow – hopefully for you and your vine supplier not a large number – and get replacements on order. The number of losses you can expect will depend on a whole host of factors – site preparation, planting conditions and post-planting care being very important – but even in very well managed vineyards some losses are inevitable. Some graft failure is to be expected and there will always be vines that are broken, run-over and otherwise destroyed. I always used to say if the losses were lower than 1 per cent then that was a great result, 1-2 per cent about normal, and if much above that, something has gone wrong. Today, with the spectre of TDs looming over all vineyards, one cannot be quite so confident, although I have planted many vineyards in the last decade with losses after three years, well below 2 per cent. Whatever the number, get replacements on order before the winter and before your supplier has run out of the varieties, clones and rootstocks you need.

*This is how your vines should look by the end of the year of planting*

## The 'don't do anything in the first year' school of vine training

There is a school of thought that says vines should be left alone in their first year, either completely or partially, in order to toughen them up and teach them about the real world and only start bothering with them in their second year. Whether this 'sink or swim' style of management is borne out of laziness, indifference, or unwillingness to spend money on them, I have no idea, but it exists. I suspect in warmer and drier climates and where weeds and fungal diseases are not such a problem this may be done. Also, if you already have several hectares of cropping vines and have just replanted a small area, then there is no urgency to get them into cropping and a long-term approach like this may have some validity. Not however, in the UK. Many is the time I have seen, in UK vineyards, recently planted vines lying on the ground or barely supported and with multiple shoots growing out at all angles and heard the owner say: 'Oh I am letting them find their own way for the first year' or something equally nonsensical and then they wonder why half their vines die and the other half take five years to produce a crop. Sorry, but I cannot be doing with this way of caring for (if that is the correct description) young vines.

## Weed control

Weed control is probably THE most important single task to get right in newly planted vineyards and is dealt with fully in *Chapter 14: Weed control*.

## Vineyard alleyways

There are three basic ways of looking after the vineyard alleyways, the ground between the rows of vines, in the establishment phase: cultivating them, growing something in them or keeping them free of vegetation with herbicides. Each system has its benefits and drawbacks.

Typically, vines will be planted into bare, cultivated soil and for a while, all will be peace and quiet. Then, within a week or two of planting, a green mist will appear on the surface of the soil as the weeds and grasses announce their intentions which, unfortunately for you, are not very friendly. Their sole purpose in life is to smother or strangle your precious vines. In warmer, drier climates, especially in more traditional winegrowing regions, vineyard alleyways (as well as the undervine areas) are often cultivated for the first few years, if not for the whole of the vineyard's life. Cultivating the soil is done so that the vine is persuaded to root more deeply in order to look for moisture at deeper levels. It also aerates the soil and, when compost or fertiliser is spread, enables this to be incorporated into the soil. Cultivations will take place at regular intervals, as and when the weed growth requires it, using spring-tine harrows, disc harrows, power harrows or rotary cultivators. In young vineyards in the UK, say in the first and second years when no crop is being taken, cultivating in the rows is possible, although not seen very often. Why is probably because it requires extra equipment and machinery which will in all probability only be used in the establishment phase of the vineyard and because traditionally, UK vineyards have been grassed down (either naturally or seeded) so that a firm working surface is created as soon as possible. Given the problems we have seen with TDs in some UK vineyards, which might be associated with weak root growth, plus the fact that on average we are seeing drier, warmer summers, I would not be against keeping a vineyard cultivated for the establishment phase, although would be happier to see mown alleyways in vineyards once they start cropping as this provides a better working platform and, in addition, helps use up some of the available moisture.

In regions where summer rainfall is low and soils are consequently drier than they are in the UK, keeping the vineyard alleyways cultivated throughout the year doesn't pose a huge problem at harvest time. Given typical conditions during many UK vintages though, cultivated alleyways would soon become mud baths for tractors and pickers alike and are not to be recommended. One way around this, often seen overseas, is to alternate rows with one row cultivated and one row grassed-down or sown with a green manure. This allows for some vineyard operations – spraying and picking – to stick to the firm, grassed-down rows whilst giving some of the benefits of cultivations to the vines. After two or three years the rows can be alternated, cultivating the grassed-down rows and seeding the previously cultivated ones. The use of green manures is discussed in *Chapter 7: Vineyard nutrition* in the section on *Green manuring*.

My preferred option for vineyard alleyways during the establishment phase is to do nothing, apart from keeping them topped with a rotary mower. Whilst this may look unsightly for the first year, or even the first two years, over this time a very satisfactory multi-species grass and weed sward will establish and provide a good working surface for both people and tractors. Many different grass and weed species will establish, providing habitat and food for predator insects and, the best benefit of all, the sward will be slower growing than sown grass. The vines will also have a year or two without much competition from the alleyways, giving them a better chance of rooting properly. Often vineyard owners have insisted on sowing grass seed in the alleyways soon after planting and find that within weeks they have what amounts to a silage field which needs cutting every week or ten days. Grass seed manufacturers sell seed on the basis that it will grow and provide lots of green matter – almost the opposite of what you want in a vineyard. Sure there are 'orchard mixtures' which are often sold as being 'low growing and shade tolerant' but in my experience they still grow too much. And anyway, why pay several hundreds of pounds for something you can get for nothing and which works better? You also want to avoid planting anything that might increase the amount of nitrogen available to the vine which might make it more vigorous than is good for it. Therefore mixes which contain clover, alfalfa and other legumes which, assuming their roots are populated by the right bacteria, can fix nitrogen from the air and will return some of that nitrogen to the soil, should be avoided until you know the vigour status of your vines. Let nature take its course and provide you with a natural carpet.

The third route, the chemical route, is one not often seen in UK vineyards (or for that matter oversees either now) and I suspect it is not advocated so much these days, although it certainly was. In other UK fruit crops, apples, pears, hops, blackcurrants and other soft fruit, 'total herbicide' is still often used and, done well, is an effective way of keeping the floor of the orchard, garden or plantation free of weeds. This allows the plants being cropped to benefit from reduced competition and have access to water and nutrients, both of which grasses and weeds also need to survive. However, vines in UK vineyards are not usually short of water and their deep roots allow them to access enough nutrients to survive, so some of the benefits of total herbicide are lost. Another benefit is that bare soil, being darker, warms up more quickly and stores its heat and this may be a benefit worth considering for vines. In addition, if the vineyard is one with a spring frost problem, then bare soil, being drier than grass, stays frost-free for longer and, in conjunction with other frost control techniques, may help. Biddenden Vineyards in Kent have used total herbicide on most of their vineyards for decades and manage to both make it work and harvest good grapes.

The disadvantages of total herbicide, especially at this stage where the vines are still young and will have foliage at, and close to, ground level, are the problems involved with getting the material on to the vineyard at the right time and in the right weather conditions (dry and still), plus the cost of both the chemicals and the application. Given that you will almost certainly require at least two applications – one pre-budburst and another in the midsummer after flowering – and possibly a third after harvest as a pre-winter clean up, the material costs could be in the region of £225-£300-ha (£91-£121-acre), plus the tractor costs and time. Having the right herbicide spraying equipment will certainly help with both getting the material on at the right time and getting effective coverage. If you are considering total herbicide in your vineyard, a machine like Micron's Spraymiser HiFlo, fitted with their Undavina spray head and guard would be ideal. The problem of 'poisoning' your soil through using herbicide for total weed control I personally feel is not one to worry about, although from a PR point-of-view, this might not go down so well with some people. Herbicide use is discussed in more detail in *Chapter: 14 Weed control* in the section on *Herbicides*.

## Training young vines – year two

Assuming most of your vines have made adequate growth by the end of their first season – and some (hopefully many) will have grown to 1.5 m or more – then the question of how to prune and train them in the second year has to be tackled. When I was first involved with UK viticulture, I always preferred to get the vines off the ground as quickly as possible and would always retain whatever good ripe wood of lead-pencil diameter (around 6-7 mm) that had grown. This ensured that as much fruiting wood as possible was retained and I can cite plenty of instances where two-year old vines have cropped at up to 5 tonnes-ha (2 tonnes-acre) without any short-term or long-term harm to the vines. However, with vines protected from herbicides with spray-guards I would now recommend cutting them all back to a short one or two bud shoot and going through the whole 'year one' process of shoot selection, side-shooting and tying up again.

Whilst this may seem drastic, if the vines have made good growth in their first year, they are certain to make even better growth during year two and by the end of year two, pretty well all vines should be up and running and able to carry a single fruiting cane for year three – the first fruiting year. If your vines have not made good growth in their first year, then there is no other option but to cut them back to a one or two bud shoot and work out why they didn't grow as much as they might have done. The one thing to remember about young vines is that what you see above is a direct reflection of what is happening down below and good cane growth equates to good root growth and it's good root growth that is the purpose of the establishment phase.

At the end of year two, before the winter sets in, is another time to walk the vineyard and count up the number of replacement vines required and get them on order.

## Pest and disease control

In the 'old days', when the main varieties grown in UK vineyards were German cross-breeds plus Seyval blanc, it was quite common to start spraying against diseases at the start of the first cropping year (usually year three). This didn't seem to worry the vines and I don't recall it leading to any real disease problems. Today however, it seems short-sighted not to put at least two to three maintenance sprays on to vines in their first and second years – assuming that year two is not a cropping year. Obviously if you are proposing to crop your vines in year two, then a full spray programme will be needed. Chardonnay especially seems particularly prone to Downy Mildew in its youth. Whether this is because we now enjoy warmer

growing conditions, or (and this is my theory) French *pépiniérists* are not so rigorous in their disease control as their German counterparts, who can say? The fact is that without some first-year sprays it often succumbs to Downy Mildew. As well as Downy Mildew, it would be senseless not to include some sulphur against Powdery Mildew. *Botrytis* is probably going to be less of an issue without a crop but again, a few maintenance sprays against this wouldn't do any harm.

Slugs and snails can sometimes be a problem with vines in their establishment phase, especially with growers using tree-guards. The warm, damp environment seems to be to their liking and young vine leaves certainly are. Some growers routinely sprinkle some slug pellets into the tree-guards immediately after planting which seems to solve the problem.

## Conclusion – Establishment phase

The aim of the first two (or maybe three) years of a vine's life, the period I have called the establishment phase, is to allow the vine to develop a root system that will support a small crop in year three. If your vines are weak in their growth, then they will have a small root system and cropping should be delayed until year four. You have no idea what the first cropping year will be like; it could be the driest or wettest season on record, the warmest or the coolest. A young vine, overburdened with fruit, will struggle in adverse conditions and stress is never good for the long-term viability of a vine. The thing to always remember is that what you can see growing above ground is a reflection of what you cannot see below ground – the vine's roots. Good vigorous growth above ground level at this stage will mean the vine is putting down roots, searching for moisture and nutrients and preparing itself for fruiting. The opposite, poor growth above ground level, typically indicates slow root growth and the vine should be allowed to take some time to catch up.

*An example of a badly-trained vine*

# Chapter 12
# Management – cropping years

## The winegrower's year

The timetable of the winegrower's year will vary according to many factors and no two sites, varieties, pruning, training and trellising systems or years will be the same. All dates and timings are therefore approximate. The timetable that follows is a general guide and more options can be found in the sections that follow it.
- Pruning – can start at any time once vines are dormant and wood is ripe. Typically January, February, March, although December is not unknown in larger vineyards. Must finish before buds start swelling in mid-April.
- Training and tying down – will follow pruning and should be completed before budburst.
- Fertliser – soil and petiole samples will have been taken during the previous growing season and fertilisers can be applied during the dormant season.
- Disposal of prunings – prunings can be pulverised and left to rot down in the vineyard or taken out and burnt. Best done during the dormant season and before alleyways need mowing and before herbicide applications.
- Repairing trelliswork, replanting vines – vineyard maintenance including replacing broken posts and anchor wires and replanting of missing vines, should take place ideally prior to budburst.
- Alleyway management – depending on alleyway management system, mowing or cultivating should start once grass and/or weeds start growing and continue until growth stops in the late autumn. Specialist operations, such as subsoiling or root pruning, will ideally take place when the ground is at its driest, i.e. mid-summer to pre-harvest.
- Weed control, undervine – weeds beneath the vines can be dealt with in several ways: chemical, mechanical, mulching. Each technique will have its own timetable. Weeds must be dealt with before they start growing and kept under control throughout the growing season. Often a post-harvest 'clean-up' is beneficial. Spot treatment of troublesome weeds (nettles and docks for instance) may need to be carried out using a knapsack sprayer at almost any time of the year.
- Pest and disease control – spraying often starts just before budburst and will continue at regular intervals (every 10-14 days depending on varieties and weather

conditions) until 2-3 weeks prior to harvest, depending on products used and relevant harvest intervals (HI). Post-harvesting applications may also be necessary. See more about HIs in *Chapter 16: Pest and disease control* in the section on *Harvest intervals and residue levels.*

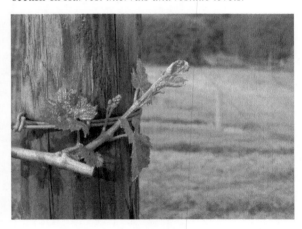

*The start of the growing season*

- Shoot removal, trunks – shoots growing below the fruiting wire will need removing once they appear, typically in late April to mid-May. Usually this is only carried out once, although a second round might be necessary, particularly in younger vineyards.
- Shoot thinning – excess shoots, especially in the crowded crown of the vine, should be removed when they can be easily rubbed off, typically in May-June. Removal once the shoots get woody is to be avoided.
- Tucking in – once shoots get long enough to be tucked in and depending on variety and rootstock, this will begin in late-June, July and continue until vines reach the top of canopy and trimming starts. Most vines will require tucking in at least twice in the growing season.
- Flowering – the most important period in the year as it determines crop size. Typically takes place in the UK between the third week of June and mid-July (often around Wimbledon fortnight), but timings will vary according to the year, the site and the grape variety.
- Shoot trimming (hedging) – will start once the shoots have grown above the top wire, typically at around the end of flowering. As the season progresses, both side growth

and top growth will require cutting. Tipping during flowering can also be carried out.

- Deleafing – depending on variety and rootstock, most vines are best deleafed twice: once just after flowering, and again around the time of *véraison*. A third pre-harvest deleafing might also be carried out, depending on leaf cover and variety, in order to speed up hand harvesting. White grapes are much harder to see than red grapes beneath a full canopy.

- Crop thinning – when vines have set a heavy crop and for certain varieties and particular types of wine, some crop thinning might be required. Normally this will take place once bunch close has occurred and before *véraison*, although other timings are possible.

- Picking – once grapes are ripe for the type of wine to be produced. Will depend on variety and weather during the growing season, but for early varieties and in early years it might be the beginning of September and with late varieties, as late as early November. In 2013, Chardonnay was still being harvested on 20 November.

## Pruning, training and tying down – first cropping year

The first task facing the vinegrower at the beginning of the year is pruning. For traditionalists, 22 January is the date to start as this is the day of the patron saint of vinegrowers, St. Vincent.[1] In reality pruning can start whenever the vine has shed its leaves and the wood has 'ripened', i.e. lignified, turned brown and hardened off. In most UK vineyards and in most years this would not happen much before mid-November and often later and many growers wouldn't think of pruning until after the New Year. If your vineyard is young and has little wood to prune out and remove, then this is a quick and easy task and can be left until the weather warms up, say towards the end of March. There is no advantage to be gained in pruning earlier. Don't be concerned if your vines start to 'bleed' – exude sap from the cut end of canes – this is quite normal and is purely a sign that the ground is warming up and the roots are starting to stir. A vine can bleed for several days and the ground beneath the end of the cane will get noticeably wet, but this will not harm the vine.

The vines will be ready to crop when they have grown a length of ripe cane of around 6-7 mm diameter – in Germany they say as 'thick as a lead pencil'. Any thinner than that and the cane is less likely to bear viable buds; any thicker than that and – well that's an interesting question. Canes thicker than 10 mm are certainly not unknown and with some varieties, especially if they on a vigorous rootstock and in their first few years, can have canes up to 15 mm diameter, although this is rare. These thick canes also typically have long internodes, quite possibly a sign that they have been growing in shaded conditions and are therefore likely to be less productive than thinner canes. However, if thick canes are all you have to work with, then better thick canes than no canes at all.

Assuming your vine has grown a length of cane above and beyond the fruiting wire, then you have the opportunity to leave a length of fruiting wood for the coming year. The length of wood you leave should not exceed half the distance between the vines, i.e. if your vines are planted at 1.20 m apart, then your single cane should not be longer than 600 mm. A little bit longer is no great crime, but avoid the temptation to leave a cane that stretches almost to the next vine. This is a young child-vine and mustn't be sent up too many chimneys on its first day. Trim the cane slightly over the correct length, take off any tendrils (although this is purely cosmetic and leaving tendrils on does no harm) and leave the cane pointing upright. Tying down can wait. Any small pieces of excess cane can be cut into two or three and thrown into the row. The mower will deal with those, assuming you are mowing the alleyways. If you are cultivating then it is still probably OK to leave any excess wood behind in the rows as such a small amount will not interfere with your cultivations. It may not be the same in future years when the volume of old wood is larger. If the vine has produced some cane above the fruiting wire, but not so much that you are able to leave 600 mm of ripe cane, then you have two options: leave as much ripe cane as there is, so that some fruit will be produced; or trim it back to the height of the fruiting wire and let it spend another year in a non-fruiting mode and hope it produces some ripe canes for the next year. Any vines that have still not produced much in the way of a trunk, may well be in trouble and replacing them should be considered.

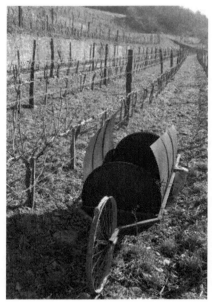

*A chariot de feu for burning prunings as you prune*

Traditionally in the UK, almost all growers left the wood from pruning behind in the vineyard – usually putting two row's worth of wood into one row – and cutting it up with a prunings pulveriser. In France one often sees growers using a *chariot de feu* to burn them as they go (and I have even seen one in a UK vineyard) whilst others gather them up and remove them off-site for burning. With concerns that TDs may be spread by from one vine to another, more UK growers have started to remove prunings and burn them. Whether this helps or not is open to speculation, although it cannot do any harm. There are also machines which will gather up the prunings and turn them into faggots which can be sold to barbequers, but the machines are too expensive for the scale of most UK vineyards. Whilst I can understand the wish to 'clean up' the vineyard by taking out old wood, I cannot quite get my head around the science. All the trimmings from summer pruning, plus all the leaves, plus a fair few rotten bunches of grapes and other detritus, plus the old wood that forms the permanent framework of the vine remains behind in the vineyard whether or not you remove prunings. Removing the prunings hardly turns the vineyard into an operating theatre. Still, if it makes you happy, take the prunings out.

Once you have been through the whole vineyard, pruning to one cane all those vines that have grown a good length of cane and trimming back to a suitable point all those that have not made the grade, you can think about tying down. There is no need to do this immediately after pruning, although this does often happen. The best time is when the canes have got a little more suppleness in them and can be bent over at ninety degrees without snapping. Take the cane at the point of bending in your left hand (assuming you are right handed) and gently bend the cane over, trim it to the correct length, twist it once round the wire and attach it with a tie. If your vineyard is on a slope, then bend it downhill (this helps even out the budburst).

Tying materials are many and varied and they have been partially discussed in *Chapter 10: Machinery and equipment*. Although Max Tapener machines can be used, they are not really suitable as it is difficult to get a really tight tie around both cane and wire and the tape tends to slide along the cane and the cane slips out. Better to use paper-covered wire ties, remembering that if you use these on the stem of the vine, tie them very loosely. If they are too tight, they will cut through the wood as the vine's stem grows and expands. Plastic covered wire ties are not to be recommended as they have sharp edges and after a day of tying down, you will have very sore fingers. Other proprietary clips are sold, but personally I cannot see the use of them. At some stage you will need to tie the stem to the planting stake with something more robust than the Max Tapener machine and there is a very wide range of products available. Whatever you use, my advice is to use something that can either be unfastened and opened up as the vine's trunk expands, or something that is elastic enough to stretch as the trunk grows. I have used plastic 'Chain Lock' (also sometimes called 'Ladder' type ties,

pictured here) which is cheap and easy to use.

It comes on a roll and if cut to the appropriate length can be opened up and expanded as the vine ages. It will last almost indefinitely.

The other type of tie I can recommend are the 'Tree Fix' rubber ties (below) which are easy to use and will not cut into the vine as it expands. They are made in several sizes so make sure you use the right size according to the age of your vines.

After you have finished tying down, if you have a vineyard with all the vines carrying a single cane of around half the distance between your vines, you should have a potential yield of 30-50 per cent of the vineyard. In reality, taking into account vines that have not made it to the fruiting wire and vines with canes shorter than the correct length, it is safer to work on a potential crop of ⅓ of what one might expect in a mature vineyard, i.e. around 2.5 tonnes-ha (1 tonne-acre).

## Pruning, training and tying down – subsequent cropping years

After the first year of cropping, your vines should have grown a substantial amount more wood and be ready for the full pruning experience.

The aim of the vinegrower is to leave each vine with its full complement of fruiting wood, plus a spur (or 'thumb') to provide next year's fruiting canes – the 'replacement' canes which give the system of 'cane replacement pruning' its name. The fruiting wood should more or less fill up the space allowed for each vine – leaving a gap of around 100 mm between the ends of each vine's canes – and both the fruiting canes and the spur must come from below the fruiting wire. Ideally the canes want to come from above the spur and the spur wants to be around 100-250 mm below the fruiting wire. However, as the vine gets older it may be necessary to select a spur position further below the fruiting wire than this and as long as it's not too near the ground (where it might get hit by herbicide) it doesn't really matter how low it is. *In extremis* a shoot coming from just above the graft could be trained up as the trunk, but this would usually only be in the case of problems with TDs such as *Esca* where the vine needed rejuvenating. The reasons that the canes and spur should always come from below the fruiting wire are, that if they start appearing above the fruiting wire: tying down becomes problematic, fruiting wood is lost, and the trunk may stop producing shoots from which the spur can be formed. A mental sign saying 'always below the fruiting wire' should be hanging in front of everyone as they prune cane replacement pruned vines.

Many books will also talk about the vine being 'in balance' and in my experience, in relation to UK vineyards, this is a difficult concept to understand. It is worth reproducing what appears in the Oxford Companion to Wine (OCW) written by Richard Smart, its viticultural editor:

*'Vine balance is a viticultural concept little appreciated by wine consumers, yet one which is essential for producing grapes for premium wine-making. A vine is in balance when the leaf to fruit ratio[2] is in the correct range. The amount of early season shoot growth should also be in balance with the vine's reserves of carbohydrates. Vine balance concerns vigour and it can be managed by the viticulturalist, with balanced pruning and water stress the principal tools. One of the best measures of vine balance is the ratio of fruit yield to pruning weight, now often called the Ravaz index, following its promotion by the French researcher of that name. - - - A balanced vine has shoots of moderate vigour with no shoot tip growth during fruit ripening. Leaves are of moderate size and number so excess shade is avoided, with both leaves and fruit well exposed to sunlight. Unbalanced vineyards are either too vigorous—in which case poor ripening results from shading and competition between the ripening grapes and shoot tips for carbohydrates—or not vigorous enough—in which case there is insufficient leaf area for proper ripening. Monitoring shoot tip growth is seen as an important management tool for vine balance'.*

The theories about pruning and how to do it are all very well, but none relate to UK conditions and I have found very few of any use in practical terms in UK vineyards. Given that your inter-vine spacing is set at planting and your trellising has been designed to carry your fruiting wood on a single wire (or perhaps on two wires in an arched-cane system), then the best you can do is to lay down as much wood as the space allows, leaving a small gap between the canes belonging to the neighbouring vines and definitely not crossing the canes over each other (except in extreme cases – frost prevention being one – of which more later). The 'Ravaz Index', mentioned above, is arrived at by dividing the yield per vine by the weight of pruning wood, giving you a figure of between 0 and around 15 which is an indication of the vine's vigour. This same technique is described on page 26 of *Sunlight into Wine* (although not called the Ravaz Index) and suggests that you categorise your vines into low, medium and high vigour, and prune accordingly. A figure of 30 buds for each kilogram of pruning wood is also advised by Smart in the OCW, although he also adds: 'experienced vine pruners can achieve a similar effect by looking at each vine, judging how it grew last growing season, and adjusting this year's number of buds accordingly'. We also of course do not have the critical element that Smart mentions above: that of 'water stress', i.e. the availability of (and need for) irrigation, with which to control our vines.

My problem with these systems, based upon weight of fruit, is twofold: vines growing in our conditions tend to be relatively vigorous whether they have a high yield or low yield (or even no yield such as in many vineyards in 2011 and 2012); and yields are so dependent on the weather at flowering that they often bear little relation to the amount of wood that the vine produces. I also do not quite understand how, with a cane pruned system, one is meant to vary the amount of wood left after pruning. Sure, you can shorten the canes to the point where there are no canes

at all, but how do you lengthen them without altering the trellis system? This may be fine with spur pruned vines, but cane pruned? I just don't see how.

Therefore 'balance' in a vine in the UK is something that you have to work at even before your plant. Given the UK's climate, its lack of days over 30ºC, its annual rainfall, especially that which falls during the growing season, and it's usually fertile soils, excess vigour is something we have to tackle by using lower-vigour rootstocks, high density planting and with appropriate vineyard and canopy management techniques. With these we can attempt to tame the vine's vigour – something incidentally more difficult in young vines than in vines of twenty-plus years old – and the rest is down to prayer. Even when we have taken all the above vigour-reducing measures, the level of crop is often due to flowering conditions over which we have little control. In addition, I do not think that vines growing in UK vineyards respond to yield in the same way that some textbooks think they ought to. In most years (years with extremely dry summers are possibly an exception) vines carrying what is by UK vineyards a very large crop – say 20-30 tonnes-ha (8-12 tonnes-acre) – do not show any great reduction in vigour compared to vines carrying a tenth of that yield (or even no yield at all), except perhaps in very dry summers. Perhaps if UK vineyards had large yields more often and we routinely had dry summers, then our vines would show a definite vigour difference between low and high yields, but as things stand at the moment, I don't see it. Some varieties are also inherently more vigorous than others and this has to be factored into the equation.

My recommendation is to take each vine on its own, judge how well it has grown in the previous year, and prune it accordingly. If the vine has grown plenty of pencil-thick canes and you have two suitably positioned canes to leave, plus a spur for next year, then prune away and fill up the wires. If your vine has struggled to produce canes and what canes there are, are short and pretty thin, then you have problems! In these cases you prune short, perhaps leaving only one cane, or perhaps only a few short spurs, and see what happens. If next year it has recovered, then fine. However, if next year it has died, then dig it up and plant a new one. If your vine has produced canes that are too short near the head of the vine and there are longer ones further along the cane, avoid the temptation to select the longer ones as this will seriously spoil the shape of the vine and may well exacerbate the problem. Leave the vine with one or two short canes coming from the correct place at the head of the vine and hope, that with a smaller crop, it can sort itself out in the year ahead. Avoid also the option of spur pruning the vine as this almost always results in the vine bearing too many buds and only weakens it, not makes it stronger.

Of course, if you find that your vines are hugely vigorous, producing masses of canes which tend towards 10-12 mm diameter and your crops are poor and intermittent, then Houston, you have a problem. What you can do about it in the short term is debatable. If the rootstock, the variety or the clone is the issue, then these cannot be changed. Your vineyard management might be a contributory factor and maybe you need to look at that.

You could try growing green manure in the rows in order to use up more moisture and resorting to more shoot and deleafing to try and improve cropping levels, but this is not a certain path to follow. Root pruning might also help (see section below on *Alleyway management*). Most probably the long-term solution (short of grubbing and replanting) is to re-trellis but this will undoubtedly be an expensive way round the problem, but one that might help. Using a training system, such as Scott Henry, is a text-book solution, but (as I said in the section on *Pruning and trellising systems*) not one that many UK growers have used successfully. Taking out every other row and re-trellising to GDC (which is something Lamberhurst Vineyards did to around 10-ha of their vineyards in the 1980s) will probably make looking after the vines cheaper, but is unlikely to reduce the vigour much, nor increase yields.

The mapping of vineyards for vigour using sensors that detect the amount of foliage in the canopy is a technique that is slowly gaining respectability. Sensors are normally mounted on the side of the tractor or sprayer, and each time the tractor passes through the vines, a snapshot is taken and, tied into the position of the vines using GPS. In this way a vigour map can be built up showing which areas of a particular vineyard are less vigorous or more vigorous. The different areas can then be individually treated with respect to a wide range of inputs and operations: fertilisers, irrigation, pruning, canopy management and harvesting. In the UK this technique is very much in the experimental stage, but in the long-term might prove very useful in fine tuning a vineyard, especially say where a very high quality crop was required: select the block with the lowest vigour, shoot select to open up the canopy, green harvest to reduce the yield and wait for riper grapes. On the other hand, on more vigorous blocks, leave more buds to try and increase the yield and help tone down the natural vigour in the vines.

*Richard Smart attempting to find some grapes in an English vineyard in 2012*

## Alleyway management

The management of the vineyard alleyways will of course depend on what system you have opted to follow in your vineyard: mowing, cultivations or total herbicide and this has been discussed fully in *Chapter 11: Management – establishment phase* in the section on *Vineyard alleyways*.

In the case of mowing, the system is quite simple – mow when the grass gets long enough and keep on mowing for as long as the grass is growing. An early 'clean up' mow after pruning and after the prunings have been pulverised, burnt *in situ* or taken out and burnt, will make things neat and tidy. It is also good practice to keep the grass as short as possible towards harvest. This helps keep the vineyard as dry as possible and maybe helps keep *Botrytis* at a lower level. It will also make a slight contribution to warding off pre-harvest frosts as short grass holds less moisture and doesn't freeze so readily. Those opting for cultivating or total herbicide will have their own timetable dictated by a combination of the weather and soil conditions. The use of green manures in alleyways is discussed in *Chapter 7: Vineyard Nutrition* in the section on *Green manuring*.

If your vines are suffering from poor drainage there are various remedies available (apart from installing tile drainage which, in an existing vineyard, is a difficult and costly exercise) including subsoiling in the row. What implement you use and to what depth you can subsoil will depend upon the equipment available, especially your tractor. If you have access to a tracked machine (crawler tractor or small bulldozer) which can fit down your rows, then subsoiling, using a two or four-tined subsoiler and working at a depth of 500-700 mm, ought to be possible in most soils. With a four-wheel drive tractor, you will probably only manage a two-tine subsoiler and the depth will depend on the soil and surface conditions. With a low-powered two-wheel drive tractor your options are very limited. One way around the lack of tractor power is to use a powered subsoiler such as the *McConnel Grassland Shakaerator* already mentioned in *Chapter 6: Site planning and preparation* in the section on *Cultivations*. Subsoiling is best done when the soil is as dry as possible, so after harvest is generally NOT a good time. After subsoiling, the earth will have been lifted and it is a good idea to give it as long as possible to settle before driving on it. The best time is actually after you have done the last pre-picking mow and if you do every other row one year and the other rows the next year, you can avoid the subsoiled rows at harvest time and hopefully leave them for the whole winter to settle down.

Root-pruning is a technique that has, in other viticultural regions, been shown to be valuable in helping control vigour, but is seldom used in the UK. Classic root pruning consists of dragging a sharp-fronted tine at about a depth of 500 mm down either side of the vines at about 300-400 mm from the line of the vines – the actual distance will depend on your equipment and how close your tractor can get to the vines. In warmer climates, where natural rainfall is less plentiful than in the UK and where in many instances irrigation is used, root-pruning might have more effect than I suspect it would in UK vineyards. The fact that UK vines tend to bear a lighter crop than in many overseas vineyards may also be a factor in its effectiveness. I think that variety and rootstock choice and planting density probably have a bigger effect upon vigour than anything else. However, if you had an over-vigorous vineyard planted with a rampant variety on a high-vigour rootstock, then root-pruning might help.

## Canopy management

Under this heading are all the post-pruning tasks associated with the vine and its shoots (canes) and leaves – the canopy. They range from spring tasks – shoot removal and shoot thinning – via tucking-in and leaf-trimming, to deleafing and crop thinning. Exactly when this starts will depend upon such factors as when budburst occurs and when flowering takes place. This will vary according to the earliness or lateness of the spring, the quality of the site in terms of shelter, exposure and altitude, plus the variety, clone and rootstock in question. Budburst is principally controlled by root growth which in turn is stimulated by a rise in temperature in the soil. The books will tell you that this should happen once the soil temperature at around 300 mm deep reaches 8-10°C, but in my experience this is something of a moveable feast. Wet soils will always warm up more slowly than dry soils, so drainage may also be an issue with regard to the timing of budburst and vine variety is certainly a factor. The books will also tell you that rootstock is also a factor, although I have not noticed this to be so. In some years budburst can be as early as the start of April; in other years 3-4 weeks later.

## Canopy quality

At the heart of canopy management is the concept of what I call 'canopy quality' and it is a concept that needs to be understood in order to grow the best grapes in any climate, let alone a climate as challenging as the UK's. In cool climates, the quality of the canopy can make the difference between a good harvest and a great harvest and between a fair harvest and no harvest.

Cool climates are challenging because the vine is a sugar producing plant and we judge the ripeness of the vine's fruit, the grapes, by the level of sugar they contain. Within reason (and very dependent on the vine variety in question and the style of wine aimed for) the higher the sugar in the grapes the better. We not only judge the level of ripeness by the sugar level in the grapes, we also take acid levels, pH levels and the slightly nebulous concept of 'physiological ripeness' – which includes flavours, tannins, aromas and general 'fruitiness' of the grapes – into account before deciding when to pick. All these are impacted by two inter-related natural elements: sunlight and temperature. Again, in general terms, the more sunlight and the higher the temperatures for the vine variety you are growing and for the style of wine you are producing, the better. In addition, cool growing conditions do not just affect grape ripeness and therefore, wine quality, they also affect yield levels, and therefore vineyard viability.

Without a mixture of both – quality and yield – growing vines becomes an unrewarding enterprise.

In the UK, all of the conventional climate assessment parameters that are used internationally to judge viticultural regions for their ability to grow vines and ripen grapes say we are not just cool, but *über*-cool. The average temperature during the growing season, the number of degree days, the Latitude Temperature Index, the mean temperature of the warmest month, the number of days when the temperature rises to 30°C and above – all of these are lower than any other vineyard area growing the same varieties and we cannot change these. Therefore, in growing vines in such a cool climate, we need to attempt, through whatever economically sustainable means possible, to overcome these natural hurdles. Site selection, rootstock, clone and variety, wine style, planting density, pruning and trellising systems, and vineyard management – all of these need to be selected or carried out with two over-riding objectives at the forefront of our decision making process: what can I do to make my vineyard warmer and what can I do to get more of the available sunlight on to the leaves of the vine and, at the right time, on to the grapes. I appreciate that much of the above has been discussed before in earlier sections of this book, but it is worth going back over old ground at this juncture.

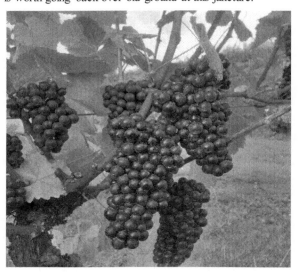

In the vineyard, the canopy is where it all happens. You have chosen your site, your rootstock, your clone and your variety. These cannot be changed. You have also chosen your row width and inter-vine spacing and they too cannot easily be changed. You will have started out with a pruning and training system in mind, and will have installed your trelliswork accordingly. What happens next is at the heart of canopy quality. The concept of 'balance' has been discussed already in this chapter in the section on *Pruning, training and tying down – subsequent years*, but it is not until your vines get into their stride, probably in cropping year two or three, that you will be able to assess the quality of your canopy and judge whether you have 'balance' or not. In any event, as I have already commented, 'balance' is a concept with which I have a problem in a UK vinegrowing context.

*An ideal canopy showing well-spaced fruit without too much leaf cover*

The aim of the trelliswork is to hold the fruiting wood in such a way that the annual shoots grow away from the winter buds and, in a cane pruned VSP system, direct them upwards so that a narrow 'hedge' is formed, which can be contained and eventually trimmed. Although a vine's leaves are actually quite efficient at capturing non-direct light, that is, light reflected from other leaves and from other surfaces (the ground for instance), and in warm to hot countries shade can actually be of benefit as it stops bunches getting sunburn, in a cool climate this is not the case. In cool climates, a vine's leaves need all the direct sunshine they can get and therefore, given that the sun is moving from one side of the canopy to the other, the canopy should ideally be no more than three to four leaves thick so that the sunshine will shine directly on to one layer of leaves and partially on to a second layer on each side. Maintaining a thin canopy will not only help sunlight to interact with as much of the leaf area as possible, but will also allow air and light to penetrate in order to dry out the leaves, shoots and grapes – thus aiding disease control – and allow pesticide sprays to reach their target.

How such a canopy is achieved is the subject of the next few sections, but always remember that the canopy is something you have created. You have determined the planting density, the inter-vine distance, the number of buds left at pruning, the architecture of the trellising, and whether you have spreaders or not. You have also decided whether you have allowed every bud that bursts to develop into a shoot and whether every shoot and every side-shoot remains throughout the growing season. You can also decide whether to leave every leaf that grows, or whether some need to be removed, and how many and at what time. You can see for yourself whether the canopy is open and whether you can see through to the other side. You can also see whether there are yellowing leaves inside the canopy, a good indicator of a crowded canopy. You can also decide to leave every bunch that is there after flowering or whether some ought to be removed.

In short, the grower has a great deal of control over the canopy and although there may be financial and other resource-based considerations to be taken into account, it is no good looking back at what might have been, when what could have been was in your hands.

## Shoot removal - trunks

After pruning, tying down and dealing with the pruning wood, the next task is to remove any unwanted shoots (water shoots) from the trunk of the vines. Once the establishment years are over and the vine has developed a permanent trunk, any shoots that appear on the first 300-450 mm of trunk (measuring from the ground) should be rubbed off whilst they are still fresh and young and haven't started to turn woody. This will probably be in late April to mid-May. The exact height to which you should clean the trunk will depend on the height of your fruiting wire and do not be tempted to remove shoots too near the wire which you might then need to form the spur (thumb) required for the year after. Most growers will carry out this task manually, wearing gloves and running a hand up and down the trunk to the required height. Others will use a shaped hoe which does much the same job, but without the back-bending. Machines also exist which are fitted with stout bristles that brush the shoots off. Some growers use a herbicide (called Shark) which desiccates the shoots so that they wither and drop off. In my experience, using a herbicide to burn off water shoots still leaves a few shoots on the stem, those situated nearer to the fruiting wire, which will need removing by hand. At least though some of the work will have been done, reducing the amount of bending down.

Timing again is critical and it is not always possible to treat all varieties, all clones, and all rootstocks at the same time and to the same effect. Often a first flush of shoots will emerge and be rubbed off, only to be followed by a second, later flush which will require a second round of removal. With time, the vine's trunk will run out of steam and stop producing many water shoots, although there will always be a few and the task will always need doing. Growers using 'high graft' vines will not have to undertake this task (although this in itself is not a valid enough reason for using high graft vines).

Remember also when carrying out this task, that sometimes a water shoot should be retained. Vines suffering from TDs, especially *Esca*, can sometimes be regenerated by taking a water shoot emerging from just above the graft and training it upwards over a couple of seasons. Then, once the new shoot is robust enough to take over, the trunk can be cut off just above the point where the new shoot emerges and take over as the new trunk. In some regions – I am thinking of Alsace and Burgundy – this is a very widely practiced and it is not unusual to see up to fifty percent of the vines in a vineyard thus treated.

*Deleafed and ripening nicely*

## Shoot thinning

The other spring task, one that I believe isn't done enough in UK vineyards and one which I also believe would help achieve better flowering and the production of better canes with more viable buds, is shoot removal, especially around the crown of the vine. This area, at the top of the trunk, is often very crowded and is where many water shoots will emerge. Water shoots may not be very noticeable in the first few cropping years, but as the vine gets older and the size of the crown increases, there is more opportunity for these shoots to appear. Left untouched, the canes that develop from these shoots, which often do not bear any inflorescences, will crowd the canes coming from the spur left for next year's replacement canes and will just add additional leaves and cover in exactly the place where they are not required. If in mid-summer (after flowering) you see yellowing leaves in the centre of the canopy it is definitely an indication that your canopy is too crowded as these leaves have not been getting enough light to keep them green. In cool climates it is important that as many leaves as possible are exterior leaves and as few as possible are interior leaves.

The reason that the task of shoot thinning is not done more often in UK vineyards is probably one of tradition and practice – in spur pruned vines this work is absolutely routine – and also the question of risk and reward. Growers probably cannot relate the time taken, and therefore the cost, of carrying out this work with any tangible reward. I am convinced though that they are missing an important element in getting more consistent and better yields. Remember, the more air, light and heat that gets to the canes being left for next year's fruiting, the more likely those canes are to produce viable, flower-rich buds. In a 2009 study[3] of the flowering process, the following was stated: 'Environment and cultural practices influence flowering, either directly or indirectly via their impact on photosynthesis and nutrient availability. Cultural practices encouraging light penetration into the canopy favour flower initiation, while practices resulting in shading have a detrimental impact.' In *The Grapevine* (p. 68), the authors state: 'late spring is the critical period – shading at this time has a greater effect upon fruitfulness than shading earlier or later in the season' and (p. 70) that: 'there is generally unanimous agreement that modifications of the light microclimate in the bud renewal area is mainly responsible for the improvement in budburst, fruitfulness and yields'.

The removal of 'blind' shoots, i.e. those shoots coming from buds along the cane which are barren and bear no inflorescences (or possibly one very meagre one), plus shoots which are stunted and which are carrying very little in the way of leaf, is again, something that has not traditionally been done in UK vineyards. Blind shoots which are vigorous grow to full length and which carry a full complement of leaves, will be contributing to sugar production, despite not carrying any grapes. These can be left if they are not crowding other, crop-bearing shoots. But, if they are shading and crowding crop-bearing shoots and bunches within the canopy, they can be removed. Short, stunted shoots are probably best removed in any event. In the normal course of events, I would not expect many growers to go to the trouble of this level of shoot thinning, except perhaps where you were trying to harvest a really ripe crop of grapes for high quality still wine.

*Inflorescences showing well*

## Tucking-in

Once your vineyard is past the establishment phase and as it develops its full complement of fruiting canes, you will need to start doing some proper canopy management. Essentially this is the process of managing the annual shoots that grow from the buds left at pruning. Once the shoots (often referred to as canes) get to around 300-450 mm long and start impeding the progress of tractors and sprayers up the alleyways, the task of 'tucking-in' can begin.

Exactly what needs doing and when, will depend on the decisions taken when you planned the trellising in your vineyard. If you opted for moveable training wires (catch wires), these will already have been lowered to the bottom of the posts, in which case you need to wait until the shoots have grown beyond the point to where you propose to move the wires. If using steel posts, you can move the wires to wherever you want on the posts, as the hooks will already be there, although the position of the chain hooks on the end-posts will limit radical movements. If using timber posts, you can only move the wires to where the first pair of hook nails is positioned. As you lift the wires, the foliage will be trapped between them and be guided on its way towards the top of the canopy. In the first cropping year, when your vines will only have at most one fruiting cane and some may not have a cane at all, some of the shoots will refuse to be trained in this way and will obstinately fall down between the wires. This is to be expected and in subsequent seasons, when all your vines have their full complement of canes, this will not happen. In the first cropping year therefore, you may need a few ties or some clips, of which there are many different makes and types, to hold the wires together. If on the other hand your vineyard posts are fitted with spreaders of one sort or another, many of the canes will hopefully find their way up between the wires, allowing you to close the wires up (assuming they are of the closing up variety) once the canes have passed through. Inevitably there will be some tucking-in required even using spreaders, but less than with moveable wires.

Like so many things in the vineyard, timing is key and your site and its soil, your varieties, clones and rootstocks plus of course, the season's weather, will all play their part in determining exactly what needs doing when. To start with, you just have to keep your eyes firmly on what is happening to the shoots, work out what manpower you have available and how long it might take you to get around all your vines and work backwards to a starting point. With tucking-in you cannot start too early – otherwise there will be nothing to tuck-in – and it is one of the jobs that is better done with say four people in one week than one person over four weeks. You will soon learn which blocks need doing first, which blocks grow fastest and which can be left to last. Some varieties, and in the case of Pinot noir, some clones, are very much more upright in their habits and helpfully send their shoots in a more heavenwards direction than others. Some varieties and some Pinot noir clones are decidedly droopy in their habits and do everything they can to escape the confines of the catch-wires.

As the vines continue to grow towards the top of the canopy, and by flowering many varieties will have reached the top wire and above, a second round of tucking-in will be required. Those with a second set of wires to be lifted will bring them up from ground level and into the second set of positions or hooks. Those with wire spreaders will close up the second set. Quite often, and especially in a cool, wet year when vine growth will be more vigorous than in warmer, drier years, a third tucking-in will be required.

## Flowering

Not long after budburst you will notice that the shoots are (hopefully) carrying some embryo flowers, the inflorescences. These, barring frost and other calamities, will expand and eventually flower and, after pollination, turn into bunches of grapes. As the canes grow towards the top of the canopy and complete the leaf-wall, the flowers will grow larger as they approach flowering. As I have pointed out already in various sections of this book, yield is one of the most important factors in determining the viability of a vineyard and yield is very dependent on how the flowers pollinate. In order to persuade the flowers to turn into as many grapes as possible, getting as much air, light and heat as possible into the centre of the canopy – where the flowers are mainly positioned – is one of the ways of ensuring good pollination. In both *Sunlight into Wine* (p.16) and *The Grapevine* (p.178-182) there are methods of assessing 'canopy quality' which, for the small grower, are quite complicated and long-winded and I doubt there are many UK growers who have ever taken the trouble to perform such a test. However, it is good to be able to visually assess the state of your canopy in order to determine whether it is open or crowded. If you look through your canopy at about the point where the majority of the inflorescences are positioned (around 1.0 m from the ground), you should be able to clearly make out the inflorescences on the vines (and later the bunches), plus the next row of vines. If you cannot, the chances are that your canopy is too thick. Later on in the season, the presence of light green and yellowing leaves inside the canopy is a clear sign of a crowded canopy.

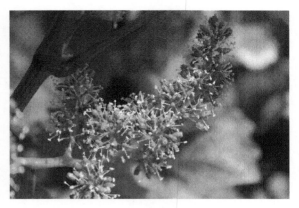

*Mid-flower with some caps still on*

The exact time of flowering is dependent on several factors. Site, variety and rootstock all play their part, but the temperature is the most important factor. Again, the books will tell you that the average daily temperature needs to reach at least 15°C before flowering can start, although Peter May, in his book *Flowering and Fruitset in Grapevines* gives details of various studies which challenge this. The UK is so much cooler than almost all other vinegrowing regions that I suspect very few of the 'rules' apply to us. Between the 1970s and '90s, flowering in most years would start in the second week of Wimbledon, i.e. the first or second week of July. Since global warming has cast its magic spell on the UK, flowering has started earlier and today, except in a really late season such as 2013 where it didn't really start until almost mid-July, flowering now typically begins in mid to late June, depending on the variety. As I said above, times of flowering are dependent on many factors and in an early season and with an early variety such as Rondo, flowering can start a full two weeks ahead of say Chardonnay. As you can see from the table below, it is July before the average daily temperature reaches 15°C.

Unlike some fruit crops, insects play almost no part in the pollination of vine flowers, so encouraging bees and other insects in the vineyard will not help. All commercial

| East Malling Research Station, Kent. 1971-2000 | | | |
|---|---|---|---|
| Month | Mean 24 hr Min Air temp °C | Mean 24 hr Max Air temp °C | Average |
| April | 4.5 | 12.7 | 8.6 |
| May | 7.3 | 16.4 | 11.9 |
| June | 10.2 | 19.4 | 14.8 |
| July | 12.4 | 22.0 | 17.2 |
| August | 12.2 | 22.1 | 17.2 |
| September | 9.9 | 18.9 | 14.4 |
| October | 7.1 | 14.9 | 11.0 |
| Data source: Met Office www.metoffice.gov.uk | | | |

vine varieties are hermaphrodite and therefore have both male and female parts on the same flower. The distance the pollen has to travel from the ends of the stamens to the ovaries is only a few millimetres and there is research to suggest that with some vine varieties, much of the pollination takes place before the flower caps (which cover the whole flower) fall off.

Research also suggests that in years with favourable flowering weather, pollen can become airborne and wind pollination between flowers can occur. Certainly in my experience, in years when the flowering conditions are ideal, the flowers give off a rich, citrus and honey-toned perfume, whereas in cool, wet years, no scent at all is given off during flowering.

Given warm dry weather and a light breeze, flowering can take place within a few days, but in years with poor conditions, flowering can take place over two or three weeks, or in the case of <u>really</u> poor years (such as 2012) even longer.

The dangers of a protracted flowering are that crops are likely to be much smaller and the grapes, because they have not been formed at the same time, will not ripen at the same time, thus making crop sampling and the prediction of a harvest date difficult. When the flowering

weather is cool and wet, vines will often suffer from what the French call *coulure* where many flowers fail to set and are shed at or after flowering or *millerandage* (also commonly known as 'hen and chick' setting[4]) where many of the berries stay on the flower and will ripen, but remain very small. These 'chicks' will get very sweet quite early in the ripening period, becoming attractive to wasps and birds, and will often succumb to *Botrytis* or rot of one type or another and simply fade away as harvest approaches. In any event, they seldom amount to much in terms of weight.

*Classic millerandage as seen in many UK vineyards in 2011 and 2012*

If you notice that some of the inflorescences have withered and turned brown, this is what is known as Early Bunch Stem Necrosis (EBSN) and whilst it can be due to a shortage of nutrients or trace elements, the most common causes are low temperatures and shading in the canopy. EBSN seems to affect some varieties more than others and in a UK context, Seyval blanc (in some vineyards but by no means all), can suffer badly in some years. Apart from keeping your canopy as open as possible and encouraging as much light as possible to penetrate the canopy, there is little you can do to influence flowering (short of some sort of covering which is discussed in *Chapter 15: Protected growing*). It goes without saying that keeping the vines free of disease and nutritionally satisfied is a pre-requisite to good flowering. As has already been mentioned, a shortage of molybdenum has been shown with certain varieties (most notably Merlot and in countries other than the UK), to make flowering more difficult and some UK growers are now applying molybdenum in pre-flowering foliar feeds. Whether this helps flowering is an unresolved question, but the cost is low and it appears to do no harm.

## Shoot trimming

The second aspect of canopy management is shoot trimming – often known as 'hedging' – which is the removal of excess growth from both tops and sides of the canopy. In smaller vineyards, this can be done with secateurs, shears, or a hand-held powered hedge cutter, whilst in larger vineyards, a tractor-mounted powered leaf-trimmer will be needed. These are described in *Chapter*

*10: Machinery and equipment.* The exact timing of the first and subsequent trimmings will depend on the growth of the vine, but the aim is to keep the leaf-wall as thin as possible (within reason) and the tops trimmed to around 100-150 mm above the top wire of the trellising. The time to carry out the first trimming is when the shoots grow away above the top wire and before they get to the point where they start to flop over. In a normal season, trimming would take place at least twice and possibly in a 'growy' year, a third time. Shoot trimming will encourage the development of side-shoots which will contribute to the supply of carbohydrates, but will also contribute to canopy density, so this also needs taking into account when deciding when to trim. As with tucking-in, you will soon get to know which blocks require trimming first and which require additional trimmings. However, with a tractor-mounted trimmer (especially with a double-sided one) this task is relatively quick to carry out.

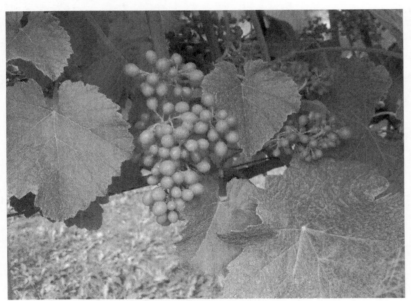

*Flowering over and grapes at 'petit pois' stage*

In some countries, a first trimming takes place during flowering (generally once the first flower on the cane is fully open and some of the caps have fallen) in the belief that it helps pollination. The aim is to divert some of the carbohydrates being produced by photosynthesis away from the shoot tips, which need all they can to keep growing, into the inflorescences. This view is supported by May in *Flowering and Fruitset in Grapevines* who states that: 'tipping of the shoot is perhaps the only manipulative operation that has consistently resulted in improving fruitset under non-restrictive environmental conditions'. May then quotes a researcher who says that: 'it has to be done when about half the caps have fallen' and follows this by stating that: 'tipping done before the start of flowering or after it has ended has no effect'.

However, tipping at this stage of the season is seldom carried out in UK vineyards and I have often wondered why. It may be that it is not seen as having much influence over flowering, given that environmental factors are much more likely to be in control. I also suspect that it is also because quite often, with our tall leaf-walls, the shoots have often not reached the top of the trellis by the time the first flowers are open and therefore in order to tip the canes, it could not easily be mechanised and one would have to use a hand-held trimmer in order to get below the top wire and avoid the posts. This is possible in a small vineyard, but not really practical in a larger one. In *The Grapevine* (p. 40), the authors state that: 'it is better to trim relatively early, e.g. close to or at fruitset, thereby allowing a large number of lateral leaves to reach maturity (and thus maximising photosynthetic capacity) around the time of *véraison*'. They then add: 'the presence of active shoot tips after *véraison* is an indicator of vine imbalance, where soil conditions are favouring continued shoot growth'. To which I would add: is an indicator of the unusual growing conditions that exist in UK vineyards. Given that the UK typically has its warmest weeks after fruitset (mid-July), and that typically we get rainfall during the summer, 'active shoot tips' are a very common sight.

Flowering can also be influenced by at least two other techniques: girdling and chemicals, neither of which have much place in commercial vineyards growing grapes for winemaking. Girdling, also known as cincturing, is an age-old practice whereby a small band of bark (containing the vascular cambium) is removed from the cane bearing the shoots which have the inflorescences on them. This disrupts the flow of carbohydrates from the leaves to the trunk and roots of the vine and makes them available to fuel the flowering. This is done just prior to flowering using a special girdling knife or tool and if done correctly, the layer of bark soon grows back. It is a technique routinely used in table grape production where size of grape and looseness of bunch is important. It undoubtedly works with wine grapes, but it is time consuming. The late David Jackson (who was then head of viticulture at Lincoln University at Christchurch in New Zealand), showed me how to do it in the small vineyard I had at Scott's Hall. It appeared to help, but was so labour intensive that I did not see it as a practical technique to improve fruit-set.

Chemical thinning is widespread in orchards of almost all types of fruit – apples, pears, citrus, olives, plums, and nuts – and also in grapes, although again, usually table grapes and not wine grapes. The most widely used product in the UK is called Cerone, which contains the chemical Ethephon, and has an off-label approval for use on apples (including cider apples). In France a product called Sierra which contains Ethephon (or *éthéphon* as it is called in French) is permitted on grapes of all types. The website of the *Institut Français de la Vigne et du Vin* (IFV) has some interesting data on its use and also provides the useful information that hand *éclaircissage* (bunch thinning) takes

40 hours-ha (16 hours-acre) at a cost of €495-ha (£420-ha, £170-acre), whereas thinning with Sierra costs €163-ha (£138-ha, £56-acre).

## Deleafing

The leaves of the vine are its solar collectors and their task is to collect sunshine and turn it, via the miracle of photosynthesis, into carbohydrates (starches and sugars). These power the plant, end up in the grapes, which we harvest, and are stored in the woody parts of the vine which enable it to overwinter and burst into life in the following spring before any leaves appear. Up until a shoot grows about eight fully expanded leaves, it is dependent upon stored reserves within the vine and until a leaf grows to about one third to a half of its maximum size, it is a net consumer of carbohydrates, drawing on reserves stored in the plant or being created by other leaves. However, once a leaf reaches this size, it then becomes a net exporter, sending carbohydrates back to the plant and its fruit until such time as it approaches its full size which is around five to six weeks after the leaf first appears. Once a leaf reaches its full size, the rate of photosynthesis is maintained for a further two to three weeks, but then starts to decrease and, as younger and still-expanding leaves, particularly those situated on side-shoots, take over, its contribution to the overall sugar production machine reduces significantly and eventually gets to a point (about ten weeks after it first appeared) where it is down to around ten per cent of its peak rate of photosynthesis.[5]

The oldest leaves on the vine are by definition those nearest the winter cane. This is the very area where many of the vine's flowers are situated and where many of the buds required for next year's fruiting are growing and deciding whether to lay down the potential to produce inflorescences for next year's crop. As these oldest leaves are no longer major contributors to the vine's sugar factory, some of them (but not all of them) can be removed at the appropriate time without causing any detrimental effect upon either this year's or next year's crop.

As I have pointed out in several previous sections of this book, air, light and heat are the most important elements in both stimulating and securing crop production and therefore deleafing in the fruiting zone plays its part in allowing these elements to reach the parts that matter. It does this in two ways: by opening up the canopy to air, light and heat; and by opening up the canopy to pesticides, particularly for the control of *Botrytis,* which can be very damaging to recently pollinated inflorescences when there is flowering residue – spent pollen stamens and flower caps – left on the bunch and also to the buds on next year's canes. In the post-*véraison* period, when ripening gathers pace, opening up the bunches to air and light will help reduce both malic and total acid levels, improve fruit flavours and, with red varieties, help to give better colour and riper tannins.

In a 1988 paper *Viticultural and oenological implications of leaf removal for New Zealand vineyards* written by Steve Smith (now an MW and viticulturalist at Craggy Range), Richard Smart, Ian Coddrington and Mark Robertson, and presented at the 2nd Cool Climate Wine Symposium, it was demonstrated how leaf removal improved yields, helped with *Botrytis* control, had no significant affect upon sugar levels and reduced total acidity levels, particularly malic acid levels. This ground-breaking work proved beyond doubt that the practice had huge benefits in cooler climates. This paper is available at www.englishwine.com/wgigb.htm.

The question of when to start deleafing is an interesting one. In past times (pre-1990) very little in the way of deleafing was done at all in UK vineyards, or if it was done, only in the two to three weeks prior to harvesting so that the final anti-*Botrytis* spray could be applied and the crop would be easier to see and access at harvest time. Today, the date of deleafing has got much earlier and my experiences over the past decade, but especially in 2011 and 2012, both years with difficult flowering conditions, was that a light deleafing soon after flowering, before bunch-close (and certainly well before *véraison*) was very positive. By 'light' I mean the removal of around one third of the leaves in the fruiting zone, that is to say in the first 400-500 mm above the fruiting cane (assuming flat *Guyot* pruning).

These leaves will almost certainly be the oldest ones on the vine and as I have pointed out above, are contributing far less to carbohydrate accumulation than their younger neighbours and the emerging side-shoots. Research, all done overseas in climates warmer and drier than the UK's and in vineyards where yields are typically higher than ours, show that an early deleafing may not increase yields as the flowering process is negatively affected by the loss of photosynthetic capability. With this I have no disagreement. However, I believe that the UK's growing environment is so unusual that the benefits of an early post-flowering deleafing far outweigh any negatives.

A 2011 Luxembourg study[6] on methods of controlling *Botrytis* stated: 'Manual leaf removal in the cluster-zone just after bloom [flowering] provided a significant reduction of bunch rot infestation without any input of chemical substances. Subsequently, this treatment can be recommended as an important tool in any bunch rot protection strategy for integrated as well as organic viticulture.' It suggested removing two leaves per bunch per cane, i.e. a cane with two bunches would have four leaves removed, the nearest ones to the bunch in question. Whilst some research has shown a reduction in yield by deleafing at this stage (as has been mentioned above), the benefits of a clean crop and the ability of being able to leave grapes to ripen fully, rather than having to pick them because of deterioration in quality due to *Botrytis*, easily outweighed any reduction in crop.

The best practice is to perform one light deleafing shortly after flowering is finished and well before bunch-close so that a good fungicide spray can be applied which will penetrate into the middle of the bunch. For the control of *Botrytis*, this is the most important spray as, if not protected, disease will often start inside the bunch and work its way outwards, only appearing when sugars reach around 5-6 per cent potential alcohol (44-50°OE). The next round of deleafing will be done just after *véraison* so that the fruit is exposed, thus allowing it to dry out more easily and be more visible which will make picking easier and quicker. Less vigorous varieties and vines on less vigorous rootstocks may require less deleafing to achieve the same end – clean, healthy fruit for the pickers. In years when flowering is protracted (2012 and 2013 come to mind), it may be necessary to deleaf once the primary bunches have gone through *véraison*. This might then be the best time to bunch thin, removing those bunches which are the slowest to change colour. In some vineyards, another pre-harvest deleafing will also be helpful and speed up picking.

How you perform your deleafing will of course play a part in how many times it is carried out. Hand deleafing is a time consuming and therefore costly, procedure and in a vineyard planted with 2.00 m wide rows can take up to 120 man hours per hectare (48 hours-acre). Performing this task by machine, while it may not be so accurate and some bunches may get partially sliced in the process, is so much quicker that it means it's much more likely to get done at the right time.

Some growers have experimented with using sheep penned up into the vineyard to remove leaves. I have tried this myself, but you need to make sure that you pen the sheep into a relatively small section of vines (although of course it does depend on how many sheep you have) and wait until they have taken the available grass down to the point where they are hungry, and look for the next best thing – vine leaves. They will start nibbling these before they take an interest in the grapes (which at this time will be hard and acidic) and will carry out a partial deleafing. The problem I found was that the sheep will also rub up against individual vines and break or bend planting stakes, plus they will put their feet up on the wires in an attempt to reach higher leaves. I also found that the constant patrolling of the electric fencing used to pen the sheep up, plus the fact that you needed to move the sheep (and the fencing) before spraying could take place, made this a time-consuming method of deleafing. Much easier to employ labour or get a machine.

In some vineyards overseas, I have also seen the removal of side-shoots in the grape zone which is certainly a time consuming practice and one that cannot be mechanised. If you had a variety that was ultra-susceptible to *Botrytis* or perhaps a block of grapes that you were attempting to get super-ripe, then this is also something to consider. However, I would not remove every last side shoot on the vines unless I was sure that this did not negatively impact upon sugar production.

## Crop thinning

The question of crop thinning may appear to be an academic one given what I have said about the low yields generally seen in UK vineyards, but there have been years – 1983, 1989, 1992, 1996, and 2006 – when crops have been heavy and national yields have been around the 33-38 hl-ha level (compared to the 1989-2013 average of just under 21 hl-ha). In these 'good' years, many growers will achieve 25 tonnes-ha (10 tonnes-acre) – even with Chardonnay and Pinot noir – and some individual vineyard blocks will have produced as much as 37 tonnes-ha (15 tonnes-acre). Again, as I have pointed out, how an individual vine copes with a large crop is interesting and there is a lot of scientific evidence to show that in fact a vine responds to a large crop by upping its rate of photosynthesis and therefore the amount of carbohydrates it is producing. This means that a vine carrying say 20 tonnes-ha (8 tonnes-acre) will not necessarily be at a disadvantage when compared to one carrying half that figure and, given good growing conditions and in a well-managed vineyard where both canopy and leaf quality are up to the mark, sugar and acid levels may remain broadly similar. However, much will also depend on the lateness of the year and the weather in the two months before picking, something one cannot predict with any certainty, especially given the UK's fickle climate. Therefore, faced with a large crop, some thinning might be considered appropriate.

How much crop thinning is carried out will depend on what type and style of wine is being produced. As I showed in *Chapter 3: Site selection*, overcropping may not be a word in the sparkling winemaker's handbook, considering that in Champagne 20+ tonnes-ha (8+ tonnes-acre) is not considered out of the ordinary. However, in vineyards for still white wines, especially those made from aromatic varieties such as Bacchus, Ortega and Schönburger or for hard-to-ripen varieties such as Chardonnay, Pinot blanc, and Pinot gris for still wine, thinning so that the yield was brought down to between 7.50-10.00 tonnes-ha (3-4 tonnes-acre), would almost certainly help quality. I would also say that with almost any red variety, but particularly with Pinot noir, thinning down to around 5 tonnes-ha (2 tonnes-acres) would improve both quality and colour. Of course, exactly how much to thin to achieve this level of yield is always going to be problematical and trial and (hopefully not too much) error is the only way. Once you get to know what a light, medium and heavy crop looks like and at what levels your vineyard yields, then working out how much to remove to arrive at a meaningful reduction becomes easier, although it is never a straight-line equation.

Thinning can take place at different times. Inflorescences can be removed prior to flowering; bunches can be halved after they have set; bunch shoulders can be removed on bunches bearing them; bunches can be cut off prior to *véraison*; whole bunches can be removed in mid-*véraison* when the difference between early and late flowering can be seen more clearly, at least on red varieties (this is the most common timing); and bunches can be taken off at almost any stage up until harvest.

Removing inflorescences prior to flowering will do the job, but given that one never knows how flowering is going to proceed, is probably the most risky. Finding the inflorescences may be a problem if left too late, but removing the third inflorescence (i.e. the last) on the shoot may well give the other two a better chance of flowering. Removing bunches prior to *véraison* is probably no better or worse than removing them half-way through, so if it fits in with your canopy management schedule, then this is fine. Cutting bunches in half is a technique beloved of German growers of Pinot noir, which under their conditions appears to be especially susceptible to *Botrytis,* and involves doing exactly what it says: taking a pair of secateurs and slicing the bunch in half. They call this *traubenteilen*. This has the effect of reducing the size of the bunch, but also of causing the shoulders to droop, thus loosening the bunch and making access for air, light and sprays easier. Removing bunches in mid-*véraison* –known as *vendange en vert* (green harvesting) in France – is certainly the easiest, as there is a visual difference between early and late bunches and if it takes place just after a trimming and a deleafing, the bunches will be much easier to find. Removing bunches in the four weeks prior to harvest probably has little influence over the final quality of the grapes harvested, although it will of course reduce the yield and make picking quicker. The cost of bunch thinning at *véraison* will depend upon many factors – vine density, pruning system and crop level – but as a very general guide, a practiced hand, working in deleafed vines, ought to be able to bunch-thin 100 vines per hour, so around 40 hours-ha (16 hours-acre) in a 2.00 m x 1.20 m vineyard.

Exactly what effect thinning has upon the quality and quantity of the harvest is something over which opinions differ. In *appellations* with yield restrictions, *vendange en vert* is quite routinely done, although how close anyone can get to the actual yield required is questionable. I suspect that very few growers are prepared to thin sufficiently to reduce the yield by a significant amount and that at least in hand-harvested vineyards, instructions to 'only pick the ripest' will be used to reduce the level of the crop if this is required. In vineyards where the grapes are machine harvested no such instruction can of course be given, although I suspect there are ways around this. My experience in the UK is with removing 50 per cent of all the bunches from some Reichensteiner vines just after flowering, in order to raise the sugar level, as I wished to make some home-made *suss-reserve*. The yield was cut by around 25 per cent and the sugar level raised by around 2 per cent potential alcohol. Whether this paid for the cost of the work is debatable.

As I have already mentioned under the section on *Shoot trimming* in this chapter, grapes can be thinned chemically, although this is not permitted in the UK. In some countries, harvesting machines are used to thin, by knocking off bunches after *véraison*, but I cannot see this technique catching on in UK vineyards just yet, given that there are so few harvesting machines, and in any event, yields are seldom that large.

## Deciding when to harvest

Deciding when to harvest is always a testing process and to get it right requires experience, patience and a degree of luck. In an ideal world, your grapes would slowly ripen to the point where they arrived, unblemished and undamaged by birds and weather, to the point where their sugar and acid levels were perfect for the style of wine required. In practice, this is seldom the case. Except in exceptional years – 2011 comes to mind – when sugar levels were rising too rapidly and those wanting to make top quality sparkling wine were forced to pick Pinot noir before the potential alcohol level got too high, in most years determining a picking date is a question of waiting for acids to fall to the wished-for level. Sampling of your grapes prior to harvest will be an on-going process with

the first few plucked from the vines, tasted and rejected as being 'far too acidic'. This will be followed by some random sugar tests using a hand-held refractometer, to the point where you can begin to collect samples and test them for sugar and acidity. This is done using a temperature-corrected hydrometer for the relative density (what used to be called 'specific gravity') which gives you the sugar level (degrees Oechsle, or °OE, are the relative density minus 1,000) and carrying out an acid titration using indicators and/or a pH meter to determine the total acidity. Whilst the floating of a hydrometer in a 250-500 ml glass or clear plastic measuring cylinder is a relatively simple job, an acid titration requires some simple laboratory equipment and fresh reagents to get an accurate figure. If you have your own winery, then you will require this equipment anyway; if using a contract winemaker, then they will usually offer this service to their clients.

*Ships? I see no ships – just ripening grapes! Peter Hall in his vineyard at Breaky Bottom, Lewes, East Sussex*

Exactly how many different samples you take, and of what, will depend on your vineyard, the varieties, clones and rootstocks being grown. I prefer to collect whole bunch samples from each block. Six bunches in total, three from one side of the canopy, three from the other and make sure you take some first node bunches and some second and third node bunches. The aim is to collect a representative sample; not to astound your winemaker with how ripe your best bunches are. Remember that the only sample that really counts is the one you will collect when you pick all the grapes. Sampling ought to start at least three weeks before harvest so that you build up a picture of the time it takes for your different blocks to gain sugar and lose acidity. All vineyards, all varieties, and all clones differ in the rate they ripen, with the yield level probably playing the biggest part in the speed of ripening. The sugar and total acidity levels, as well as perhaps pH and bunch-weight, should be put into a spread-sheet and plotted on to a graph so that you can see how the grapes are ripening over time. Many factors will get in the way of a gradual rise in sugars and lowering of acid levels – something that would only happen in an ideal world – and rain in the four to six weeks prior to harvest may well cause both your sugar and acid levels to fall at certain times during the ripening process as the grapes get diluted.

| Date | °OE | Total acidity in g/l tartaric | pH | Bunch weight grammes |
|------|-----|-------------------------------|-----|----------------------|
| 08-Sep-14 | 43 | 23.0 | 2.53 | 120 |
| 17-Sep-14 | 53 | 17.5 | 2.66 | 167 |
| 23-Sep-14 | 63 | 13.0 | 2.73 | 174 |
| 02-Oct-14 | 66 | 14.1 | 2.71 | 170 |
| 08-Oct-14 | 68 | 12.4 | 2.71 | 166 |
| 14-Oct-14 | 76 | 12.2 | 2.81 | 178 |
| 16-Oct-14 | 72 | 10.2 | 2.91 | 188 |

The table above shows Pinot noir in a typical progression of ripening from around 5-6 weeks before harvest until picking on 16 October 2014. Sugars rise until just before harvest when they fall due to rain dilution, whereas acids drop in a fairly straight line.

Whilst a lot of growers tend to get excited about sugar levels, to my way of thinking it is the acid levels that really tells you about ripening. Sugar levels, taking different varieties and different yield levels into account, are much more a reflection of the weather during that year, and if you decide that you are always going to pick when the grapes reach 10 per cent potential alcohol, you will not get the best wine possible. What makes the difference between a partially ripe crop and a fully ripe crop is the acid level and in particular, the proportions of malic and tartaric acidity. At the start of the ripening period, generally taken to be at *véraison*, malic acid levels are high, but start to fall as sugar levels in the grapes rise. Whilst the level of tartaric acid in the grapes – the flesh and the skin – remains fairly constant throughout the ripening process, the level of malic acid in the flesh can fall by between 60 and 80 per cent (Iland et al. 2011). The main driver in the decline in malic acid levels is the temperature after *véraison*: the higher, the faster malic acid levels decline. In terms of taste, the higher the proportion of tartaric to malic, the 'riper' the grapes and juice will taste. Although in general, only total acid levels (i.e. malic, tartaric and other acids) are measured pre-harvest to determine a picking date, in fact it is the proportion of malic to tartaric that is just as important and can differ from year to year. If you compared ripeness levels in 2012 and 2013, even though total acid levels were similar, the much warmer post- *véraison* period in 2013 helped deplete malic acid levels much more than in 2012, giving riper tasting grapes. Acid levels of course will differ from variety to variety and will differ according to the type of wine you are making, but the difference between a wine made with a properly ripe acidity and one made from a not-quite ripe acidity is the difference between an award winner and an also-ran. Be patient and wait for those acids to ripen.

In Champagne, growers often refer to *L'indice de maturité* (IM) levels which are arrived at by dividing the grammes per litre of sugar in the grapes by the acidity expressed as sulphuric. They consider an IM of 20 to be an ideal level for Champagne. Thus a juice at 75°OE (170 g/l of sugar or 10% potential alcohol) divided by an acidity of 8.5 g/l as sulphuric (12.9 g/l as tartaric) has an IM of 20. This used to be considered a typical level in Champagne up to the 1990s, but since then their average IM levels have risen. For the years 2000-12 their average alcohol levels were 10.1% and acidity levels 7.5 g/l (as sulphuric) giving an IM of almost 24. That's global warming for you!

The one thing you do not want to happen is for any of the following to decide your picking date: a rapidly deteriorating crop; bird damage; frost; a lack of pickers; the children's half-term; and because you decided in August that this was the weekend you were going to pick and have asked all your friends to help!

## Picking

Picking can be done by hand or by machine. Denbies have used a picking machine (a Braud) since their very early days, and Buzzards Valley Vineyard in Staffordshire also now has one. All grape picking machines work in the same way, by shaking the grapes off the bunch and leaving (most of) the stalks behind on the vine. As they scoop the grapes up, they inevitably collect leaves, bits of stalk and other plant debris (plus the odd nail if using timber posts), which is collectively known as MOG (material other than grape) and which in many grape purchase contracts has to be kept below a certain level. The newest machines are better than older ones and many now have sophisticated on-board sorting devices which pick a much cleaner crop and considerably reduce the MOG level. However, given that grapes in the UK tend to be far less ripe than their overseas counterparts, I would be concerned about the small bits of (unripe) stalk that inevitably come through any sorting system and end up in the press and the effect they would have upon the herbaceousness of the resulting wine. I would certainly want to do some trials before I went ahead and machine picked my entire crop. In 2013, Gusbourne had a demonstration of a brand new Pellenc harvester on some Chardonnay, but the general consensus was that for sparkling wine, the juice was not as good as hand-harvested and whole-bunch pressed fruit. Gusbourne also had to go through the section of vineyard to be machine harvested prior to the machine going through in order to remove any diseased bunches which rather negates the cost and speed benefits of machine harvesting.

Overseas, especially in countries where labour is either expensive or hard to find (or both), machine harvesting for still wines is the norm and given the increasing size of UK vineyards, I am sure that in years to come we will see more picking machines. For sparkling wines, which are typically whole-bunch pressed, machine harvesting is still frowned upon in most quality sparkling wine regions. I suspect it will be many decades (probably never) before harvesting machines are allowed into Champagne.

However, picking machines become more sophisticated with each generation and their on-board cleaning and selection systems are far more effective than they were even five years ago. The discrimination against machine harvesting in some regions is understandable and old habits and traditions die harder in winegrowing than in many other spheres. I am sure that good grapes can be machine harvested and used for making very good sparkling wines, although I accept that 'quickly picked by machine' doesn't look quite so good on a back label!

There are several different ways of picking grapes by hand and each has its advantages and disadvantages. The first thing to decide is what to pick into and this will be determined by one of several factors. If you are picking grapes under contract, there may be a clause stipulating what you have to pick into and with some contracts, the purchaser will supply picking bins or crates, the type of which will depend on their handling equipment and/or their winemaking philosophy. When it was mainly still wine that was being produced, many vineyards used bulk bins of one sort or another, either purpose-built plastic or fibreglass bins that could be carried by tractor-mounted forks or a fork-lift and which could be stacked on top of each other for transport or storage and could often be tipped directly into a receiving hopper, crusher or press. The picking bin used by many wineries is a Dolav Box Pallet Type 800 Solid which has a base the same size as a standard 1 m x 1.2 m pallet, has a cubic capacity of 500 litres and will hold around 275-325 kg of fresh grapes (weights will depend on variety and condition and whether the bins have been well-filled or loosely filled). These are solid-bottomed bins which are very robust and with care will last decades. They cost (new) around £125 + VAT each, depending on number required, but can often be found second-hand for much less.

*Dolav Box Pallet Type 800 Solid*

The sparkling wine revolution in UK vineyards has meant that many producers now pick into small trays as careful handling from vineyard to press is all part of the *méthode Champenoise* and enables unbroken whole bunches to be tipped – usually by hand – straight into the press. There are many different types of trays used by wineries and the exact type will depend on several factors – budget probably being the most important. The best, to my way of thinking, are the type that both nest and stack (depending on which way round they are placed) so that when they are full they sit one on top of another, but when they are empty they take up around one half of the space for storage. The ones illustrated are the Allibert 11032 which cost new around £12 + VAT each (depending on the number required). They are 32 litres in capacity, have solid bottoms, hold around 12-15 kg of fresh grapes and stack five per layer on a standard 1 m x 1.2 m pallet.

Some growers prefer trays with perforated bottoms, but apart from the fact that these allow juice to leak out if any is released by the grapes (which of course shouldn't

happen as they ought to be in perfect condition), the perforations will pick up mud and dirt in the vineyard and dried juice from the grapes and they are more difficult to keep clean with normal cleaning techniques. Granted, if you have a purpose-built tunnel pressure washer for your boxes this may not be an issue, but most growers do not have this type of equipment. The solid bottomed trays are also more robust and less likely to get broken if stood upon or otherwise mishandled. If your budget will not run to new trays, there are usually plenty of second-hand fruit or vegetable trays available at around £3-5 each, but these are usually fairly flimsy and almost always perforated.

*Allibert 11032 stack and nest trays*

In the vineyard, if you are using bulk bins, you will need something to move them about with. Fixed forks or a fork-lift attachment mounted on the front and/or rear of the tractor is ideal. Pickers can then pick grapes into individual buckets or smaller bins and tip them into the larger bins. If you are using trays, assuming they hold a maximum of around 15 kg (larger ones are not advised as some pickers will only partially fill them as they will not want to lift more than 15 kg), they can be used to pick directly into, although most growers use buckets which can be filled and then tipped into the trays.

Depending on your vineyard layout and/or manpower availability, full trays can be walked out of the vineyard to the headland to be loaded on to a pallet, trailer or other carrying device. Or, as is more likely, if your rows are too long for trays to be manually carried out, you will also need some form of pallet lifting and carrying device that will fit down the rows. Again, a tractor with front and rear forks or a purpose made pallet trailer is ideal. Remember also, if you are picking into trays, that when these are loaded on to a pallet, four, five, or even six high, they will sway from side to side and unless well-restrained with straps of some sort, will easily tip over. Scrabbling around in the mud for grapes that have already been picked and were clean and pristine, but now are now muddy and damaged, is not a great experience.

I have always found it quickest to pick four rows at once – two either side of the alleyway the tractor is in – with two pickers per row, one on either side of the leaf-wall, making a picking gang of eight. Pickers can then hand their full buckets or push the filled trays under the bottom wires into the row where the tractor is. You will need a tractor driver and one 'bucket-person' to handle the buckets as they are passed under the wires and to manage the pickers, keep them up to speed, instruct them in what to pick and what to leave and to check up on the picked rows to make sure all the grapes have been harvested. If you have more than two pickers on each row, you will find that their work rate slows, they spend time overtaking each other, chatting, missing sections and generally slowing down. Of course, if work-rate is not a priority and chatting to each other part of the fun, then have as many as you want per row! If you want to pick six rows at once, this is possible, but you will find that three rows is a long way to pass trays or buckets to and fro. If you need to pick more grapes than eight pickers can pick in a day (around 2.5-4 tonnes), then you will need two gangs, each with their own tractor (and driver and bucket-person) and bin or pallet carrying facilities.

In most vineyards in the UK (and indeed in all non-UK vineyards that I have ever visited) picking is done by hourly-paid employees and they are kept up to the mark by a desire to get the job done. Some UK growers pick on piece-work with each picker or team of pickers being paid according to the weight of grapes they pick but unless you are a really large scale grower and time and/or cost are a really important factor in your calculations, I think the extra work involved in keeping tabs on who has picked what, checking to make sure that all the grapes have been harvested and not just the sections with the heaviest crop and managing the payments, far outweighs the benefits. Harvest time ought to be a pleasant occasion and many vineyard owners will provide some sort of lunch for their pickers, plus tea, coffee and snacks at the appropriate moment.　Whatever system of payment you opt for and whatever picking containers you use, all pickers will need a pair of picking secateurs and often they will also be provided with protective gloves. You will also need a First Aid kit as fingers often get snipped as well as bunches. Costs of picking have already been covered in *Chapter 2: Why plant a vineyard in the UK?* in the section on *Picking costs.*

*Job done!*

1 St. Vincent is also the patron saint of winemakers and vinegar makers. The Bulgarians have a different saint for this purpose, Trifon Zarezan – St. Trifon the Pruner, whose day is 1 February, although apparently they also worship him on 14 February as well. I am not sure how St. Valentine feels about this though.

2 According to Smart in another entry in the Oxford Companion to Wine, the 'leaf to fruit ratio' lies between 5 and 30 sq cm of leaf area per gram of fruit, with 10-15 g considered 'adequate' for most varieties although 'higher values are considered by some for Pinot noir'. I am sure someone knows how to measure leaf area, but I have never seen it done.

3 *The Flowering Process of Vitis vinifera: A Review* by Vasconcelos, Greven, Winefield, Trought and Raw. American. Journal Enol. Vitic. 60:4 (2009). This document is available from www.englishwine.com/wgigb.htm

4 You often see this referred to as 'hen and chicken' setting which makes no sense as a hen and a chicken are the same size!

5 Kliewer 1981. The information about leaf sizes and timings is based upon US data, so it may be slightly different in UK conditions.

6 *Crop cultural and chemical methods to control grey mould on grapes* by Molitor, Rothmeier, Behr, Fisher, Hoffmann and Evers (2011). This document is available from www.englishwine.com/wgigb.htm.

# Chapter 13
# Frost protection

## Introduction[1]

Frost in the vineyard can be a danger at three different times of the year: winter, spring and harvest time. There are several passive measures, ones that require no action at the time of the frost, which can be taken to reduce the level of frost damage, as well as several active methods, those requiring inputs of materials, machinery and manpower.

## Winter frosts

Winter frosts usually occur in late December, January and February, and are seldom a problem in the UK as temperatures do not usually go down low enough. The trunk of a mature vine can withstand -20°C to -25°C when the vine is completely dormant although it is possible that annual canes might be damaged at these levels. If these sorts of temperatures are experienced (and they have been in the past) the incidence of such things as Crown Gall (caused by the bacteria *Agrobacterium tumefaciens)* and *Eutypa Lata* might well increase. However, it is impractical to protect a vine against this degree of frost.

## Spring frosts

Spring frosts are by far the most important and damaging type of frosts in the UK, as well as in other northern European cool climates. They occur in April and May (and even very occasionally in June) and come in two types: advection and radiation (or inversion) frosts. An advection frost occurs when very cold, frost-carrying, air blows into a vineyard region (sometimes from a considerable distance away) and displaces warmer air. This type of frost is unusual in the spring and is more associated with winter conditions. The only technique to counter an advection frost is to avoid planting in a frost pocket. The second type, a radiation frost, usually occurs on a clear, dry night when there is little, or no wind, and when long-wave radiation from the ground to the air is not impeded by cloud cover or high concentrations of water vapour in the air. When all these factors occur together, rapid cooling of the air immediately around the vines takes place. This layer of cold air, which can fall to as low as -8°C (although in the south of the UK -2°C to -4°C is more usual) is then

trapped beneath a layer of warmer air (hence the term inversion) and cannot escape. Typically this cold, damaging layer will start almost at ground level and rise to 10-30 m above the vineyard floor. This type of frost is the one most likely to damage vines and is the one that can be more easily, although expensively, controlled.

As has been said above and stated in *Chapter 3: Site selection* in the section on *Aspect*, the best method of frost protection is to select a site that is not in a frost pocket. These 'pockets' can range in size from a relatively small area of land such as a low depression in the middle of a flat or gently sloping site, to one low-lying corner of a site where the frost cannot escape, to complete valleys covering a considerable area of land. If you do have a slope on the site and think you might be frost affected, plant with the rows in line with the slope and with plenty of space beyond the vines so that the frost can drain away. Make sure that any windbreaks, shelter belts or hedges likely to trap a frost have enough gaps in them for the same reason. However, finding a site that fits all these requirements is not always possible and, in looking for a site that is both well sheltered and not exposed to prevailing winds, you may find that your site is prone, at least in some areas of it, to frost.

Spring frosts have always been an issue in UK vineyards – not only vineyards, but in fruit crops in general – and in most years, frosts of some sort will occur. The question of how damaging they are is one of timing: an early bud burst and a late frost and vines can suffer huge damage. 1997 was a classic frost year when an early spring was followed by a -6°C on 6 May. National yields were cut to 6,460 hl when they had been over 26,000 hl the year before. At Chapel Down, where I was then winemaking, less than 1-tonne of grapes was picked from the whole 4-ha (10-acres) whereas the year before, from the same vines, 30-tonnes of grapes had been harvested. Mike Roberts says that at Ridgeview they have used their frost protection system in each of the last twelve years. In recent years (since 2009) frosts seem to have been more of an issue in UK vineyards and more growers are now using active techniques to prevent frost damage.

The extent of the damage to vines will depend, not only on the temperature down to which the frost falls, the length of time it stays there and the state of the growth of the vine, but also on such factors as the orientation of the site, the vine variety, the rootstock, the height of the vine above the ground, the condition of the floor of the vineyard, the slope on the site, the amount of space allowed for the frost to collect and/or disperse and several other factors. Each frost event on each site will have its own peculiarities. The actual temperature required to damage a vine depends on the state of growth at the time of freezing and the relative humidity of the buds; the higher, the worse will be the damage. A paper from Michigan State University says that at woolly bud stage, -3.3°C will kill 10 per cent of the buds and -6.1 °C will kill 50 per cent of the buds; at second leaf, -1.7 °C will kill 10 per cent of the shoots, -2.2 °C, 50 per cent and -5.6 °C, 90 per cent.

Of course, if your vineyard looks likely to suffer from frost, you will need some form of sensing equipment to tell you when a frost is about to occur and/or is occurring. A standard weather station is probably not the best way of obtaining the data as they are (a) usually sited in the wrong place and (b) have their temperature sensors at the wrong height. To predict the likelihood of frost you need a sensor in the part (or parts) of the vineyard most likely to be frosted first, with the sensors somewhere near to ground level, plus perhaps at 500 mm and 1.0 m above ground level. The system needs to be able to send text messages to multiple mobile telephones so that everyone involved with frost-fighting can be woken from their slumbers. With experience you will work out where in the vineyard the best place is to site sensors, at what height to have them and at what temperature they are programmed to send out text messages. You can also site additional temperature data-loggers in vulnerable parts of the vineyard to record what actually happens. Being able to predict a frost event accurately will keep the cost of preventing frost damage down to a minimum and some growers subscribe to a frost prediction service which will alert them to the likelihood of a frost in their immediate area so that staff can be warned that they might be needed to help with frost prevention measures.

On a 'frost night' the temperature will normally get towards freezing at between midnight and 2 am (although it can be earlier) and get progressively colder as dawn approaches, reaching its lowest point at around daybreak. During this period the frost will slowly roll from high ground to low, settling in even quite small dips and hollows in the vineyard – you often only notice that there is a slightly lower area in the vineyard when you see how the vegetation and vines have been damaged by frost – and will scorch any green tissue in its path. Having said that, frost can be remarkably capricious, damaging some buds but not others, touching those on the top of the cane but not the bottom and singeing one side of a shoot but not the other. A really hard frost on a dormant or barely open bud may well kill it completely and there will often be no regrowth at all. The damage to buds from a light frost is more difficult to spot and it will often only manifest itself after budburst when shoots and leaves will be deformed as they grow. Frost damage to leaves will show up as soon as the sun comes up and the frost lifts. Frost damage can also seriously deplete stored reserves in the vine, affecting the

development of subsequent shoots and accounting for lower yields the following year.

Depending on the severity of the frost (depth of temperature and length of freeze) there is usually some recovery afterwards with many vines sending out new shoots, especially from around the crown of the vine where the buds are better protected by the mass of older wood found here. Typically what happens is that some buds will be unscathed and continue as normal whilst others will shoot later and will always be behind. This gives rise to different flowering dates, different ripening dates and consequently, different harvesting dates. Inevitably, frost damaged vines will yield less, often considerably less and in some instances, nothing at all.

## Passive methods of frost prevention

In order to reduce frost damage, there are a number of passive measures that can be taken. If you have a site where frost is likely to be a problem, then planting varieties that are naturally late in breaking out of dormancy might be advantageous, although there is some evidence to suggest that in years where budburst is late, spring frosts are also late. However, from my experience, Seyval blanc is less prone to damage than say Reichensteiner or Rondo – both early varieties – but this maybe because it is a variety that is generally less susceptible to frost damage. Some varieties show a marked tendency to produce viable secondary flowers after the primary ones have been frosted (Pinot noir and Chardonnay for instance) and growing these in frost-prone areas might be considered. If you are only growing Champagne varieties, then plant the Pinots in the area more likely to be frosted as budburst is slightly later than with Chardonnay. You might also consider using a high-wire training system – GDC, Sylvoz or Blondin – as temperatures can be up to 4°C higher at 2.00 m above ground level than at 700 mm. Raising your fruiting wire say just from 700 mm to 900 mm will make a difference of around 0.5°C, so helpful, but not critical and not generally enough to avoid frost damage. Spur pruned vines will suffer less damage than cane pruned vines as the buds on spurs will gain some benefit from the body of older wood near them. Spur pruned vines are also much quicker to prune and therefore could be left until the very last, thus delaying budburst. Although these are not good enough reasons to adopt this form of pruning wholesale, if you have one area that you know is always frosted, then this might be one part of the solution.

The state of the vineyard alleyways is also important. Clean, firm, bare earth will hold on to heat during the day, even more-so if the earth is damp, when compared to rough cultivated soil or alleyways with a covering of grass or other vegetation. The heat held in the soil will be released to the atmosphere during the evening and night and can help ward off frost. Some reports suggest a rise in the temperature by 0.3°C to 0.6°C. Dark loamy soils are at less risk than light, sandy soils and vines with mulch beneath them will also be at greater risk than those with bare soil underneath the vines. Long, un-mown grass, which holds moisture, is the worst alleyway cover and much more likely to exacerbate frost damage. In some regions, growers routinely burn off the vegetation on the vineyard floor with a contact weedkiller prior to budburst, allowing it to grow back after the frost-dangerous weeks are over. If you were to take no other frost prevention measures, this might be worth considering.

Pruning later in the spring – say in late March – will delay budburst slightly and could be considered if the area liable to be frosted is small. Leaving the canes long and in a vertical position until the danger of frost is over is often stated as being a way to avoid frost damage. Vertical canes are less likely to be damaged than horizontal ones, as the frost cannot settle on them, and in addition, the first buds to grow shoots will be those at the ends of the canes, which you will be cutting off in any event, assuming that you have left the canes over-length. However, given that in the UK it is usually the third to fourth week of May before it is safe to say the danger of frost is over, leaving the canes upright means that when you do come to tie them down, they will have shoots down the whole length of them – and in most seasons quite long shoots – many of which will get knocked off as the canes as they are handled whilst being tied down. It also makes the job of tying down much slower and is generally not seen as a practical solution to the problem.

Leaving additional 'sacrifice' canes on your vines – a third or a fourth cane if you are normally pruning to two canes – is also a textbook way of coping with frost. The idea is that if you don't get frost, they can be cut off and discarded; if you do get frost, then they can be tied down. It does at least allow you to tie down two canes to start with and then it is only the sacrifice canes that have to be dealt with. What often happens if you do this is that all the buds on the sacrifice canes burst and produce long shoots (often showing multiple inflorescences) whereas the canes tied down are delayed in their bud burst and seem to lack flowers. However, in an area known to be frost prone, this is a relatively simple and cheap method of frost insurance.

Chemical sprays of one type or another have for many years been touted as preventing frost damage and every year seems to bring a new product. However, I have never met anyone who said they work. They might have a marginal effect upon delaying budburst or they might give the buds a greater degree of resistance to frost damage, but cannot be relied upon to provide total protection. Most of the sprays have to be applied between 24 and 48 hours prior to a frost event, so this implies (a) knowing with some certainty when a frost event is likely to happen and (b) being able to get on to the ground with a sprayer. The chemicals do not last for that long – maybe a week – and are not cheap (£150-ha per spray for materials was a recent quote) and given that you will probably need to use other methods as well, they do not seem (yet) to be part of a practical solution to the problem of frost damage.

## Active methods of frost prevention

Heating vineyards is probably the most used technique (both in the UK and overseas) of frost prevention and there are several different systems and materials used. The most widely used system in the UK is with wax *bougies* (candles) made by the French firm Stopgel. These are 6 litre cans of solid paraffin wax with a cardboard wick that can be placed out in the vineyard and lit progressively as temperatures fall. They cost around £6.50 + VAT each including transport. The benefit of these is that they require no fixed capital equipment, can be placed out in the vineyard beneath the vines until they are used (meaning that you can still drive up the alleyways to spray and mow if you need to) and then brought into the centre of the row when they are needed. They are also relatively simple to handle and operate and can be stored indefinitely until used. They also meet the recommendation that a larger number of small heaters are more effective than a fewer number of large ones and the number used can be expanded or contracted at will.

*A Stopgel 'bougie'*

The number of candles required in a given area is something that will depend on several factors. The manufacturers state that a maximum of 500-ha (200-acre) are required to protect against a -7°C frost in a vineyard 'with no wind' and suggest that around 200-250 ha (80-100 acre) are lit to start with and the number progressively increased as the temperature falls. You need to work out, based upon your row width and vine spacing, how many vines per candle you need, i.e. if you are spaced at 2.00 x 1.20 m then for 500-ha you need one candle for every 8.33 vines and space them out accordingly. You need to make sure that the perimeters are well heated as, if you just place them only in the centre, cold air will be drawn in from outside. You also need to place more on the windward side than the leeward side, assuming there is a breeze.

After you receive a frost warning, typically this will be when the temperature falls to around +1°C, you will need to get up and assemble your troops and, assuming the temperature continues to fall, start lighting the candles. Most growers find that a plumber's gas torch works very well. Each candle burns for around ten hours and on average you will get two to three burns per candle. The actual number used per season will depend upon the number and severity of the frosts, but in some years in the UK you might have to light up around six times, making the cost, including the candles and labour, around £5,000-ha (£2,000-acre) protected. Whilst this is a high sum (although unlikely to be this high in most years), hopefully you would be protecting a relatively small proportion of your whole site and with a good crop of grapes valued at least at £15,000-£20,000-ha (£6,000-£8,000-acre), well worth doing.

*Bougies put out in the vineyard ready for lighting*

In addition to wax candles, there are several other types of burner available, although not used much (if at all) in the UK. Burners using a mixture of waste sump-oil and paraffin (known as smudge pots) were once popular, but now seldom seen as this mixture of fuel is not very environmentally friendly (and probably illegal today) added to which the burners were heavy and difficult to move and required filling up with fuel in the vineyard where there is always a danger of spillages and soil contamination. Lighting piles of old car tyres or damp straw bales soaked with a waste oil and paraffin mixture used to be advocated, but are now definitely not permitted, although the smoke was useful in showing where the inversion layer stopped and started.

*Old style 'smudge pots'*

In Chablis – a region noted for its spring frosts – I have also seen gas burners connected with permanent pipelines to a gas tank in the corner of the vineyard and even electric heating cables strung along each row. Neither of these is used in UK vineyards. There are also tractor mounted devices that blow hot air, heated by oil or gas, into the vineyard which can be static or towed around the vineyard. Frostbuster and Frostguard, made by Agrofrost NV, are used in the UK. The units are expensive (£10,000-£15,000) and costly to run: £50-75 per hour. Nyetimber have around twenty of these – static and trailed – and say they can protect 80-ha (198-acres) from frost. They take a bit of getting used to and of course, each site will have its own peculiarities, but if frost is a real problem and you have a large area of vines, they are undoubtedly easier than frost candles.

In many parts of the world, wind machines – commonly known as 'frost mills' – which mix up the cold and warm layers of air in the vineyard, are the preferred form of frost prevention and when used in conjunction with vineyard heaters, probably offer the best solution. This is the system widely used in citrus orchards. One manufacturer states that one frost mill will protect around 4-ha (10-acres) with a 5.5°C inversion difference at 15 m above ground level. These figures are approximate as each installation and each frost event will be specific to that site. Each machine needs power – electricity, gas, diesel or even tractor PTO – and a control system. A basic gas powered unit can cost around US$30,000. Denbies Vineyard installed several Californian frost mills in the mid-'90s at a cost said to be around £250,000 only to find that as soon as they turned them on for the first time, some very irate neighbours, annoyed at having been woken up in the middle of the night by the noise and commotion, successfully appealed to the local authority to prevent their use. A new blade was designed which, although quieter, failed to shift enough air, and eventually they were sold to a New Zealand vineyard.

*Frost windmill in an Australian vineyard*

There are also frost protection units that rely on the 'selective inverted sink' principal (SIS), also known as the 'forced cold air displacement systems', which draw in the cold air and blast it upwards into the warm layer creating air circulation. Whilst these appear to be popular in some parts of the world, they are not universally liked and have, so far, not made much of an impact in the UK.[2]

Helicopters are used quite widely in New Zealand (often in conjunction with vineyard heaters and frost mills) and these are presumably effective as they continue to be used there. When I ran Lamberhurst Vineyards, its owner, Kenneth McAlpine, who both owned a helicopter and a had a pilot's licence, was interested in seeing if it worked, but both the Civil Aviation Authority and the local residents thought differently and it was never tried. A helicopter needs to be able to fly slowly over the vineyard, re-passing the affected area every 5-6 minutes, to make sure that the inversion layer remains stirred up. According to one New Zealand helicopter company's website, one helicopter ought to be able to protect 20-ha (50-acres) at a time.

Another technique, known as water aspersion, is widely used in citrus orchards and other soft fruit plantations (and often in blackcurrant fields in the UK), and involves spraying the vines with a fine spray of water as the temperature falls to and beyond freezing. Unlikely a technique as this might sound, where enough water is available (as it must be sprayed all the while the temperature is at or below freezing), it is a fail-safe method. As water freezes, it releases a small amount of heat (known in scientific circles as the latent heat of freezing) and this heat, coupled with the igloo-effect of the layers of ice that form around the canes and buds, protects them from any damage. Once the temperature has risen above freezing, the water sprays can be turned off and the ice slowly melts as the day warms up. This technique can use prodigious amounts of water – 25 mm in a six hour period would not be unusual – and there are systems using micro-sprinklers and intermittent water application in order to save water. If water aspersion system is used, it is important that enough water is available to keep the sprays running for the maximum number of days and the maximum depth of frost that is likely to occur and it is no good running out of water in the last few hours of the last day of frost. It is also essential to make sure that the soil does not become waterlogged and poorly drained soils may well suffer in this respect. There is a risk of breakage to the trelliswork as the ice formed can be very substantial and if this type of frost protection is to be used, the design and construction of the trelliswork will have to take account of this. However, it is generally agreed that where enough water is available, the aspersion system will provide guaranteed protection against frost. The costs of installing an overhead irrigation system will not be small and a considerable volume of water will have to be available prior to the frost period. A vineyard using this system might need to have at least 2.5 million litres of water per hectare of vines in store at the start of the frost period, unless it was possible to top up the water source in between frost events. However, with appropriate control systems, the system is automatic and does not require manpower on hand to operate it.

In the 1980s there was quite a large (4.15-ha, 10.25-acres) GDC vineyard at Headcorn in Kent, owned by the decidedly eccentric Major Grant, whose main business was growing potted chrysanthemums (pot-mums as they

are known) and alstroemerias (a type of South American lily) under around 3.2-ha (8-acres) of glass. In order to provide the greenhouses with water, there was a large lagoon, filled with water from the nearby river Teise. The Grant's abstraction licence allowed them to keep pumping out of the river until the end of May, so an overhead irrigation system was installed in the vineyard. At the time I was their winemaker and in 1988, when everyone else in Kent was hit by an extremely hard frost, their vineyard was protected by their frost irrigation system and yielded a huge crop. I recall that the icicles formed fell from the high wires of the GDC, about 1.80 m from the ground, right down to ground level and almost succeeded in bringing the trelliswork down with them. I also recall that the site, on heavy Wealden clay, had been land-drained at 5 m spacings (the normal spacing for vines is 10 m) as otherwise the huge amount of water used would never have drained away. Such was the frequency of the drainage runs that they all had to be marked out on the surface before any vineyard posts could be installed as Grant was worried that otherwise the pipes would be perforated.

*Frost protection with water aspersion*

Using covers of some sort, netting or shade material, to place over the vines during a frost event, may well be a practical method of avoiding some frost damage, although on its own it is unlikely to prevent damage in the event of a really hard frost, say below -4°C. To erect netting so that it can be made secure – problems with wind damage are always possible with any netting or similar product attached to vineyard trelliswork – and so that it can be raised and lowered so that normal vineyard operations can take place (e.g. spraying) requires both considerable capital investment, plus manpower inputs. And, when all is said and done, it can only be part of the solution and some other technique will also be required. See *Chapter 15: Protected vinegrowing* for more details about covering vines.

## Harvest frost

Although in many years the UK grape harvest is over by the end of the third week of October, there have been occasions both in the past and in more recent years when autumn frosts have damaged grapes. In some years, a light frost, perhaps around -1°C to -2°C, will do nothing more than singe the top of the canopy and perhaps cause some of the older leaves to fall off, thus exposing the fruit and make it easier to harvest. In years when temperatures have fallen further – down to around -4°C or lower – damage has been done to grapes although generally only the less ripe ones as grapes with a high sugar content freeze at lower temperatures than those with lower sugar content. In many cases this is a good indicator of which bunches are fully ripe, making picking easier. However, if grapes are frozen, then they must be picked immediately and wine made from them may well acquire a 'frost tone' on the palate which will need work in the winery to remove.

As to whether frost prevention measures can be used at harvest time is another matter. Most growers are too tied up with thinking about picking dates and picking arrangements to start putting out and lighting frost candles. Much easier to keep an eye on the weather and hope to harvest before a damaging frost arrives, picking earlier than planned if necessary. I guess if growers had static systems that could be turned on and off at will, they might be able to use them, but at present, this is not the case.

## Frost insurance

At one time, frost insurance was available to top and soft fruit growers in the UK (as well as insurance against hail) but this does not appear to be available any more. In some European countries, both frost and hail insurance are available.

**Note:** The UN Food and Agriculture Organisation (FAO) has produced a huge work on the subject called: *Frost protection; fundamentals, practice and economics*. It can be downloaded from:
www.fao.org/docrep/008/y7223e/y7223e00.htm

---

1 I acknowledge the paper: *Practical considerations for reducing frost damage in vineyards* by Trought, Howell and Cherry (New Zealand Winegrowers 1999) in helping me write this chapter. This document is available from www.englishwine.com/wgigb.htm.

2 www.frostprotection.com, www.frostsolutions.com and www.agrofrost.eu for full details.

# Chapter 14
# Weed control

## Introduction

The adequate control of weeds – which includes weed species, grasses and any other unwanted plant – in the 600-750 mm strip directly beneath the vines, is one of the major tasks in the vineyard. For the 'vineyard virgin', a grower completely new to the myriad of tasks that face him or her as soon as the vines are planted, it poses one of the greatest challenges. Such is the importance of weed control that it warrants a separate chapter to itself.

*There are vines in there somewhere!*

Without good weed control in new vineyards, vines will soon become choked and smothered and the weeds will compete for both nutrients and water to the detriment of the vine's root and shoot growth. In established vines, weeds will also compete for water and nutrients, will interfere with the crop if allowed to grow too tall and will make the disease situation worse by creating a damp and humid atmosphere directly beneath the fruit. Keeping the soil weed-free beneath the vines will also help raise the soil temperature, leading to an earlier budburst and better

cytokinin production, the all-important element in getting good yields. In *The Grapevine* (p.37), the authors state: 'it appears that 'warm' soils are just as important in cool maritime climates as in cool continental climates – in the latter, an early start of the growth cycle is desirable, whereas in the former [cool maritime climates, i.e. the UK], warm soils are needed to offset the slow rise of air temperature during the spring in order to increase cytokinin production. Warmer soils will usually have more root growth and potentially more cytokinin production'.

There are in reality only three practical methods of keeping the undervine area free of weeds: herbicides, cultivations and mulching. Other techniques such as flaming the weeds or grazing them with animals (short-legged sheep, large rodents?) may have their places in certain situations and at certain times of the year, but they do not in themselves constitute a year-round solution to the problem. An additional technique to control weeds in the undervine area, that of the use of another plant species to suppress weeds, does not, to my way of thinking, offer a realistic solution to the problem in UK vineyards. The competition from the other plant species is just too great and is to the detriment of the vine's development and long-term well-being. In warmer regions where weed growth is slower (or even non-existent) in the summer and vines are irrigated, undervine weed suppression with another species might be possible, but it is certainly not a widely used technique. In organic and biodynamic vineyards, where of course chemical means of weed control are not permitted, some of these less commonly seen techniques might well have their place. However, whether organic or biodynamic, vines will still be stressed if weed competition becomes too great.

## Herbicides

Herbicide spraying is a widely used and long-established method of controlling weeds in crops of all sorts, both in the UK and world-wide, and with the right materials, right mode of application and good timing, it is a safe and effective method of weed control. To my way of thinking there is a lot of nonsense written about the dangers of using herbicides in vineyards and whilst I fully understand the wish, surely shared by all growers, not to 'poison' the soil by using unnecessary chemicals, the fact of the matter is that every chemical used has been through a testing procedure for safety and as long as the materials are used correctly, then there ought not to be a problem. I also have a real issue with those who are fully signed up to the organic and biodynamic route who believe that any use of herbicides is wrong on the grounds that the soil is being irretrievably damaged and I cannot quite get my head around this view.

If the herbicides are confined to the immediate area beneath the vines in a strip of say 600 mm wide, then the volume of soil that the herbicide impacts upon per hectare in a vineyard planted at 2.00 m row width and assuming that herbicides penetrate to a depth of 75 mm, is 5,000 m x 0.6 m x 0.075 m which equals 225 $m^3$ of soil per hectare. Given that a vine will root let's say to 2.00 m (and it has of course unlimited access to much deeper regions) and the roots can spread where they want in the vineyard, then the volume of soil the vines have to root in per hectare is 100 m x 100 m x 2.00 m which equals 20,000 $m^3$ or a volume 89 times greater than the volume 'occupied' by the herbicide. Given also that the soil is regularly watered by rain, that other plants will also absorb any herbicides, and that almost most permitted herbicides break down upon contact with soil or over a relatively short period of time (although there is evidence that Diquat persists in the soil, and should therefore be used with caution), then I find it illogical that, if correctly and sensitively used, any harm will come to either the vines, the soil or the environment by using herbicides. However, I digress.

The first requirement for successful weed control using herbicides is to have the right equipment. You will need a dedicated weed sprayer with tank, pump and spray booms of the right width (or adjustable) and with appropriate nozzles for the area you want to cover. Do not attempt to use the same tank for both pesticide and herbicide spraying. A weed sprayer would normally fit behind the tractor and be mounted on the three-point linkage, although if you have access to a quad-bike or similar, it is worth looking at weed sprayers mounted on these. Nozzles for strip spraying are best mid-mounted so that they can be seen without having to keep looking behind. Most weed sprayers will have nozzles fitted to both sides so that two strips can be sprayed at once, but with each nozzle independently switched on and off so that single-side operation is possible. A tank of 250 litres will give you sufficient material to spray 1-ha (2.5-acres) of land, so if you are spraying a 600 mm wide strip in a 2.00 m wide rowed vineyard, this will give you enough liquid to spray 3.33-ha (8.2-acres) of vineyard. The exact rate of liquid applied per hectare will depend on several factors – the herbicide used, type of nozzle, type of weed to be sprayed, timing of application – so it is difficult to be too specific about the exact size of tank required, but 200-300 litres is typical. There are also a number of herbicide spray systems which use low-volume technology including CDA (controlled droplet application) and firms such as Micron Group, with their 'Undavina' range, are worth looking at.[1] With their low pressure tyres they can get on the land when a tractor might not and can be very useful in vineyards. For spot-treating weeds and for places where

you cannot get a tractor, a decent hand-powered 20 litre knapsack weed sprayer will also be required. You will require different nozzles for different spray widths, plus, if you intend to strip-spray or spot-treat near young vines, a spray hood.

If the vines are correctly protected, the ground around them can be sprayed as soon as they are planted and whilst it is important to be nervous about harming the vines, if the job is done with the right equipment and herbicide, the lack of weeds will benefit the establishment of the vines hugely. My preferred method of weed control in young  vines is for each vine to be protected with a 600 mm high x 125 mm diameter spray-guard (see left) which has a ventilated top section, but is closed at the bottom to allow for careful spraying of the ground around the vines. Yes, some weeds will grow up the inside of the spray-guard, but these can be removed when the vines are shoot-singled and side-shooted as they are large enough to get a hand down inside. At first pruning, depending on how the vine has grown and what your policy is about first year pruning, the guard can either be left *in situ* or lifted up over the planting stake which should be attached with a removable clip.

My advice is to get a residual (pre-emergent) herbicide on as soon as the soil has settled after planting and before any seedlings start to appear and then be prepared to apply a further one or two sprays using a relatively benign contact material (i.e. not a translocated herbicide) during the first year. Then, after leaf-fall, review the situation and maybe put on a pre-winter spray. Next spring, spot-treat any clumps of nettles (which typically start growing fairly early in the year) and then get a residual on before any weeds start growing and aim to put a contact spray on once the first flush of thistles are no more than 100-150 mm high. Let them get higher than that and it is too late. Once you follow a regime like this, weed control becomes easier and simpler as less weed seeds are present and perennial weeds get dealt with. Of course there will always be problem patches of ground and weed species which may become resistant to the herbicide you are using. In which case you need to spot treat and probably change the herbicide you are using or increase the rate for a spray or two.

Whilst you must consult your chemical supplier about the choice of herbicide, I have used both residual (also called pre-emergent) and contact herbicides on newly planted vines without any damage being done. The use of translocated (i.e. systemic) herbicides in young vineyards is probably best avoided unless you are an experienced operator, conditions are ideal and your vines are fully shielded with spray guards. Different materials will be appropriate at different times of the year and will depend on the weeds to be controlled. In established vineyards, where the trunks are hardened and woody and there are no shoots or leaves at ground level, you can use a much wider range of materials than in young vineyards.

For effective herbicide spraying you need the right weather conditions without too much breeze and dry weather after spraying. Rainfastness times will differ for different products with as little as ten minutes drying time required for some contact herbicides (Diquat) but six hours required for many systemic herbicides (Glyphosate and Glufosinate-ammonium). Residual herbicides work by sinking into the top layer of the soil and locking into it so that when seedlings start germinating, they are killed as their roots come into contact with the herbicide. For this the soil needs to be damp, so a period of gentle rain after application will do no harm. In dry years residual herbicides sometimes fail to work satisfactorily as they haven't been 'watered in' sufficiently after application.

The question of timing, however, is THE most important aspect of weed control. The first thing to realise is that weeds have their own timetable and will not work to yours. It matters not to them that it is too wet to get on to the vineyard, that it is too windy to go weed spraying and that it will be raining for the next week – in fact the weeds <u>know</u> this and will use it to their advantage to outwit you. For effective weed spraying you have to keep your eyes firmly on what is happening on the ground and be prepared to get out the sprayer at a moment's notice. Once the weeds get away, get too tall and too numerous to get a decent cover of spray on to them, then the battle is lost. Of course this is a difficult task. Some weeds arrive early, others arrive late and some appear at all times. Using a residual at least gets you a head start as a proportion of the weeds will be controlled, leaving only the more perennial weeds that do not come from seeds, but from roots, thistle being a prime example.

Once the majority of the vines have formed a trunk which can take herbicides – and with good luck this will be at the end of year two – the spray guards can come off all those vines that have formed trunks and weed spraying can take place with less concern about harm to vines. Some herbicides are time-limited – Kerb Flo, a useful residual can only be used between 1 October and 31 January for instance – and it may be necessary to apply at least two applications of herbicide in the first part of the year (up to flowering) and then a third 'maintenance' application after *véraison*. A fourth 'clean up' application after harvest is not unknown. Each vineyard will be different and indeed each year will be different. In dry years, weeds tend to grow less for obvious reasons; in wet years, residuals may get washed out of the soil and be less effective and with good soil moisture levels, weed seeds may germinate more freely. Either way, the battle against weeds is one that requires constant vigilance. Herbicides may sound like a lot of work to the novice grower, but with the right equipment, the correct materials and by spraying at the right time for the weeds to be controlled, I am sure that they are a more certain and more effective way of controlling weeds than any other.

## Cultivations

The control of weeds in vineyards by cultivating, both under the vines and in the middle of the rows, is very common in Europe and also increasingly in New World regions. This is partly due to tradition and also because in many instances, one grower's vineyard is very often right next door to another's, so there is a strong disincentive to use herbicides that might drift and cause damage to a neighbour's vines. In regions warmer than the UK's and where there is often a shortage of summer rainfall, cultivating between the rows, rather than allowing weeds and grasses to establish and use up moisture, is seen as a way of conserving moisture. The practice of cultivating is therefore part and parcel of managing a vineyard and extending it to cultivating beneath the vines is second nature. In the UK it has not been traditional to cultivate either under the vines or in the middle of the rows, mainly because vineyard owners have tended to follow the established practices of most top and soft-fruit growers for whom herbicides are the norm. However, the practice is becoming more common in UK vineyards, although I suspect it will be some time (if ever) before it becomes the 'standard' system of weed control.

Almost all under-vine cultivators (and also under-vine mowers) work in a similar way and have a sensor arm which detects the presence of a stake or a vine and activates a hydraulic ram which swings the cultivator mechanism away from the vine and then returns it after the vine has been passed by. This leads to two problems. One is that unless the vine is protected by planting stakes placed either side of the vine (or only on one side if you can be sure to drive down the row in the same direction each time), the sensor arm will hit the vine on the trunk at about the same place each time the weeder is used. There are fears, especially with vines which are newly planted and until their stems have grown and hardened off, which might well be in year three or four, that this regular knocking might result in long term damage and may well be a contributory factor in TDs. As has already been mentioned in *Chapter 9: Trellising systems – construction* in the section on *Individual planting stakes,* the use of a stake such as a *tuteur trombone* would provide protection to a young vine against the damage that might be caused by the arm of an automatic weeder. Using individual rabbit guards around each vine might also help in this respect (although I am generally against their use) but you would have to make sure that the guard was both well staked and firmly attached to the stake.

The other seemingly unavoidable problem is that there is always a small mound of soil around the vine which the cultivator cannot reach and which, if it is piled up against the graft of the vine, will lead to roots growing out from above the graft. Quite why this seems to be more of a problem in UK vineyards than overseas is interesting and I suspect that it is because our soils are typically wetter in the summer than in drier regions and tend not to crumble and fall away from around the trunk quite so readily. The only way to avoid the scion root problem is to go through the whole vineyard on a regular basis, perhaps every two years, and manually remove any soil that has built up with a hoe. If scion roots are left to grow and establish, then the vine will become susceptible to *Phylloxera* and the benefits of the rootstock will slowly ebb away.

*Automatic weeder hoe*

There are a wide variety of different types and modes of under-vine cultivator available for use in vineyards. Some have fixed blades and no moving parts, others have powered rotary cultivators that work in the horizontal and yet others with cultivator blades that work in the vertical. However, they all seem to have difficulty in the UK's relatively mild climate and in our often damp soils where weed growth happens for much of the year and as I have pointed out above, the soil doesn't shatter and crumble away as it is turned or moved by the cultivator. Some growers report that it is necessary to have two cultivators, each with a different mode of action so that the soil beneath the vine gets attacked in a different way each time. With a single-sided cultivator costing between £5,000 and £15,000, investing in two makes this an expensive system of weed control.

Whilst mechanical under-vine cultivation might be seen as a more ecological way of managing weeds in vineyards, the amount of tractor time, and therefore fuel used, can mount up. Using under-vine cultivators requires a steady hand and at least to begin with, quite a slow speed. With a single-sided machine (meaning that each row requires two passes) you would be unlikely to travel faster than 3 km-hr which means three to four hours per hectare for a 2.00 m wide rowed vineyard. Given that you would probably need to cultivate five to six times during growing season, then this becomes an expensive operation, especially when you add on to that the biennial scion root clearing, plus the wear and tear of blades on the machine.

Having said that under-vine cultivators are difficult to use in young vineyards, what is perhaps more difficult is to start using them in vineyards where weeds have been controlled with herbicides for a few years. Soils here tend to be quite hard and whilst perhaps not compacted, take a lot of work with a cultivator to get them to move and crumble and in addition, there are bound to be weeds and grasses that have put down established roots which add to the problem. If I was determined to use an under-vine cultivator, I would use herbicides for the first three years and then, with the soil beneath the vines as clean as

possible, start with a cultivator that had a powered blade. I think that a static-bladed cultivator would merely bounce along the compacted soil.

However, if you can manage to get to grips with cultivating beneath your vines, and maintaining a weed-free strip, the benefits of earlier soil warming, as was pointed out at the start of this chapter, are probably worth having.

## Mulching

When I studied at Geisenheim in 1976-7, before I planted my first vineyard at Tenterden in Kent (now Chapel Down), I saw the technique of mulching with black plastic 'film' and decided that this would be the technique I would use. The vineyards which Kenneth McAlpine had recently planted at Lamberhurst had also used plastic mulch, so I felt safe that the technique would work. A plastic-laying machine was found and adapted – it had been built to lay 2.0 m wide mulch for strawberry beds – and 750 mm black plastic film sourced and purchased. Planting commenced, by hand, on Easter Monday, 11 April 1977, and after every day's planting, I got on my tractor and, with the help of someone who generally had to sit on the back of the plastic layer and guide the wayward film as it unpeeled off the roll, laid it over the planted vines. I clearly remember the first few attempts at laying the plastic – the unburied edges, the plastic laid too tightly so that it broke the grafts – but after a few attempts we worked out how deep to plant the vines and how tightly to lay the plastic. With a few hiccups, we successfully managed to plant 9,300 vines and covered them with almost 12 km (7.5 miles) of film.

As far as weed control went, the black plastic worked exceptionally well. The vines were not hampered by any weed growth, save the few weeds that sprouted in the same hole that the vine was planted in and in the holes which the crows made as they stomped up and down on the plastic looking for food. The soil beneath the film was always moist and undoubtedly warmer that the uncovered soil as the black film sucked up the heat. The only problem was the edges where the film was buried – of the 750 mm wide film, around half was exposed and half buried – and given that I was cultivating the centres of the rows, there was a 300 mm strip on either side of the plastic that had to be kept weed-free with herbicides (which is about the same amount as would be sprayed if you were just using herbicides).

What I didn't know at the time was that the film I had naïvely ordered from a local supplier had not been made to 'plastic mulch standard' – I was unaware at the time that there was such a standard – and it only had 1.5 per cent of carbon black, the additive which both colours the film and prevents degradation by ultra-violet light. The consequence was that after less than a year, the mulch started to deteriorate and after numerous letters to the supplier, the manufacturer and to both ICI and British Cellophane, the leading manufacturers of plastic film in the UK at the time, plus tests of the film that had been supplied and used, it was agreed that the film was not suitable for long-term outdoor use. The suppliers eventually accepted that whilst I had told them what the film was for, they had not told the manufacturers this, the consequence being the low level of carbon black. I forget now whether we received any financial compensation or not, but the whole experience was an eye-opener for me and I quickly learnt that you need to spell everything out, preferably in writing, when ordering products whose failure might have long-term consequences and costs!

The result of the slow deterioration of the film was that some of the soil around the vines was covered and remained weed-free, but in some places the film disintegrated into ribbons and the weeds soon poked through, especially in areas where the film's colour bleached out and light could get underneath. This made weed control a haphazard affair and after a further twelve months we decided that the plastic had to come up. This was fine, even if hard, dirty work, where the film was exposed, but where it was buried – and completely undamaged and sitting comfortably beneath a solid covering of soil, weeds and grass – the plastic proved impossible to move. We therefore just cut it along the edge and left it there where it remained for many years and I expect you could probably still find remnants of the wayward film today if you looked.

For my next vineyard, three years later, I ordered film directly from British Cellophane and specified 4.5 per cent of carbon black and with a thickness of 125 μm rather than the 80 μm of the earlier product. For this vineyard we had decided to use ungrafted, unrooted cuttings from our 1977 planted Seyval blanc and, after laying the mulch, merely stuck the lengths of cane, dipped on the end with hormone rooting powder, through the plastic and waited for them to root. This they did with a great degree of success and this became one of our best – and certainly our cheapest – vineyard. This vineyard has now been grubbed, but there are definitely traces of this film in the vineyard even after thirty-five years!

Today, however, unless there were exceptional circumstances, I wouldn't recommend using plastic film for mulching. There are various reasons. Apart from the cost of buying and laying the film, plus the cost of removing and disposing of it once it starts to deteriorate, there is the problem of keeping the buried edges free of weeds. To do this you end up with having to spray around 300-350 mm on either side of the film (as I have pointed out above, this is about the same amount as you would spray around the vines without mulch). I also am worried that having such a moist, warm, weed-free environment around the vines makes them lazy and doesn't force them to root deeply in search of moisture and nutrients, something I feel the vine should be encouraged to do at all costs. You might also find that vine weevils, snails and slugs are also attracted to the continually moist soil beneath the mulch, all of which can damage the tender shoots and leaves of a young vine.

I have seen growers use Mypex, a woven weed-suppressant which, although much more expensive than plastic film, is much stronger and can withstand the occasional tractor wheel and heavy foot traffic, and comes with a five-year guarantee. This is a permeable product and as such lets the soil breathe, but I am not sure it offers many other benefits and you still have the 'edge' problem

to resolve as the weeds and grasses very soon encroach and root through the fabric.

Organic and biodynamic vineyard owners face a considerable challenge in the area of weed control and one of the ways to tackle weeds is with mulches. Whilst the problem of how to keep the buried edges of the plastic film or Mypex-type fabric clear of weeds is even greater in the absence of herbicides, if this can be solved – hand mowing and strimming works on small areas – then this does answer the problem in the early years when mechanical methods of weed control cannot safely be used or in situations where tractor-mounted mechanical weeders are inappropriate, i.e. in small vineyards where the cost cannot be warranted.

*Black polythene mulch*

Mulching with loose materials, such as compost or wood chippings (or a combination of both) can be effective in controlling the weeds, although there are drawbacks. On anything other than a small scale, you need a dedicated side-delivery spreader which can take sufficient material to cover a reasonable length of vineyard row with each filling. These can cost between £12,000 and £20,000 so not for the smaller vineyard owner. They can also be hired (at around £200 per day for spreader only, no operator), but getting one that can fit down narrow rows and which can turn in the average vineyard headland can be a challenge. You also need quite a large area of hard-standing which can be reached by road-going tipper lorry (that is unless you are close enough to the source of the mulch material to have it delivered by tractor and trailer) and ideally some machinery there at the time of delivery to heap up the compost as it arrives. Otherwise, the area you need to store the material before starting to spread it will be huge. For effective weed control, enough material needs to be applied to fully cover the soil to a depth of at least 75 mm, although the accuracy with which this can be judged is difficult and you need to do a test row or two to get the rate of delivery correct for your needs. Spread any less thickly than this and the weeds and grasses will start to poke through quite quickly and, especially at the edges (assuming you have grassed-down alleyways), the cover will deteriorate.

Compost is readily available from waste sites that process green waste and a lot of it is PAS 100 compost meaning it has been produced to BSI PAS 100 specification. This covers every aspect of the compost's production and content, including the amount of 'non-organic' material such as glass, stone and plastic that is allowed in it. There will be some evidence of plastic in it, particularly bits of the blue plastic bags that every corner shop uses, plus bottle tops and other hard plastics that people include in the 'green' waste that they put out for the dustmen, but these should be to a minimum. If you are considering buying non-PAS 100 compost, make sure you know what you are getting. The PAS 100 specification also includes the amount of food waste (including meat waste) that is allowed, plus the amount of nutrients that are contained in it. WRAP (Waste & Resources Action Programme) state that 1 tonne of PAS 100 contains around 8.1 kg of nitrogen (as N), 3.3 kg of phosphate (as $P_2O_5$), 6.6 kg of potassium (as $K_2O$), 2 kg of magnesium (as Mg) and 1 kg of sulphur (as S) so that these need to be taken into calculation when considering applying other fertilisers, especially if you are in a NVZ. Although the nitrogen is the largest nutrient in the compost, because it is contained in a form which requires time to break down, it is released slowly. The same goes for the other nutrients. Also note that PAS 100 has a slight neutralising effect upon the soil (about 10 per cent as effective as limestone), so pH levels will be raised, especially in the area immediately below the mulch. If you are using woodchip it ideally needs to be made from hardwood, not pine, and the chips need to be fairly coarse, otherwise they also break down too quickly.

As for the cost of using loose mulch, this very much depends on such factors as the cost of delivery of the material, whether you have your own spreader, the width and thickness to which you spread it and the time interval between applications. PAS 100 compost is almost free at the point of production, but the haulage can be expensive, depending on how close you are to your nearest plant (WRAP publish a list of producers). Road-going tipper lorries, especially large 8-wheelers, will not usually go very far off a metalled road and will only tip on to good firm ground. If you happen to be within tractor and trailer distance of a compost plant then you win twice: you can pick the compost up and transport it cheaply and can probably get it very close to the point of use. To get PAS 100 compost to one Kent vineyard cost around £200 per 20 tonne load using a tipper lorry which was able to get to good hardstanding near to the vineyard site where it could unload. Twenty loads were delivered (around 400 tonnes) and spread, using a professional contractor who came to the site with both spreader, loading machine and drivers. The compost was spread in a strip about 600 mm wide and to a depth of 75-100 mm in the centre of the strip and the 400 tonnes covered 6,900 running metres. The cost of the machinery was £780 (13 hours at £60 per hour), plus £160 haulage each way to and from the site, a grand total of £1,100. The total cost of this (2009 prices) was £5,000 or 72 p per metre or 87 p per vine planted at 1.20 m apart. PAS 100 contains quite a lot of small material (25 per cent less than 10 mm in size) so consolidates and breaks down and is absorbed by the ground relatively quickly. In the above example it was really used as a soil conditioner and

vine nutrient rather than as a pure weed suppressant and required some additional herbicide treatment in the second year. However, the spreading rates and costs are probably quite accurate for coarser material which would break down more slowly.

*Side-delivery compost spreader*

For woodchip, the costs are slightly higher, although the material used was organic. On a vineyard near Guildford, a large articulated lorry load of around 90 $m^3$ of organic hardwood woodchip cost around £1,150 per load delivered and one load covered around 2,000 running metres. It took two people around three days to spread woodchip on 2 ha (5-acres) of vines planted at 2.00 row width (so 5,000 running m-ha) which means that the whole job cost around £4,000-ha (£1,619-acre) which equates to 80 p per metre or almost £1 per vine at 1.20 m. This includes the cost of the material, unloading it and stockpiling it, the hire of the spreader and spreading it. In this example, as the woodchip started to weather and break down, particularly in areas where there was a heavy weed infestation, some weeds grew through and had to be pulled by hand before the situation was bad enough to warrant a second application of material. Once the weed situation came under control, an application of a fresh layer of material was needed around every two years, although the sides of the mulch needed an annual weeding.

In newly-planted vineyards, the use of loose mulch such as PAS 100 compost, is probably as good a way as any of making sure that the vines establish well. Not only are weeds suppressed without the use of herbicides, but the vines will get both extra humus and a small amount of slow release nitrogen to help them develop.

With loose mulches, there is the same problem of scion roots as you get with under-vine cultivators and therefore from time to time (every two years perhaps) every vine where the graft is not visible must be checked for scion roots and, if found, they must be removed. Planting the vines slightly higher out of the ground than normal, say with the graft 75-100 mm above the ground level, would probably prevent this happening. Using high-graft vines certainly would.

Other mulch materials such as spent mushroom compost or hop waste might work just as well, but given that most of the cost is in the transport and spreading, it doesn't really pay to use materials that are second-best. In Germany and France, I have seen straw used, but it tends to blow away if it doesn't get well soaked as soon as its spread – probably less of a problem in the UK than warmer regions – but it also takes a long time to settle down and form a weed-suppressing mulch. Unless you are very lucky, there are usually quite a few weeds, plus their seeds, in the straw, which have a habit of germinating. Straw will also often attract mice which can damage the shoots of newly planted vines, and ring the bark on the trunks of more established ones. It is also a fire hazard. However, in low density, wide-rowed vineyards, straw mulch might work very well and would certainly be cheaper than compost. Side-spreaders which take large round bales are often used on strawberry beds and with some adaptation could probably be made to work in vineyards.

*PAS 100 compost strip spread below vines*

I have also considered the 'mow-and-throw' system much used in low-cost regions of Australia where a grass crop is encouraged to grow in the middle of the rows in the spring and then mown and the cut grass thrown (by the mowing machine) under the vines as a mulch. Whether this would work completely in the UK's damp summer climate is open to question and there would bound to be some growth of weeds under the vines. However, given that the grass keeps on growing in most summers (unlike in Australia) constant toppings up of the mulch would help. With systems such as GDC and Blondin, where some weed growth below the vines can be tolerated, this system could be considered. You would need a mowing machine however, that was suitable and really did lay the cut grass in a tight strip beneath the vines. There are also swing-arm under-vine mowers, but these suffer from the same problem as under-vine cultivators (the propensity of the activator arm to strike the vine on the trunk at the same point each time) and are not to be recommended in vines.

Whatever loose organic mulches are used, they will in time break down and be taken into the soil by worms and other organisms which will raise both the levels of organic matter in the soil, as well as the numbers of worms – both admirable things in themselves. However, loose mulch covering the soil around the vines will tend to keep the soil wetter and therefore cooler, and this is a factor that ought to be considered. As has been pointed out at the start of this chapter, the warmer the soil, the earlier the budburst and the greater the production of cytokinins.

## Weed control – summary

Whatever system of weed control you decide to use in your vineyard, there are only two requirements: it has to work and work first time. I have so often seen vineyards in their first season completely swamped by weeds which have got beyond the point of spraying and where manual weed pulling and hoeing, or mowing and hand strimming, have had to be used in order to get the weeds down to a point where they can be tackled with herbicides. My preferred route is the herbicide one, but this is only my personal preference and with the right equipment and know-how, one of the other methods can be made to work, although none are cheaper or easier alternatives.

1 www.micron.co.uk/viticulture/undavinas

# Chapter 15
# Protected vinegrowing

## Introduction

Plants have been grown under protection of one sort or another since at least Roman times. Pliny wrote about the use of 'muscovy-glass' (his name for mica) to ripen both fruit and vegetables in the first century AD and in the 1200s the Vatican had what we today would call 'cloches' made from small glass panels mounted in metal frames, similar to stained glass windows. Although fairly primitive, the first true greenhouses appeared in France and the Netherlands in the 1500s and were soon being tried in the UK. The first large heated greenhouses and conservatories appeared in the UK in the early 1600s and became common in the gardens of royalty, the nobility and the well-to-do by 1630. When the first vines were grown in UK greenhouses is not known for certain, but by the mid-1600s table grapes were being grown and are mentioned in several books. Although John Rose, gardener to King Charles II, who wrote *The English Vineyard Vindicated* in 1672, doesn't mention growing vines other than in the open air, I feel sure that he would have had vines in his greenhouses. He was after all the man who had, in 1671, presented the King with the first pineapple (pictured below) to be grown in Great Britain and therefore had great experience of this method of growing fruit.

Over the next century or so, the growing of vines under glass became something of a craze and dozens of

different varieties were being grown and even new ones developed in the UK. In 1769, a Black Hamburg vine was planted at Hampton Court under the direction of Lancelot 'Capability' Brown with a cutting taken from a vine at Valentines Manor, Ilford, Essex which had been planted in 1758. The Hampton Court vine was, until an even older vine was discovered at Maribor in Slovenia, the world's oldest and today has a girth of 4 m (13-feet) and the longest cordon is 36.5 m (120-feet) long. It often produces over 300-kg of fruit. The Victorian era was undoubtedly the high-point of protected grapegrowing in the UK and dozens of books were written about how to do it. The best known was written by Archibald Barron, Superintendent of the RHS Gardens at Chiswick, whose *Vines and Vine Culture* first appeared in 1883 and ran to five editions, the last being updated by his widow in 1912. In the final edition there was a chapter on *Commercial Grape Culture, or the Growing of Grapes for the Market*, in which Barron writes about the extraordinary increase in the cultivation of 'grapes for sale or market purposes over the past few years'. He says that the popularity of grapes is due to the public's sudden demand for tomatoes, which were then becoming very popular. Growers were able to erect glasshouses, plant them with vines and during the first four or five years while the vine was making wood and not producing fruit, crop the glasshouse with tomatoes. Once the vines were established and fruiting, tomato growing would stop.

Barron says that the centres of table grape production were the Channel Islands, Hertfordshire, Worthing, Finchley and Galashiels in Scotland and that: 'several of the Vineyards or Grape-growing establishments are of a leviathan character'. One grower, Rochfords at Cheshunt in Hertfordshire, had over 50-acres (20-ha) of glass in total, with half of it devoted to vines and expected to send between 300 and 400-tons of grapes annually to Covent Garden. At 2 shillings a pound, this equated to a return of £224 an acre – worth around £38,540-ha (£15,600-acre) at today's values. Grapes were also sent by *fast steamer* to New York and arrived about ten days after cutting in good condition. Sadly, many of these enterprises ended during the First World War when both manpower and fuel became short and expensive, although a few growers in Worthing did keep their greenhouses producing grapes until the 1930s. The chapter in Barron ends with a paragraph on *Grape Growing in Belgium and France* and reports on similar vine and tomato establishments to those found in England that sent large quantities to the markets. It ends by saying that the French had put a tax of five francs a kilo on non-French grapes coming on to the Paris markets, the result of which was that the Belgians sent all theirs to the English markets.

Vines in British greenhouses also had their darker side. It was in 1831 or 1832 that Powdery Mildew was first seen in a greenhouse in Margate, Kent and named *Oidium Tuckerii* after Mr Tucker, gardener to Mr John Slater, whose greenhouse and vine it was. The first time *Phylloxera* was seen in Europe was in another greenhouse, this time in Hammersmith, London in 1863, when a vine appeared to be suffering a mystery attack. Some damaged leaves were sent to Professor John Westwood, the *Gardener's Chronicle's* 'Insect Referee'. He reported back that he could come to no firm conclusion about the insect 'for want of a knowledge of a male' [sic]. This lack of a male also baffled the French for several years, they too having discovered it in 1864 on some vines in Pujaut, a village a few kilometres north-west of Avignon, belonging to a wine merchant, Monsieur Borty.

In more modern times, glass cloches were used by two pioneers of twentieth century UK grape growing: Ray Barrington Brock at his Oxted Viticultural Research Station; and Edward Hyams in his garden at Molash, near Canterbury. In 1952 Hyams wrote *Grapes Under Cloches* which drew heavily ('rather too heavily' Brock told me!) on Brock's two published works: *Outdoor Grapes in Cool Climates* (1949) and *More Outdoor Grapes* (1950). Hyams also wrote *The Grape Vine in England* (1949) and edited *Vineyards in England* (1953), a masterly work which consisted of twenty chapters, many written by different specialists (although Hyams himself wrote six of them and Brock, two) covering every conceivable aspect of grape production in the British Isles. It included chapters on the cloche and greenhouse cultivation of vines.

In the era of commercial UK vineyards, several growers have tried growing vines under cover, mostly under polythene-covered, aluminium-framed tunnels. According to Gillian Pearkes in her 1982 book *Vinegrowing in Britain*, Colonel George Nangle 'pioneered tunnel-grown vines in South Devon', although I can find no other information about the Colonel. One of the earliest commercial growers to use tunnels must have been the Sampsons at Loddiswell Vineyard near Kingsbridge, Devon. Reg and his wife Betty (who was a well-known amateur winemaker, wine judge and author of *The Art of Winemaking*) had started a trial plot of vines (outdoors) in 1972 and in 1977 had decided to 'go professional' and they planted 6,000 vines. Following some very wet summers they experimented with polytunnels and found that the vines did well, giving more regular yields and higher sugars. Their wines were well received and they won several medals including the SWVA's 'Best Wine' trophy in 1986 with their 1985 Loddiswell Medium Sweet. According to my 1989 book *The Vineyards of England* they had 'approximately 0.9 acres' (0.36-ha) under plastic. I remember visiting the vineyard one wet summer – we camped near Dartmouth for a hateful week during which it

never stopped raining – and remember seeing the tunnels on a steep hill above the farmyard. They had closed sides, but open ends, which helped with the ventilation as the Sampsons were concerned lest disease take over. The tunnels were quite low and each contained two rows of vines. I don't believe that there was enough room to drive a tractor inside, so if they were sprayed, it was probably by hand with a lance or knapsack sprayer. The Sampsons always put the quality of their wine, which was very good for the time, down to the grapes coming from their tunnels.

Another Devon grower, who has been growing vines under tunnels for many years, is Mark Sharman at Beenleigh Manor near Totnes. The Cabernet Sauvignon and Merlot vines were planted in the late 1970s by Mark's cousin, Marian Ash, who, with her husband and with some help from Gillian Pearkes (who probably supplied the original vines), grew them unprotected until they were established and then covered them. The vines struggled for moisture inside the tunnels, so an irrigation system was installed. The wines produced were, according to Mark 'thin, pale and acidic'. After several years' neglect, Mark bought the vineyard in January 1989 and says he 'managed to produce a small vintage of surprisingly good quality' in that year. Over the years, his wines have won many major awards in the UKVA's competition including the Bernard Theobald trophy for 'Best Red' with the 1990, 1995, 1998 and 1999 wines, the President's Trophy for 'Best Wine' in the small volume section for the 1990, 1995, 1999 and 2001 wines and a Gold Medal for the 2003 vintage – an impressive tally by anyone's standards. I guess the relative lack of success since 2003 coincides with the changes in the UK's climate and the better wines being made (out of doors) from varieties such as Dornfelder, Pinot noir, Regent and Rondo.

On the Isle of Wight, an island well known for its glasshouse industry, Anthony Goddard grew 0.4-ha (1-acre) of Gewürztraminer in polytunnels on the grounds that he loved the wine from this variety (albeit from Alsace) and as he already had 4.13-ha (10.2-acres) of the standard varieties growing in the open and knew all the pitfalls of growing vines in the open, he thought he would cover his bets. From memory, his tunnels were of a very superior type, around 5.50 m (18-feet) wide and high enough for a tractor to be driven through them. They also had sides that could be lifted up to about 1.00 m off the ground to aid ventilation. The cost, as I recall it, for the 0.4-ha (1-acre) of tunnels was somewhere in the region of £10,000, excluding the cost of the vines and the trelliswork. Although the vines grew well, fruited well and were disease free, Goddard admitted himself that the grapes were never very special and didn't do much to enhance his wine. My guess is that it was the wrong variety to grow under cover as its acidity is fairly low to start with and the conditions inside a tunnel, even a tunnel in the UK, were just too warm for it.

In more recent years, Martin Seed at his small vineyard at Worthenbury in Wrexham, North Wales, grew around 0.25-ha (0.60-acres) of Pinot noir, Chardonnay and Sauvignon blanc in small tunnels. He planted the vines between 1991 and 1999 and until around 2005 he grew quite respectable crops of high sugar grapes. 11-14 per cent natural alcohol was regularly achieved and his wines, made at both Tenterden Vineyards (by myself) and at what was then called Valley Vineyards by John Worontschak, won several awards. Because of the northerly position (latitude 53°N) there was always a danger of spring frost, so each row of vines had its own hot water pipe running along it, heated by a gas-fired boiler in one of the tunnels. The vineyard has now been grubbed.

*Worthenbury Vineyard*

## Protected vinegrowing

Using some form of netting or textile cover over your vines to protect them from frost, poor flowering weather and as an aid to ripening, is something that has been considered often in the past. I recall a New Zealand company marketing something called the 'Kerilea Cloche' which was in effect a mini-greenhouse that covered every row of vines.[1] Whilst it undoubtedly worked, the cost of the frames and supports, plus the cost of the covering, plus the cost of putting it on and taking it off at the appropriate times of the growing season, made it far too uneconomical for UK grapegrowers. For other crops – cherries, late season raspberries and other high-value crops – overhead covers are quite widely used. The Vöhringer company, which make Voen covers, state that they cost around €40,000-ha (£16,000-acre) to install and with cherries give a 15 per cent increased crop of much larger cherries which, because cherries are priced according to size, made the crop worth over twice as much and paid for the installation in two years. In vines, the difference might be in having almost no crop to having a good crop and if you say grapes are worth around £1,500-tonne after picking costs, and say you can get an extra 5 tonnes-ha (2 tonnes-acre), an additional income of £7,500-ha (£3,035-acre) per annum might also seem worthwhile. However, this doesn't account for the costs of putting the covers up and down or the cost of replacing the covering. The relatively high cost of these covers is because they require an additional post and wire system to be erected over the plants/trees. In vines however, there is already an existing trelliswork and this is an advantage that can be used.

Recently, Richard Smart has developed, in conjunction with a company called Capatex,[2] a covering made of an 'almost transparent film with special properties for light and UV' which can be attached to the training wires and draped either side of the vines and trap them in an envelope. The film is 400 mm wide and should cover the fruiting zone. It is suggested that the vines are first covered 'from around bud break to late May' which 'could help mitigate a late frost'. The covers can then be rolled up and 'stored' on the wires until they would be replaced over flowering and then from *véraison* to ripening. The capital cost is around £9,000-ha (£3,642-acre) for vineyards planted with a 2.00 m row width, with annual costs for the three moves of £1,200-ha (£486-acre). The film is designed to last for 'three to four years continual exposure' so by using it as outlined above, the film might well last longer. Therefore, assuming that you get five years use, the annual cost is around £3,000-ha (£1,200-acre) which – if it works – might be quite cost effective. An initial report from Richard Smart, based upon covering one 100-metre row of Seyval blanc in 2013, showed a very significant increase in yield (up by a factor of three) with sugar and acid readings about the same as outside uncovered grapes.

Given the difficult harvests of 2011, 2012 and 2013 and the spring frosts that growers have experienced since 2009, I can quite see that some UK growers might consider using one or other of the above systems of protection. If you were starting a new vineyard, where you could allow the space needed for the supports and could make the structure used to carry the overhead covers part of the overall trellising system, then the cost of the 'cherry cover' type of protection could probably be lessened. Once one grower proved that better and larger crops of grapes suitable for winemaking could be achieved on a regular basis, then this type of protected growing might well be taken up by others. It wasn't that long ago in the UK that cherries and strawberries were both outdoor crops. Today, most large-scale commercial growers of these fruits wouldn't dream of it and in fact, many supermarkets will only take cherries and strawberries if they have been grown under cover!

*Cherries growing under full cover in Kent*

---

1 The Kerilea Cloche is today sold by Redpath in New Zealand www.redpath.co.nz

2 www.capatex-agro-textiles.com

# Chapter 16
# Pest and disease control

## Pest and disease control

**Note:**
- The term 'pesticide' covers products used to control all pests, diseases and weeds in the vineyard and immediate surroundings.
- Before buying or using any controlled pesticide, advice should be sought from a BASIS registered advisor.[1]
- All operators are required to have the necessary qualifications and/or supervision before using any controlled products.
- The advice given below relates to pest and disease control on grapes grown in the open air for wine production. Products used on grapes grown under protection (glass or polythene) or for eating may be subject to different rules on dilution and application rates and HIs.
- The storage of pesticides and the disposal of pesticides, pesticide residues and empty containers must be carried out in an approved manner.
- The official UK 'Code of practice for using plant protection products' (PB 11090) can be downloaded from the DEFRA and HSE (Health and Safety Executive) websites or at www.englishwine.com/wgigb.htm.
- The UKVA's *Full & Label Extension Approvals* (known as the 'Green Book') is published annually and lists all approved materials, plus a suggested spray programme which acts as a guideline for growers. It is free to UKVA members, £30 to non-members.

## Introduction

All other things being equal, a mastery of pest and disease control (particularly disease control) is probably the most important skill a UK winegrower can acquire. Why? Because the UK has plenty of rainfall, often during the height of the growing season; because our cool climate fosters vigorous shoot and leaf growth at the expense of fruiting; and our canopies are often shaded – all ideal conditions for the development of fungal diseases. Pests and diseases not only damage and destroy the current crop, they can also damage the future crop by reducing the fruiting potential of the buds for next year. This is one of the reasons why yields in UK vineyards are (a) very variable and (b) relatively low. However, pest and disease control is not only about chemical control. Under what is

termed an Integrated Crop Management (ICM) approach to the problem, vineyard hygiene, vineyard layout, canopy management and under-vine and alleyway management are also part of the mix and these will also be discussed in this chapter.

ICM (and its counterpart Integrated Pest Management – IPM) are terms often used, but which have a myriad of different meanings. DEFRA, on its *Integrated Crop Management* website, offers several meanings, one of which I believe best suits UK vineyard owners. It states that ICM is: 'a management system which employs controlled inputs to achieve sustained profitability with minimum environmental impact, but with sufficient flexibility to meet natural and market challenges economically.' Therefore, whilst a reduction of inputs in the form of pesticides, fertilisers and other carbon-based products (fuel for instance) is a desirable aim and care for the environment and its inhabitants an obvious goal, one has to bear in mind the 'profitability' of the enterprise and the 'market challenges' that confront it. One could have a vineyard in the UK planted entirely with a proven pest and disease resistant variety (Seyval blanc comes to mind) and use mechanical weed control (supplement by hand hoeing when required) and carry out all operations using manual and maybe horse-power, but whether that would be the best way of creating a profitable, sustainable enterprise is open to conjecture.

There is often a reluctance on the part of UK vineyard owners to realise that by planting most varieties of vines in what is a relatively inhospitable climate they have signed up to the task of looking after them and in almost all cases – even when they have chosen to grow their vines organically – looking after them with some form of chemical control. And, if they are keen to safeguard the considerable amount of time, energy and money they have ploughed into their enterprises, they must become good at the one task which can really help them do this, that of adequate pest and disease control. I quite understand the reluctance to spray – it is messy, time consuming and expensive – but in my experience it is one of the major factors between success and failure in growing grapes in the UK.

UK vineyard owners must also be aware of the 'honeymoon period'. Like many marriages, everything in the vineyard can often be hunky-dory for the first year or two (or even three) and when vines are young, root systems are still developing and the amount of wood left at pruning may not be filling the fruiting wire, disease pressures may well be light and crops can be exceptionally clean and ripe and of good quality. However, a few years down the line, problems start. When the vines have got a bigger root system with more access to water and nutrients and you have laid down the full complement of fruiting wood, the canopy can suddenly become crowded and diseases will very quickly start to show. Be prepared for this and be prepared to spray preventatively.

Pests and diseases fall into several distinct categories. There are pests such as rabbits, hares, deer, badgers, foxes, wild boar and any other mammals that take a shine to vines and grapes and these have been dealt with in *Chapter 6: Site planning and preparation* in the section on *Fencing*. Luckily for UK vineyard owners, many of the wide range of insects and mites which, in their various forms, can damage vines and grapes, are absent from our shores – at least for the present – and the very few that ARE found in UK vineyards are discussed. Wasps, snails and slugs are then covered, followed by *Phylloxera*, which is probably the worst pest of all, since attacks are nearly always fatal if vines are grown on their own roots, a practice most commercial growers avoid in regions where *Phylloxera* is endemic. The final pest to be dealt with is birds, not quite a pest in the same sense as the others, since eradication is not a solution, but nevertheless, one that can be extremely costly.

Diseases too, fall into several distinct categories. There are the fungal diseases, of which the three major ones – Powdery Mildew, Downy Mildew and *Botrytis* – are discussed in detail, plus a range of others less commonly seen in UK vineyards, but nonetheless to be guarded against. Finally viruses are covered. Trunk diseases (TDs), some of which have been present in UK vineyards for many decades and others which have appeared more recently and which have been the subject of considerable debate amongst UK vineyard owners, are dealt with in *Chapter 17: Trunk diseases*.

## Vineyard conditions

The job of good pest and disease control – and more so with diseases than pests – starts with getting the right physical conditions in the vineyard. Selecting a low vigour rootstock will, for most varieties, be one important step towards creating an airy and open canopy. Your overall canopy height should be appropriate for your row width so that the fruiting zone gets the maximum amount of light and is not shaded. Your fruiting wire should be at the appropriate height for the row width and kept tensioned so that the vines can be tied down correctly. Your training (catch) wires should be fitted with chains so that moving them up and down is easy and you should consider wire spreaders if you feel that your canopy is too dense and could be improved by opening up.

Pruning must be correctly carried out so that the canes do not overlap and the spur for the replacement cane is below the fruiting wire (assuming a two-cane flat *Guyot* pruning system). Although there is some debate about its contribution to disease control, some growers feel that

burning the prunings, either in the vineyard in a *chariot de feu* or taking them out and burning them on the headland, helps keep the vineyard healthier. In addition, if TDs are of a concern, then painting the pruning wounds may also be helpful. The use of powered secateurs, especially when vines get older and the wood to be cut and removed gets thicker, allows pruners to make the pruning cuts exactly where they want them and helps keep pruning wounds clean and at the right angle. This reduces the chances of TDs entering the vine via wounds and makes wound painting more effective. Undervine management should aim to keep a weed-free strip of around 600-750 mm at all times as allowing weeds and grasses to build up directly beneath the vines will only increase the humidity in the fruit zone. Your alleyways, unless you are growing a green manure crop, should be kept mown short during the growing season, right up until harvest, so that moisture retention is at a minimum and the vineyard floor dries out as quickly as possible.

Two to three weeks after bud burst, if the crowns of your vines are crowded with excess shoots, some shoot thinning should be carried out to open up this area. This will help get air and light on to next year's replacement canes. Canopy management, in the form of deleafing and shoot trimming, is an essential part of disease control and the aim must be to keep the canopy thin, permitting light and air to get on to both the crop and the canes for next year's fruiting and to aid maximum air circulation and spray penetration. An open, airy and light-penetrating canopy is the foundation of good pest and disease control. The advice given in the 2011 Luxembourg study on methods of controlling *Botrytis*, already mentioned in the section in *Chapter 12: Management – cropping years* in the section on *Deleafing*, is worth repeating as I believe it reinforces the rôle of canopy management in disease control: 'Manual leaf removal in the cluster-zone just after bloom [flowering] provided a significant reduction of bunch rot infestation without any input of chemical substances. Subsequently, this treatment can be recommended as an important tool in any bunch rot protection strategy for integrated as well as organic viticulture.'

## Nutrition

The nutrition of your vines, whilst really a secondary consideration, can play a part in the health of your vines if things are not correct. The leaves of your vine are their power-plant and unless they are well looked after, well maintained and running at full speed, the vine will suffer. Apart from lower levels of grape ripeness, stored reserves of carbohydrates will be less and consequently, in the spring and at times of stress (which in the UK, with our cool, wet springs can often occur together), your vines, like humans who are under-nourished and stressed, will be more likely to succumb to diseases. In particular, just because the crop is nearing ripeness and even after picking in years when the harvest is not very late, the vine can still continue to photosynthesise and can produce carbohydrates until the leaves senesce and fall off. The leaves must therefore be kept in good condition so that photosynthesis can continue for as long as possible. Obviously making sure your vines are well balanced with the correct nutrients, both major and minor, will help keep the leaves in perfect working order. As already mentioned in *Chapter 7: Vineyard nutrition*, keeping your vines well supplied with trace elements and spraying with products containing potassium phosphite (such as Nortrace Phyte P-Plus) will help the vine build a natural resistance to diseases.

## Machinery requirements

In *Chapter 10: Machinery and equipment* I said that: 'Your sprayer is the most important tool in the vineyard and will help you win the battle to keep your vines and your crop clean and pest and disease free' and for good measure added: 'Do not try and economise' on your sprayer. Both of those statements are true. Apart from your tractor, which also needs to be reliable and trustworthy, your sprayer is really your insurance against crop loss and must perform on demand. Unless you have a large vineyard, your sprayer will probably only get used for one or two days per fortnight and in dry years, even less than that. In addition, it will be used to carry and spray corrosive chemicals and therefore must be kept clean and well maintained.

*A Drake & Fletcher 'Victair' sprayer – designed over 60 years ago, but still a very effective sprayer*

There are a large number of sprayer types and sprayer manufacturers and the type you buy will depend upon several factors. The size of your vineyard and vineyard layout may well determine whether you have a mounted or trailed sprayer, although your budget may also be part of that decision making process. My advice is that you want to try and cut the non-spraying time of your spraying day down to a minimum and this means keeping the filling time to a minimum. Given that you have a spray tank of water conveniently situated in or near the vineyard – a tank mounted on a stand which can, in a few minutes, deliver under gravity the same amount of water that your

sprayer tank holds – then mixing up materials and filling your sprayer can be kept to the smallest time possible. Therefore, when buying a sprayer, try and get the largest size tank that you can afford and which suits the area of vines you are likely to have to spray.

Mounted sprayers seldom have tanks larger than 600 litres as a tractor's three point linkage will not carry more weight, whereas trailed sprayers can have tanks up to 3,000 litres. Mounted sprayers are of course cheaper as they do not have a chassis and wheels. They can also turn in much less space so are suitable for the smaller vineyard or in vineyards where the headlands are tight. However, they are more difficult to hitch up and attach to a tractor, whereas a trailed sprayer is easier and quicker. The size of pump and fan that you need will depend on the row width and layout of your vineyard, and the type of sprayer you have. Sprayers with axial fans, with the nozzles placed around the outside of the fan, typically have fans around 600-700 mm in diameter which is fine for 2.0-2.5 m wide rows. There are also sprayers with 'snakes' that can be directed to different parts of the canopy where the air is delivered down the snakes with the spray coming out of fingers placed in the air stream. These tend to have smaller fans – around 450-550 mm. Finally there are also sprayers with tangential flow (or cross-flow) fans mounted vertically. Despite claiming various benefits – reduced drift and better penetration – sprayers with this type of fan are seldom seen in vineyards.

On most sprayers, pump output, spraying pressure and fan speed are adjustable, so remember that you can always reduce the air output from a larger fan: you cannot increase it from a smaller one. Most modern sprayers have dual nozzles which can easily be switched from one output volume to a lower or higher one (or turned off completely) making it very simple to adjust sprayer output to the canopy size. The canopy will expand as the season progresses, requiring larger and larger liquid volumes. Selecting the correct nozzles for the right product or occasion is important and switching between air-induction nozzles and hollow-cone nozzles is all part and parcel of effective sprayer use.[2] The best advice is to go to a dealer who is used to dealing with orchard and vineyard sprayers and seek their advice. Under the 2012 Sustainable Use Directive (SUD)[3], your sprayer will have to be inspected by 26 November 2016 (unless it is under 5 years old) and pass an MOT, so keeping it serviced on a regular basis is essential and having a helpful mechanic on your side will pay dividends. Sprayers will then require an MOT once within five years up to 2020 and every three years after that. New sprayers will need an MOT once before they are five years old. Full details can be found on the National Sprayer Testing Scheme's website www.nsts.org.uk.

In *Chapter 10: Machinery and equipment* I said that in recent years, so-called 'tunnel' (or 'recovery') sprayers have been used in UK vineyards with the Lipco[4] brand being the most popular (although several manufacturers make them). Although they are expensive to buy and really only suitable for the larger vineyard, they are undoubtedly cost-effective in the long-term, owing to the amount of spray material they save. Andrew Landers, in his book *Effective Vineyard Spraying*, states that a saving of an average of 35 per cent (much more in the early growth stages) can be made. Given that spray materials will come to at least £1,000-ha (£400-acre), then on 10-ha (25-acres), this is an annual saving of at least £3,500. Also, because much of the spray is recovered, you can work for much longer between fill-ups, thus saving time and expense.

Whether tunnel sprayers are as effective at controlling disease is another question. Some say that because the spray is re-circulated, two things happen: one is that the spray gradually loses its potency and effectiveness by this repeated use; the other is that as the sprayer passes around the vineyard, it tends to spread disease about. Landers says in his book (p. 92-6) that this is not the case, and that this is a story put out by competing sprayer manufacturers. Whether this is true or not is another matter, although they are not universally popular. Some makes and models of tunnel sprayers also do not have fans inside them, relying on hydraulic pressure only to carry the spray into the centre of the canopy. Whether this is sufficient in a crowded, dense canopy such as is often seen in UK vineyards is also open to question and I would always advise getting a sprayer with fans. It should also be noted that for tunnel sprayers, under the LERAP (Local Environment Risk Assessment for Pesticides) scheme, the default buffer zone (of which, more later) for pesticides, for which a buffer zone is required, is 5 m from any watercourse (wet or dry) and cannot be reduced even following a LERAP assessment. Full details can be found in the LERAP *Broadcast Air-Assisted Sprayers* guide (PB 6533) available from the DEFRA website.

*Lipco tunnel sprayer in operation*

## Vineyard weather stations

In some UK vineyards, growers have installed vineyard weather stations which monitor a large amount of weather data and, in theory, can be used to predict the likelihood of certain diseases. Using variables such as rainfall, temperature, humidity, leaf wetness and wind speed, these weather stations claim to be able to predict when Powdery and Downy Mildew and *Botrytis* are likely to occur. This gives growers advance warning of likely disease events, enabling them to time their sprays for maximum effect. However, the sensors can only sample the situation in one spot in what might be quite a large area of vines, and

therefore there are bound to be inaccuracies. I also suspect that the algorithms most vineyard weather stations are using are not based upon UK weather data or UK vineyard conditions and therefore greatly mis-read the likelihood of disease. Although we are wetter, cooler and windier than many warmer climate regions, this does not mean that we suffer from disease as much as the data would suggest (see the section on *Botrytis* below). The weather stations that I see tend to suggest much more frequent spraying than in reality actually occurs, which is quite the reverse of what is intended. On balance, having a weather station in your vineyard is something of a luxury and there are plenty of good growers who do not have them. Whilst they can record all the weather data you will ever need, how you use it is another matter. For frost sensing, a standard weather station is probably not that suitable and the requirements are discussed in *Chapter 13: Frost protection*. A weather station will also be useful if you have problems with spray drift in that it will help confirm what the wind speed was at the time of spraying.

## Spraying practices and techniques

How you spray, what you spray and when you spray will depend very much on a range of factors. The sprayer you have, the vine varieties you are growing, and the plant densities, row widths and trellising systems will all play their part in determining your spray programme. The weather during the year will also be critical in determining both spray frequency and timing. Dry years will be generally good for growers and disease pressure will probably be lessened, although do not get lured into the trap of thinking that because there has been little rain, there will be no disease. Powdery Mildew is spread by wind and actually favours dry humid conditions.

In general, one should aim for disease prevention rather than disease control. Keeping vines clean, at least in the early part of the season, up until the start of flowering (typically the end of June) ought to be straightforward. Once the canopy fills out and side-shoots start to appear, spray penetration will be more difficult and timely deleafing and shoot trimming will help open up the canopy to light, air and sprays.

The first task of good pest and disease control is to get a suitable spray programme from a BASIS registered advisor and, at least to start with, stick to it. Your spray programme should be designed to take account of the varieties you grow – if you are growing disease resistant hybrids your spray requirements will be very different from if you are growing disease prone varieties – although in general terms the spray programme will be much the same for all *vinifera* varieties. Once you get through a cropping season or two, you will hopefully get a feel for how your vines and your site behave in respect of pests and diseases and learn to adjust your spray programme accordingly. Whilst it may be desirable to spray as little as possible, to act on information about the likelihood of disease due to climatic factors, the reality in most vineyards is that spraying is like house insurance. You don't wait until you see the first signs of subsidence or the first flickers of flame before you take out insurance: you act pre-emptively. In time, and with experience, you will discover which blocks require less spraying, which require more and which weather conditions favour your vines and which don't. Until then, spray first and ask questions afterwards. Of course this is not to advocate spraying too often, or using more material than necessary – the cost of time and chemicals is high enough not to want to waste them. But allowing diseases to develop and then attempting to halt them, let alone rid your vineyard of them, is not a recipe for an easy life and certainly not a way of saving time or money. Timing is often the key to good disease control, all other things being equal. The saying 'the difference between a good farmer and a bad farmer is ten days' is nowhere truer than in the area of disease control.

Standard spray programmes generally allow ten to fourteen days between sprays, but this interval needs to be adjusted according to the prevailing weather conditions and disease pressures. If it so happens that the day you intend to spray on is going to be at the start of a five day wet period, then you may need to bring the date forward and perhaps spray on day nine or day eleven rather than leave it until it stops raining. There may also be occasions when disease pressure is very high and the vines are growing rapidly when a seven day spraying interval might be appropriate. If, on the other hand, the weather is dry, the vines are in balance and the canopy management is up to scratch, then allowing the interval between sprays to lengthen may not cause any problems. Of course the size of your vineyard and the time it takes for you to hitch up, fill up and get a spray on your whole vineyard will also dictate when you spray. With a small vineyard that can be sprayed in a few hours, finding a rain-free gap to get a spray on with time to let the spray dry and be absorbed in the case of systemic materials, is far less a problem than in a large vineyard which might take a day or two to spray completely.

Using the right water volume for the growth stage and for the disease is also often a large part of getting good disease control. Using sulphur to control Powdery Mildew requires good coverage with spray, as sulphur is a contact material and has no systemic action. This is especially true in the later growth stages when canopies can become crowded and shaded. In Germany, the following recommendations are made:
- Budburst to appearance of inflorescences: 100-400 litres-ha
- Pre-flowering: 200-800 litres-ha
- Mid-flower to post-flower: 250-800 litres-ha
- Post-flower: 300-800 litres-ha
- Pea-size: 1,400-1,600 litres-ha
- *Véraison* and post-*véraison*: 1,600 litres-ha.

The range of volumes is given to accommodate different row widths, different trellising systems and canopy management techniques. If your rows are 1.5 m wide, then per hectare volumes are going to be higher than if your rows are 2.5 m wide. Likewise, with a well-trimmed, deleafed canopy, less water volumes will be required than with a crowded canopy. In the UK we tend to talk about low volume and high volume. Low volume (LV) spraying is taken to mean 200-600 litres-ha (18-54 Imp.

galls-acre) and high volume (HV) spraying at least 1,000 litres-ha (89 Imp. galls-acre) and often as high as 1,200 litres-ha (107 Imp. galls-acre). 100 gallons an acre (1,125 litres-ha) was always considered 'normal' for spraying apples and pears with a full canopy.

In Germany they also express spray amounts not as in the UK, where fixed amounts of product per hectare are given, but in quantities per 100 litres of water. This means that as the water volume per hectare required to spray the ever-growing canopy rises, so does the amount of product, keeping the concentration of product that hits the vines much the same. Therefore, with a product such as Switch, just after flowering you might use 180 gm of product in say 500 litres-ha of water, whereas in the final spray before the start of the 35 day HI, the amount of product would have risen to 240 gm in 700 litres-ha of water. In the UK, the recommendation for Switch is 800 gm-ha at the maximum rate.

Apart from lengthening spray intervals, another way to save on both sprays and time is, in the early stages of the season, before the first tucking-in, is to spray more frequently, but spray every other row. Assuming your row widths are not too far apart – I would not consider this technique would work well with a 3.50 m GDC vineyard – and you have (a) a sprayer with a suitably sized fan, (b) a sheltered vineyard and (c) the wind is not blowing too hard, then perhaps spraying every other row on a seven day cycle might save a couple of spray rounds without jeopardising vine health. Of course you need to remember which rows you have sprayed (having every row numbered definitely helps with this) so that you don't end up spraying the same row twice.

Andrew Landers has written a very good paper called *Improving spraying efficiency* which is available at www.englishwine.com/wgigb.htm.

## Weather conditions

When you spray must also take account of the prevailing weather (especially wind) conditions in order to avoid spray-drift. The 'Code of practice' (PB 11090) suggests spraying when the wind speed is: 'a steady 3.2-6.5 km-hour' (light breeze) and blowing away from 'any sensitive areas or neighbour's land'. It also suggests avoiding spraying: 'when there is little or no wind', 'when there are low winds on warm sunny afternoons' and 'when temperatures are above 30°C'.

## Legal requirements

As might be imagined, there are many regulations governing every aspect of pesticides – purchase, handling, storage, use and disposal – and every grower must make sure that they are fully up to speed with the current ones. You should also note that under certain conditions and when using certain products, it may be necessary to give notice to beekeepers, neighbouring property owners and to put up notices to warn visitors and footpath users that spraying is taking place or that spraying has recently taken place. There may also be 're-entry' periods (see below). Pesticide users must also have somewhere to fill and clean the sprayer and this must be so constructed that any spills of products, unused spray or wash-down water does not reach a watercourse. Collecting these and having them removed by a licenced contractor is probably the easiest way for the small producer to deal with these legally.

## Operators

All users of pesticides in a professional capacity will, as of 26 November 2015, require to be trained and hold the relevant 'certificates of competence'. These are issued by the National Proficiency & Training Council (NPTC) and most vineyard owners will require the following certificates: PA1, the foundation module which covers the safe use of pesticides, environmental factors and legislation; PA3A for broadcast sprayers with air assistance, i.e. most fruit sprayers; PA3C for boom sprayers without air assistance, i.e. most weed spraying booms; and probably PA6 (option A or AW) for hand-held applicators, i.e. knapsack sprayers. If you were born prior to 1 January 1965, 'grandfather rights' exist which exempt you from these requirements, but do not exempt you from storing, handling and applying pesticides in a safe manner. If you are a holder of 'grandfather rights' you can take a NPTC Level 2 Award called 'Safe use of pesticides replacing grandfather rights' which will allow you to continue applying pesticides after 26 November 2015. The courses and tests mentioned in this paragraph are offered by several different providers and full details can be found on the NPTC's website www.nptc.org.uk. In any event, before taking any NPTC courses, the precise equipment to be used must be discussed with your training provider. Such things as axial flow fans and CDA (Controlled Droplet Application) and ULV (Ultra Low Volume) sprayers may well require particular modules.

Under certain conditions, a person holding the relevant certificate can supervise someone who has not yet obtained their certificate, but you must: 'be able to see the person doing all parts of the job including: preparing and mixing the pesticide; filling equipment and making sure the dose levels are correct (calibrating); applying the pesticide and; cleaning equipment and disposing of washings, leftover pesticides, and the containers'. In other words, you cannot 'supervise' unless you are physically present during the process of using the pesticide. As might be imagined, there are large fines and even imprisonment if you fail to comply with any of the above. If you are using a contractor to apply pesticides (which includes weedkillers), you must make sure that the operator (and not the contractor) holds the relevant certificates and always ask for written confirmation that they do hold them. If you do not, and something goes wrong, it might count against you in the event of an insurance claim.

Products controlled by the pesticide regulations may only be bought if the purchaser is sure that they are for use by someone holding the correct certificates. After 26 November 2015 it will be an offence to purchase controlled products if the buyer has not ensured that the user holds the correct certificates. Suppliers of pesticides may also refuse to sell you products if you cannot show them the correct certificates.

## Products

There are many different products that can be sprayed on to, under or around vines, including pesticides – a term which covers weedkillers, fungicides, insecticides, acaricides, molluscicides and probably a few other-icides as well – plus wetters, spreaders, foliar feeds, fertilisers, physical barrier forming products, growth regulators and various other materials. Not all of these are subject to pesticide regulations. Those that are, are listed in the UKVA's annual 'Green Book'[5]. Here you will find all products that either have a full label approval, i.e. its use on outdoor grapes will be on the product packaging itself and on any data-sheets about that product, or the product will be what used to be called a SOLA product (Specific Off Label Approval) but which is now called an EAMU (Extension of Authorisation of Minor Use) product. These products will not have outdoor grapes listed on their packaging and any user must, by law, be in possession of the appropriate EAMU documentation (all the current ones are in the Green Book) and follow the instructions for such things as dose rate, water volume, tank mix for specific application, maximum number of applications, minimum interval between applications, method of application, re-entry period and HI. Products also have to be stored in the correct manner and Section 5 of the 'Code of practice' (PB 11090) should be consulted. There is a wide range of products which have 'all edible crops' approval and which might be suitable on vines. Before using these, it is advisable to ask the supplier and/or manufacturer for their specific approval before using them on wine grapes.

## Adjuvants – spreaders, wetters, surfactants, buffers

There is a wide range of additives which can be added to the spray tank in order to do a number of different things: enhance pesticide performance; reduce drift; lower the surface tension to help adhesion; reduce spray droplet size; help create bubbles if using air-induction nozzles; help the spray stick on to the target and make it more rainfast; and change the pH of the solution (buffering). Some products already have adjuvants added and other products work better if the correct adjuvant is added to the tank. Protectant and contact products work best without adjuvants as they are designed to work by remaining on the surface of the leaf. Before using an adjuvant, it is best to obtain advice from your BASIS advisor as not all products are compatible with all adjuvants. Cornell University also has a good 'fact sheet' on 'Agricultural Spray Adjuvants' which can be found on www.englishwine.com/.

## Re-entry periods

To date, no re-entry periods – the time between product applications and re-entry of people (owners, employees, and visitors) into the vineyard – apply for current pesticides permitted to be used in UK vineyards, but it is likely that in the future they will. Rules regarding footpaths crossing or adjacent to vineyards have also yet to be agreed. It is good practice, however, to put up notices warning people with access to vineyards, that spraying is about to take place, is taking place or has recently taken place. In that way, you have everything covered. You should also warn people that their dogs should be kept on a lead in case the dogs decide to lick, eat or brush against recently sprayed vines or weeds.

## Harvest Intervals and residue levels

Most controlled pesticides have a Harvest Interval (HI) which is the number of days which must elapse between the last application of the product and when any grapes are picked. The main reason for having a HI is for the safety of the public so that pesticide residues do not get into the food chain. However, this is not always the whole story. Rovral WG for instance, a valuable product used to protect a wide variety of crops against *Botrytis,* has a fourteen day HI for grapes, but on tomatoes grown under protection and strawberries grown both indoors and outdoors, the HI is only two days. The reason? On tomatoes and strawberries, both fruits mainly eaten raw and sold very much on the basis of appearance, damage by *Botrytis* is financially painful and Rovral helps prevent it in transit, storage and display until purchase. On grapes, the problem is that residues of Rovral would have a damaging effect upon yeast growth and therefore might upset fermentation, especially if a low-vigour, naturally occurring, yeast was being used. HIs are not always about public safety.

The HI can also depend upon the rate of product used and/or volume of water applied per hectare (the concentration rate). Mancozeb for instance has an HI which varies between 63 days and 28 days depending on these factors. Some products do not have a HI at all, but for sound winemaking reasons it would be unwise to spray them too near the harvest. Sulphur, which until about ten years ago used to have a 56 day HI in the UK, now has none at all. Since the use of coal in the home and in many power stations has diminished, the amount of sulphur in the atmosphere, and hence falling on the land, has dropped, meaning that many soils are becoming deficient in sulphur. It is therefore widely used on a range of agricultural crops as a foliar feed and has ceased to be classed as a pesticide. However, in other countries, the same sulphur approved for use on grapes in the UK (Kumulus DF for instance) has a 21 day HI in Germany and France, but on the UK label merely says 'do not apply near to harvest on grapes intended for wine'. In Germany, copper-containing sprays for vines have a 21 day HI, whilst in the UK they have a zero day HI. The reasons that it would be unwise to spray both sulphur and copper too near to harvest is that residues can give rise to problems in the winery: hydrogen sulphide in the case of sulphur and a copper *casse* in the case of copper.

The correct HI should also be adhered to – and indeed in some situations, very dry years perhaps, even exceeded – as residue testing by supermarkets and other large wine retailers is becoming far more common, especially (I would imagine) since the horsemeat contamination problem. Almost all controlled pesticides have a MRL (Maximum Residue Level) which varies according to the product and the crop it is used on and for wine, the MRL is that for wine grapes. Current GC-MS (gas chromatography-mass spectrometry) testing can detect residues as small as 0.01mg-kg which, according to Geoff Taylor of wine industry analysts Corkwise, is the equivalent of 'one grain of salt in 100,000 litres' of wine and is way below all MRLs. The MRL on Scala for instance (active ingredient of which is *Pyrimethanil*) – and being an anti-*Botrytis* product is probably one of the last to be applied and which has a 21 day HI – is 5 mg-kg, some 500 times greater than the current GC-MS detection rate.

However, even though residue levels are below the permitted MRLs, there are concerns that a cocktail of residues, each of which are below permitted levels, taken together might be shown to be detrimental to human health. The last thing a supermarket wants is a news story that reads 'Pesticides in wine can lead to brain damage' (although of course the headline 'Alcohol in wine causes brain damage, liver failure, violence, deaths etc etc' would be treated as a 1 April joke!). If it was found that grapes and/or wine had residue levels higher than the MRL for the product concerned, undoubtedly DEFRA would prosecute and naturally all wines would have to be withdrawn and, in all probability, destroyed. What this would do to the reputation of English and Welsh wine doesn't bear thinking about.

## Buffer zones

Many products have buffer zones – the distance you have to leave between your sprayer and the 'top of the bank of any static or flowing waterbody or ditch which is dry at the time of application' – and these have to be adhered to. Products fall into two classes: LERAP A, products which are not eligible for a buffer zone reduction; and LERAP B, products which are eligible for a buffer zone reduction. If using a horizontal boom sprayer (such as might be used for herbicides) you cannot spray either LERAP A or B products 'within 5 m of a watercourse or within 1 m of the top of a bank of a dry ditch'. However you can, with certain LERAP B products, reduce the 5 m buffer zone if the assessment has shown the products and your spraying technique to be safe. For 'broadcast air-assisted sprayers' (i.e. most vineyard sprayers), there is no distinction between LERAP A and B products and the buffer zone required will be on the label or the EAMU. Buffer zones will also vary according to whether you are spraying a full or reduced rate of the product which has a buffer zone. Buffer zones can also be reduced where there is a windbreak between your sprayer and the watercourse, but only when the windbreak 'is formed from broad-leaved trees or shrubs, not conifers'. The windbreak must also be managed to protect the crop from the effects of wind or spray-drift, extend the full length of the boundary between the crop and the watercourse, be 2.0-m higher than the crop, have no gaps 'including those resulting from systematic stripping of lower branches' and have leaves visible over its entire length. If you are spraying pesticides at less than 75 per cent of the approved rate, the buffer zone can be reduced by 3 m; if using at 50 per cent of the approved rate, the buffer zone can be reduced by 6 m; and if below 25 per cent, the buffer zone can be reduced by 12 m. Note however that reducing the rate of the material might seriously affect its effectiveness. The LERAP *Broadcast Air-Assisted Sprayers* guide (PB 6533) gives full details.

## Resistance

If you use the same product repeatedly over several seasons and on the same crop, it is possible that the problem you are trying to control will become resistant to the product. Given that insecticides are little used in UK vineyards, this problem is likely to occur with fungicides and most likely to occur with what are called 'single-site' fungicides. Margaret McGrath in *What are Fungicides?* explains:

> *'Single-site fungicides which are active against only one point in one metabolic pathway in a pathogen or against a single critical enzyme or protein needed by the fungus. Since single-site fungicides are highly specific in their toxicity, having little effect on most organisms, they can safely be absorbed into plants, thus these fungicides tend to have systemic properties. As a result of this specific activity, fungi are more likely to become resistant to the fungicide because a single mutation in the pathogen usually allows it to overcome the action of the fungicide, such as by preventing it from binding to the active site in the fungus. Typically, older contact fungicides have multi-site activity and thus usually affect many fungi in different classes. Through the development of in vivo screens, and due to the increase in the stringency and number of regulatory tests required to register a new active ingredient, fungicide manufacturers have found it easier to develop single-site systemics recently. As a result, fungicide resistance has become a more important concern in disease management'.*

In the past, there have been several instances of almost complete fungicide resistance to certain products. In the UK, growers used to use a product called Benlate (containing *benzimidazole*) against *Botrytis* but it gradually became less and less effective and scientists even discovered strains of fungi that needed *benzimidazole* to survive! After thirty-three years of use it was withdrawn from the market.

The factors that cause resistance are very varied, but include frequency of use, dose rate, whether the product is used singly or repeatedly, the target disease, and the strength of the disease to build up resistance. These are, in turn, influenced by other factors such as the method (and quality) of application, the timing of application and adverse weather conditions. In short, the causes of disease resistance are many and varied and must be guarded against. In order to make this easier, all approved pesticides have been given Mode of Action (MoA) codes which are grouped according to their biochemical mode of action. Products with a MoA code that starts with an M – such as sulphur which has the MoA code of M2 – are multi-site acting and generally less likely to cause resistance if used repeatedly, although they do not necessarily give the best level of disease control. Products

with a MoA code that consists of a number – such as Teldor (the active ingredient of which is *Fenhexamid*) which has a MoA code of 17 – are single-site products and therefore more likely to lead to resistance if used unwisely. Therefore, in designing a spray programme, it is best to alternate products and not repeatedly use those with the same MoA codes and when tank mixing, try and use products having different MoA codes. It should also be noted that some products contain more than one active ingredient and therefore have more than one MoA code. Switch, for instance which contains the active ingredients *Cyprodinil* and *Fludioxinil* – has two MoA codes: 9 and 12. Any spray programme which has been drawn up by a BASIS registered professional should take account of MoA codes.

## Disposal of unwanted pesticides and empty containers

The disposal of unwanted pesticides, whether diluted for use or undiluted, and of empty pesticide containers, is strictly controlled. The best way to use already mixed pesticides is, of course, to spray them on to the crop and only mix-up the correct amount. In theory this is fine: in practice less so. Given that the ends of the rows often get under-sprayed compared to the rest of the vineyard, I always think it legitimate to finish spraying by giving the outside of the vineyard one (extra) round of spray. But if you genuinely have excess spray to dispose of, then you need to follow the rules. For empty containers, the easiest way is, after triple-washing them, use a licensed disposal contractor (or take them to a licensed disposal site) or ask your supplier (who must also be licensed – and many are not) to take them away.

## Record Keeping

The 'Code of practice' (PB 11090) gives guidance on record keeping:
- Storage records - Not mandatory, but advisable.
- Treatment records - Mandatory.
- COSHH assessment - Depends on the product used and circumstances.
- Environmental Risk Assessments - Depends on the product used and circumstances.
- Exposure monitoring - Might be necessary if staff exposed to certain products.
- Maintenance records of Respiratory Protective Equipment (RPE) - Only if RPE used.
- Health Surveillance Records - Only if using staff that require health assessment.
- Disposal records - Required if moving or disposing of waste.

## Identification of pests and diseases

Before embarking on any pest or disease control, correct identification is essential. With experience and practice, many of the major pests and diseases can be quickly and easily identified without recourse to hand lenses or books. Others however, such as a light brown spotting on the leaves, might be caused by a disease, a herbicide spray or insect damage and require proper identification before treatment can be prescribed. As a minimum I would advise vineyard owners to invest in a small hand lens, say 10x magnification and with a lens of at least 18 mm diameter (23 mm is better), plus a book or two, although there are of course multiple pest and disease identification websites which can be consulted. I use the following resources:

- *Diseases and Pests* Edited by Phil Nicholas, Peter Margery and Malcolm Wachtel. Winetitles, Ashford, South Australia, 2011.
- *Compendium of Grape Diseases* Edited by Roger C. Pearson and Austin C. Goheen. APS Press, Minnesota, USA, 1988.
- *UC-IPM Online* This is aimed at Californian growers, but is a very good resource for pests, diseases, weeds and many other vineyard problems. www.ipm.ucdavis.edu and follow link via 'Agricultural Pests' to the 'Grape' pages.
- *Ontario Grape IPM* www.omafra.gov.on.ca/IPM/english/grapes. Look for Diseases & Disorders.
- *Winetitles* Australian wine book and magazine publisher has very a very good disease diagnosis website: www.winetitles.com/diagnosis

## Pests

Until relatively recently, UK vineyards were remarkably free of vineyard pests and compared to vineyards in warmer climates, were almost pest-free. The University of California's 'UC IPM' website for instance, lists twenty-four insects and mites to watch out for. The UK escapes lightly, partly due to the relatively cool climate (as most vineyard pests prefer warmer conditions), but also because: UK vineyards tend to be isolated from one another; our vineyards have a wide variety of plants in their alleyways providing plenty of habitat for predator species; and because most vineyards are part of a mixed agriculture landscape that also provides habitat for predators. However, this situation – as it is in many other spheres of both agriculture and everyday life – is changing and there have been several instances in the last ten years, of vineyard pests causing damage at levels where treatment becomes necessary. European Grapevine Moth (*Lobesia botrana*), called *Eudemis* in France, Vine Moth (*Eupoecilia ambiguella*), called *Cochylis* in France, Grape Berry Moth (*Paralobesia viteana* or *Endopiza viteana*), Light Brown Apple Moth (*Phalaenoides glycinae*) also known as LBAM, and Summer Fruit Tortrix Moth (*Adoxophyes orana*), also known as SFT, have all recently made appearances in the UK, particularly in warmer years. To say that these moths were regularly found in UK vineyards would be an exaggeration, but if growers see physical damage to any part of their vines and grapes, then they must be considered as a possible cause and, if it is felt that the damage is of a level to cause commercial damage, sprayed against. Of course, once you start using insecticides, especially broad spectrum insecticides which do not target a particular species, the numbers of natural predators will start to decline and this should be taken into account before you start using them. In order to monitor moth numbers (and not trap them), pheromone traps ought to be employed to decide whether to spray an insecticide or not.

Overseas, several types of pest (mainly the *Eudemis* and *Cochylis* moths) can be controlled with what the French call *confusion sexuelle* and which in the UK we call 'mating disruption'. This is carried out by hanging small tabs, containing the pheromones of the female of the species to be confused, around the vineyard so that the males, instead of mating with real females, wear themselves out hunting down plastic capsules. In order for this technique to work correctly, a large area needs to be covered – BASF say a minimum of 5-ha for their RAK product – and 500 capsules per hectare (200-acre) need to be distributed. Costs are high with the materials costing around £215-ha (£87-acre), plus the labour to hang the tabs out. Because of the requirement to cover large areas in order for this technique to work, it is being used successfully in regions where co-operatives dominate and where growers are able to work together. In isolated vineyards, such as we typically have in the UK, it is less likely to prove effective. In the UK, blueberry growers were given an emergency approval to use a mating disruption tab – the Exosex LBAM MTE – against LBAM and this is proving successful. Despite 'vineyards' being mentioned on the manufacturer Exosect's website, it is not currently cleared for use in UK vineyards, although this may change.

Mites have been present in UK vineyards for many decades, but until recently, did little economic damage. Grape Erineum Mite (*Colomerus vitis*) also known as Erinose or Blister Mite, was occasionally seen on leaves, especially in hotter, drier years, but apart from looking a little bit like *Phylloxera* leaf-galls and thus occasioning a slight increase in the heart rate, did little damage and always seemed to be controlled by sulphur sprays, However, in the last ten years, Grape Vine Bud Mites (*Eriophyes vitis*) have started to make an appearance – in my experience especially on Chardonnay – and once established, they seem quite difficult to eradicate. The clues are in the first few weeks of budburst and, if Bud Mites are present, buds can be blind, shoots stunted and leaves deformed and there may well be lower than normal levels of inflorescences. In other countries these mites are often a contributory factor in what is called Restricted Spring Growth (RSG). Unlike Erineum Mite, these Bud Mites spend most of their lives inside the buds and are therefore more difficult to spot as their damage is largely hidden and much more difficult to control. The recommendation to control these is two to three early sprays of sulphur at a high rate – 10 litres-ha – one at woolly bud, one at bud burst, and maybe another after that. Whether this is a long term solution remains to be seen. Red Spider mites, of which there are two types, European Fruit Tree Red Spider mite and Two-Spotted Red Spider mite, are quite common in some crops in the UK – hops, blackcurrants, cane fruit, protected strawberries – and have been seen on vines in the UK, but only very occasionally. They like warm dry conditions (which is why they can be found on vines in greenhouses), so perhaps a pest to look forward to!

Other insect pests such as capsid bugs (of which there are several types) and thrips (thunderbugs) have always been seen in UK vineyards, but their damage has never been of economic importance and they were therefore not worth spraying for. Capsids, which like living in clumps of nettles and other tall weeds, will sometimes cause damage to leaves, especially on young vines. Thrips can cause scarring and russeting on grapes which could make berry splitting more likely, but again, at non-commercial levels. Capsids however, are also predators of several species of insect, so may be doing some good as well as harm.

*Capsid damage on a young vine leaf*

Spotted Wing Drosophila (*Drosophila suzukii*), first seen in Europe in French vineyards in 2010, has been causing damage in the UK in soft and stone fruit crops, but has not yet been seen in grapes. It is however, a pest to be aware of. Growers, especially those with early ripening, softer-skin vine varieties (which it appears to prefer), should consider the use of detection traps (such as the Biobest Droso-Trap) for monitoring numbers. The 2014 Green Book has some good advice on monitoring this pest, plus the measures that need to be taken should it be found.

The multi-coloured Asian Lady Beetle or Harlequin Ladybird (*Harmonia axyridis*) has also been seen in UK vineyards, but not in numbers enough to cause problems. This ladybird, when disturbed, exudes a substance called 'reflex blood' which, if it gets into juice, can possibly taint the wine, depending on numbers. However, given that the numbers of this insect are currently very low and given that harvesting machines are not often used in the UK, no problems have been reported with this pest.

Pollen beetles (of which there are many different sorts) are often seen on inflorescences during flowering, but it is not thought that they do any harm and may even possibly aid pollination. They are generally only seen during warm weather, so perhaps ought to be generally welcomed rather than worried about.

Other pests which might appear include scale insects, of which there are two main types – brown and woolly –

which might affect vines, which usually gather on the trunk or under the bark on older vines. They don't appear to cause much harm on outdoor vines (although can be a problem on greenhouse vines) and before an insecticide is used, an assessment of the scale (no pun intended) of the damage should be made. A petroleum oil (Croptex Spraying Oil) has an on-label approval against scale insects and this product, sprayed on to trunks during the dormant season, might help. In the past, both Vine Weevil and Dock Sawfly have been known to attack young vines in the UK, but on established vines are seldom a nuisance. The literature mentions aphids as being a problem, but I have never known them to be. It is quite probable that the use of relatively high rates of sulphur on vines, which starts early in the season, coupled with our sometimes challenging weather, keeps most pests down to levels where they are not noticed. So far, the UK has not seen any of the wide variety of sharpshooter leafhoppers which in other countries are the vectors for ailments such as *Flavescence dorée* (Grapevine Yellows) and Pierce's Disease, as our climate is not yet that warm.

Wasps will always be a problem when there is ripe fruit about, especially if the fruit is damaged or rotten, and they have an easy entrance to the sweet flesh. In UK vineyards, wasps have usually been a problem in early years when sugars are high, before the weather starts to turn cold; with early varieties such as Siegerrebe, Ortega, Optima, and Rondo, especially when individual grapes are damaged and start to rot; and when poor flowering conditions have given rise to *millerandage* and there are a significant number of small seedless grapes which ripen fully, well before the seeded grapes on the same bunch. If your vineyards are also near apple orchards where there is a supply of fallen fruit, this too may attract them. The remedy against wasps is to firstly track and destroy their nests. How you do this exactly is part of country folklore, but looking in likely spots – dry banks and old farm buildings – is a start. Following their flight paths is probably the best way as they tend to fly in a fairly straight line from food source to nest. Capturing one and tying a piece of white cotton to it so that you can follow it home is another, but I have never seen this done, but can believe it might work (although probably illegal). Having found nests, they can be eradicated using approved materials.

The second method of controlling wasps is to trap them *in situ* with wasp traps. However, Chris Cooper in the UKVA's Green Book points out that this technique is now construed as 'mass trapping' and is not authorised for grapes in the UK. Therefore, wasp traps now have to be renamed as 'wasp monitoring devices' and the technique referred to as 'precision monitoring'. You can also spray an insecticide against wasps, although its effect may be short-term and fairly limited. Three products – Clayton Lanark, Tracer and Hallmark with Zeon Technology – are currently approved for use on grapevines in the UK.

In young vineyards, where vines have yet to develop a woody trunk, slugs and snails can sometimes cause problems, damaging both canes and leaves and stunting extension growth. In this instance, slug pellets are often effective. Slug and snail damage will often occur inside rabbit guards of the tree guard type and slug pellets may need to be sprinkled inside them as soon as they are put on. I have also known snails to attack mature vines, but this only in a vineyard that had been repeatedly flooded and where incoming silt off neighbouring fields had carried with it huge quantities of snails and snail eggs. Getting rid of these was much more of a problem and despite trying various molluscides it was only the hard winters of 2009-10 and 2010-11, when temperatures fell to -10ºC, that killed them off.

## Phylloxera

Although *Phylloxera* (which is more correctly known as *Viteus vitifoliae*) has to be classed as a 'pest', it is not one in the same sense of any of the above. It cannot be eradicated by spraying or soil drenching and the only practical remedy is to use *Phylloxera* tolerant rootstocks. It has been found in the UK many times since vines were first imported in the 1950s in both open vineyards, as well as in garden centres selling potted vines. Given that it is endemic in virtually all European vineyards (as well of course as in most vineyards world-wide), eggs can easily be missed when vines are being sorted after lifting and if they are pot-grown, can be hidden in the soil. Therefore anyone buying vines from European nurseries (which is all but a very small number of amateur vineyards) the possibility of *Phylloxera* being present in your vineyard must always be considered.

If you are growing pure *vinifera* vines on their own roots (something you would only do in quantity in certain circumstances and where you appreciated all the risks involved), the first signs of *Phylloxera* may well be just a general lack of vigour in a few plants, building up over several seasons from a nucleus to a wider circle of vines. If this happens, and there is no other obvious cause (such as poor drainage) and no signs of leaf galls, then get a spade out and expose a few roots near the surface. *Phylloxera* does not like tunnelling deep – indeed it cannot – so finding them is relatively easy if you know what to look for.

If you are not growing vines on their own roots, the appearance of *Phylloxera* is likely to be as leaf galls on the leaves of hybrid varieties such as Cascade, Seyval blanc, Triomphe etc, or, and much more likely, on the leaves of shoots which have come from below the graft. This typically happens when earth or mulch has been allowed to build up over the graft giving rise to both shoots and roots coming directly from the rootstock. *Phylloxera* finds the leaves of American rootstocks much more palatable than pure *vinifera* leaves (which it almost never touches). You may also find that the vine has put out roots from above the graft, i.e. scion roots and these are highly susceptible to the root form of *Phylloxera* as they are pure *vinifera* roots. Depending on how many seasons the leaf galls have been there, you may or may not have root infestations. The root form of *Phylloxera* is, when in its youth, a fairly bright yellow and can just about be seen with the naked eye. If the *Phylloxera* have been there for a year or more you will probably also find root tuberosities (also known as nodes or knots) which are dark brown and can often be mistaken

for just pieces of old root or general soil debris attached to the roots.

If you find (or even suspect) that you have *Phylloxera* in your vineyard, it is a legal requirement that you notify FERA (Food and Environment Research Agency), the agency whose task it is to deal with 'quarantine pests' for DEFRA, and inspectors will be sent to investigate. If *Phylloxera* is confirmed, although FERA has the power to make you remove infected vines, it is much more likely these days to impose a movement control on your vineyard, restricting the movement of both plant material in and out, plus the movement of visitors to the vineyard, and let the infestation run its course. If you only have leaf galls on a few rogue shoots of rootstock, then the answer is to make sure that every graft union is exposed and inspected and the graft made completely free of extraneous shoots and roots. If you have pure *vinifera* vines growing on their own roots and they have root galls, then they will weaken and die and unless the *Phylloxera* has new hosts to migrate to, they too will die out. If you have Seyval blanc or other older hybrids either grafted on to rootstocks or on their own roots, then it is quite possible for *Phylloxera* to stay on the leaves for several years, although they can be sprayed with insecticide and they do not like high levels of sulphur. Currently, one product (Movento) is cleared for use in UK vineyards for the control of *Phylloxera*. This is a 'unique two-way' product which moves throughout the entire plant system and reduces the breeding habits of adult females and 'limits the survival of their offspring'. To date, I do not believe this product has been tried in any UK vineyard for this purpose.

It is also worth noting that not all rootstocks are as tolerant of *Phylloxera* as others. Those with pure *Berlandieri*, *Riparia* and *Rupestris* blood are very tolerant and unlikely to be damaged. However, as was seen in California with the rootstock AxR1 (Aramon x *Rupestris* Ganzin No.1), there are several rootstocks which are *vinifera* crosses and therefore not as tolerant of the pest. The rootstock 41B is a Chasselas x *Berlandieri* cross and therefore does not have 100 per cent American species blood and there are reports of it suffering from *Phylloxera* damage in overseas vineyards. Given that in the UK it is being used on high-pH soils (as it has a tolerance of 40 per cent of active $CaCO_3$) and is also 'low-medium' for vigour, growers using it should make doubly sure that *Phylloxera* does not establish itself in their vineyards. The only rootstock that is currently actively resistant to *Phylloxera* is Börner which is a *Riparia x Cinerea* crossing. This means that instead of supporting, but not encouraging the root-gall form of *Phylloxera*, it actively rejects them. For this reason it is becoming more popular in Germany.

## Birds

Bird damage in vineyards is a worldwide problem and the UK is no exception. In many parts of Europe, where vines have been grown for centuries and where many wine areas and regions consist of hundreds, even thousands, of hectares of vines and no other crops, the native bird populations have been substantially reduced by shooting and trapping. In German winegrowing regions, and very likely in other Old World winegrowing regions as well, pensioners and teenagers will be allocated their own patch of vines and during the four to six weeks prior to harvest, will spend all their daylight hours patrolling their vines with rattles (what we would call old-fashioned football rattles), lighting bird-banger ropes and generally keeping birds on the move. When flocks of starlings threaten, it is not uncommon to see quite large numbers of vineyard owners appear as if from nowhere, armed with shotguns. In other countries where vineyards are more isolated, birds can be hugely damaging and will, if left to their own devices, take almost all the crop.

The extent of bird damage will depend on many factors and no two vineyards, and indeed no two years, will suffer the same level of damage. Such factors as the proximity of woods, buildings and other safe-havens to which birds can escape and roost; the availability of other crops which might either make the area attractive, thus drawing them in, or provide easier to obtain or more satisfying food, thus diverting them from eating grapes; and the presence of overhead high-voltage wires which make ideal perching spots from where to plan their attacks will all affect the level of bird damage. The presence in the area of birds-of-prey can also deter birds, but in my experience they cannot provide anything approaching even partial protection from damage.

In years when other crops and natural foods (hedgerow fruit) are plentiful, bird damage to grapes tends to be less as these other foods are generally ripe before grapes, easier to access, and, at least in the case of hedgerow fruits, are not protected. In early years, especially with early varieties, and even more especially with red varieties or varieties that colour up as they ripen (such as Schönburger grapes which turn dark pink to tawny as they ripen), bird damage will always be greater than with those high-acid white varieties that tend to ripen later. The main attractant to the birds appears to be a combination of the sugar level and the softness of the grape – which typically go together – with darker grapes being more visually attractive (or perhaps just more noticeable) than green grapes.

In the early decades of the revival of viticulture in the UK, birds were often cited as the main problem facing vineyard owners. The first vintage at Hambledon in 1955, the first vintage of the modern era, was largely eaten by birds. Major-General Sir Guy Salisbury-Jones had engaged a winemaker from Bordeaux, Monsieur Chardon, to come and help with the winemaking. Unfortunately, the 1955 *vendange* in Bordeaux was very late and by the time Chardon arrived, the birds had eaten most of the Hambledon grapes. Salisbury-Jones recounted the story:

*Every day the lovely green bunches grew less. Here and there, tucked away under the foliage, a few bunches still defied the invaders. Elsewhere, only the naked hideous stalks remained. It reminded me of moments in the First World War, when some lovely wood, under the ceaseless pounding of the guns, would slowly be transformed into a gaunt array of skeletons that had once been trees.*

Salisbury-Jones was not the only vineyard owner to face the same problem. Growers had limited options: pick early before the bird damage got too severe, the result of which was some fairly green, high-acid, thin wines; double (and often re-double) efforts to scare birds off with a wide array of devices, static, audible, and visual; mount early morning and early evening patrols armed with a shotgun; or net. Most tried a combination of all, although picking early was never the right option. Scaring devices work for a time and work better with some species, but audible ones (gas cannons, bird scaring 'banger' ropes and recorded distress calls) tend to upset the neighbours. The current National Farmers Union (NFU) 'Bird Scarers Code' advises that they should not be used more than four times per hour, not within 200 m of 'sensitive buildings' and not before dawn or after dusk. Vineyards with footpaths running through or near them may also find that they receive complaints if audible devices are placed too near.

Devices such as black cotton strung along the rows (long-used in fruit orchards to deter bullfinches from taking apple and pear buds) worked against some species but proved a nightmare to both pickers and machinery. Humming tape, spinning discs, magic mirrors, CDs strung

along rows and a range of other devices barely worked and if they did at all, it was very short-lived. Two devices which do appear to work are helium-filled kites (such as the Allsopp Helikite shown above) and birdscaring 'hawk' kites. These devices, which can 'fly' above the crop, are relatively maintenance free, and can be moved around the vineyard, are cheap enough – at least in relation to the value of the crop they are protecting – for there to be enough per vineyard for them to provide some protection. The product made by Scarem (www.scarem.co.uk) which is mounted on a 10 m telescopic pole is effective. The company claim that one 'hawk' will 'protect approximately twenty acres' (8-ha) of land is probably true for arable crops such as rape when pigeons are a nuisance, but for grapes I would suggest at least one kite per 2-ha (5-acres) and to move them to different locations on a weekly basis.

In the early '80s, a product called Mesurol, which was widely used at the time in New Zealand vineyards, proved very effective at discouraging birds and several UK growers used it for a few years until it was withdrawn from use for this purpose. It was known as 'electric fencing for birds' as once they had tasted grapes sprayed with Mesurol, they never touched them again. According to the literature at the time, it was said that it constricted the bird's throats and made them gasp a bit (this is probably not an accurate technical description of the effect). Unfortunately, it wasn't good news for wildlife if it got into watercourses, so it was banned. Mesurol (the active ingredient of which is *Methiocarb*) is still sold in the UK and used as a seed dressing – to stop birds eating seeds after they are sown – and as a slug and snail bait (i.e. killer). If you have ever wondered why the birds don't eat slug pellets after you have sprinkled them on your garden, this is the reason! I also note from Bayer's Australian website that it is permitted in vineyards against snails and slugs. Other sprayable products based upon such things as chilli pepper and garlic were (and still are) sold as 'natural' sprayable bird deterrents, but the risk of the product persisting on the grapes and possibly passing into the wine and tainting it was always too great. In the US, a product called RejeX-it Migrate which contains Methyl Anthranilate is approved for a wide range of species and crops including grapes. It claims that 'one treatment can last up to three weeks' and that for wine grapes there is only a five day HI. They recommend a use rate of around 47 litres-ha (19 litres-acre) at a product cost of £750-ha (£304-acre), so by no means cheap. Whether it works or not is another matter and the advice leaflet for the product ends, somewhat ominously: 'Be realistic. Nothing is 100 per cent. There are no silver bullets.'

Netting, on the other hand, erected correctly, does work 100 per cent. Lamberhurst Vineyards were probably the largest users of whole-vineyard overhead netting and at one time had over 16-ha (40-acres) worth of Lobrene netting (made by Low Brothers of Dundee – now known as Don and Low) which was laboriously erected over the top of their vineyard rows, stitched together where the 6.0 m wide strips met and weighted and pegged down along the sides and ends. Whilst it undoubtedly worked, the cost, not only of buying it and erecting it, but also of removing it, mending it, and storing it in vermin-free storage, was prodigious.

An alternative to multi-use netting such as Lobrene was a Swiss product called XiroNet which was sold for one-off use (although some growers claimed to get two seasons out of it) and was cheap enough to tear off and burn after the harvest. It was a very lightweight yellow product, which came on a 1 m roll which, when held aloft on a purpose-made dispenser on the back of the tractor, expanded to 10 m wide. Each roll cost around £150 and covered 0.2-ha (0.5-acres), although you lost some of that area where it draped down to the ground at the sides and ends. For several seasons I used it to great effect at Tenterden Vineyards, wearing my fingers to the quick with stitching the edges of the net together where they met in the middle of the rows, and making twice-daily patrols to disentangle hedgehogs and mend holes where dogs, foxes and badgers had found their way through it. XiroNet does not appear to be made any more.

The main problem with all types of overhead netting, but XiroNet in particular (probably because of its colour it was difficult to see) is that birds, especially songbirds and starlings, are easily trapped in the net. They often hang there for hours emitting loud distress calls which, although this frightens off other birds, causes visitors and neighbours to complain (quite rightly of course) and also attracts other birds such as owls and kestrels which are after the trapped birds and then themselves get caught. Some growers have tried side-netting, hung on to the existing training wires and clipped together at the top and bottom, but birds easily find that they can hang on to the outside of the net and peck the grapes through the netting, so this technique is not completely successful. However, with the right rolling and unrolling equipment and by using cheap netting (big-bale wrap works well), this is a cost-effective way of making a vineyard semi-bird proof, although it does tend to hamper air movement within the canopy and make late-season disease problems, especially *Botrytis*, more of an issue.

In New Zealand, where vineyards are often isolated, bird netting is very widely used and (according to Mike Trought) its use is as high as 90 per cent of vineyards in certain regions. Given that there are 34,000-ha of vines in New Zealand that is a lot of bird netting. Growers mostly use overhead netting which covers several rows and drapes down to the ground or netting covering whole vineyards (or at least much larger areas) which is supported by an additional wirework frame erected above the vines. If your bird problem is severe, then this latter solution is probably the easiest and most effective. The overhead wires act as 'rails' along which the netting can be dragged to put it on, and the wirework is sufficiently high enough above the vines for it not to get tangled up with the growing shoots, a real plus when it comes to taking the nets off. Damage to the nets is also kept to a minimum. Overhead netting also allows easy access for tractors for spraying, and eventually picking, after the nets have been put on, by raising up the ends for access.

In the UK, the widespread use of nets to protect vineyards against birds started to decline in the late 1980s and today it is seen less often. The reasons for this decline are various. In the days when many of the grapes being grown were relatively low-value German crosses such as Müller-Thurgau, Reichensteiner, Bacchus, and Schönburger – Seyval blanc never seemed to suffer so much as it was both later ripening and less sweet – the cost of netting versus the costs of other systems of bird control made it prohibitive. The increase in the area down to the later ripening varieties Pinot noir and Chardonnay also probably helped as birds appear to be less interested in these. Some more isolated vineyards use it – Camel Valley still nets almost all of its vines – and it is often used on vulnerable early ripening varieties, in situations where vineyards are remote from habitation and in relatively small vineyards where the owner wants 100 per cent peace of mind and the task of putting it on can perhaps be achieved in a weekend with a few friends.

*Side netting in a Yorkshire vineyard*

A major factor in the reduction in the use of bird netting in the UK has been the decline in bird numbers over the last few decades. The early 1980s saw the start of the decline in certain bird species including starlings, blackbirds and thrushes, the birds that caused the most damage in UK vineyards. The British Trust for Ornithology's (BTO) Common Birds Census and Breeding Bird Survey shows that the UK's population of starlings, by far the most damaging species, because of their habit of attacking vineyards in large numbers, has declined by 75-80 per cent since the mid-'60s, and that the song-thrush and blackbird populations have more than halved in the same period. Also, the rise in bird species such as magpies and jays, which typically do not eat grapes, but which do prey upon birds which do, has further reduced pressure on grapes from these garden birds. In addition, there have been significant rises in the population of birds of prey. The BTO records that three commonly found UK birds of prey – buzzard, sparrow-hawk and red kite – are all showing 'rapid increase' which in some vineyards has definitely contributed towards the lack of damage from other bird species. Taken together, these factors have resulted in far less bird damage in UK vineyards. However, with natural sugar levels rising seemingly with each vintage and as some species of birds start to recover their numbers, one cannot rule out the re-appearance of netted vineyards in the future.

In some vineyards, pheasants (and occasionally partridges) can be a problem, but these are almost always vineyards situated near to a farm or estate with a shoot and especially if the shoot's release pen is within 1.6-k (1-mile) of the vineyard. Pheasants do not generally perch on the wires and get amongst the foliage like most other birds,

but take the grapes by pecking them from the ground or leaping up and taking them. It stands to reason therefore that if your vineyard is liable to be damaged by pheasants, the higher the fruiting wire the better. However, an adult pheasant can easily jump to 800 mm or more and you may still lose fruit at this height. Pheasants, especially juvenile ones, don't really like flying and tend to enter vineyards along the ground from the ends and sides. Netting the ends and sides therefore, especially the perimeters facing where the birds come from (adjacent woodland or towards where the release pens are situated), may well deter some of them.

For many vineyards, the capital costs, plus the costs of putting on and removing nets, is just too much to consider, especially those with fluctuating yields where the value of the crops to be protected is none too certain. Therefore a combination of static, silent methods such as balloons and kites, and, in areas where neighbours will not be annoyed, a limited amount of audible devices such as gas-guns and banger ropes, plus patrols at feeding times, especially with varieties susceptible to bird damage, provides adequate, if not total, protection. It may be in the future, if vineyards start to investigate protected growing systems in order to overcome such hazards as spring frosts and poor flowering conditions, then the framework used to carry the protection might also be used as support for bird nets. After all, if you are going to the considerable expense of covering your crop, you certainly want to make sure you pick every grape you grow.

Airport operators – including military airports – have developed a wide array of techniques to scare birds as a 'bird strike' can easily damage an engine and a quick look on Google under 'airport bird scaring' will bring up 223,000 results. When you start reading them – the Wikipedia page is a good place to start – you will see that they all agree on one thing: most sensible methods work for a while, but only a while. Birds get used to everything short of being killed, so if birds are a problem, try several different methods and keep rotating them on a regular basis. Under certain conditions, certain species of birds damaging fruit crops may be killed (or trapped and destroyed) for which a 'general licence' is required. These are issued (in England) by Natural England under the provisions of the 1981 Wildlife and Countryside Act. The list of species that may be killed is relatively short and includes wild pigeons and doves, rooks, jackdaws, magpies and jays, plus certain species of geese and gulls. Blackbirds and thrushes, which are partial to grapes, are protected by law and may not be harmed. Starlings, also very partial to grapes, are, somewhat surprisingly, protected by law in England (but not yet in Northern Ireland, Scotland or Wales) and may also not be disturbed or harmed. The Royal Society for the Protection of Birds (RSPB) has full details on its website.

A recent article in the Australian *Wine and Viticulture Journal* suggested that in a few years' time, fleets of drones, programmed to fly in formation up and down vineyards, even in-between the rows of vines, emitting distress calls and any other noise that might scare birds, would be available. Bizarre as this might seem, if Amazon are proposing to use them to deliver parcels, then I guess anything is possible!

*Pheasant damage confined to the lowest bunches*

## Diseases

Successful disease control in vines really requires a two or three stage approach and is not just about spraying the right chemicals at the right time (although that helps). Most diseases are made worse when canopies are crowded, shaded and slow to dry out. Light and air, those most valuable of (free) natural resources, must be encouraged, through good and timely canopy management, to penetrate into the centre of the leaf-wall. Leaves should look clean, with a good glossy finish (depending on variety) and be uniformly bright green in colour. It is only older leaves that will start to fade. The yellowing of leaves inside the canopy is a sure sign of a shaded canopy and indicative of poor light penetration. Good canopy management also requires that winter pruning is carried out correctly, excess shoots are removed after budburst, and deleafing and trimming are attended to. Excessive weed growth below the vines and long grass in the alleyways can also add to the level of moisture in the atmosphere. Any mechanical damage, such as that from hail, animals, insects, or damage by wires or machinery, will allow disease to get a hold on the vine, especially from *Botrytis.*

## Powdery Mildew - Oidium

Powdery Mildew (PM) or *Oidium*, which used to be known as *Uncinula necator* but is now more correctly known as *Erysiphe necator,* is a fungal disease native to eastern North America where it did little damage to the native vine varieties and caused little excitement. Its first European appearance was in Margate, on the north Kent coast, in 1831 or 1832. Mr Tucker, the gardener to a Mr John Slater, noticed a white powdery discolouration on a few leaves of a vine in a greenhouse under his care. These he sent to the Reverend M. J. Berkeley (a famous fungologist who wrote the *Outlines of British Fungology*) who sent an account of the 'new' disease to the *Gardener's Chronicle and Agricultural Gazette* and named it (incorrectly as it happened, as it is not a true *Oidium*) *Oidium Tuckeri*, after gardener Tucker. It didn't then make much of an impact upon European vines until the mid-1840s when potato blight (a similar disease) first appeared in Europe on the Isle of Wight in August 1845. PM soon followed.

PM soon appeared in France – the keeper of the Versailles grape-forcing houses complained of the new disease in 1846 – and it quickly spread throughout the vineyard regions, causing widespread damage. Tucker had already noticed the physical and visual similarity between his mildew and that of peach mildew which was then (as it still can be today) controlled by sprays of sulphur and it was found that this remedy worked on vines. The vintage of 1854 was the smallest in France since 1788 (a year when the French *paysannerie* no doubt had other things on their minds), caused by nation-wide attacks of PM. Only then did growers take to treating their vines with sulphur – sprayed in cooler regions and dusted[6] in warmer ones – which proved to be a very cheap and effective remedy. It was found that sulphur had the effect of increasing yields and bringing the harvest forward by 7-10 days, two factors which made the uptake of sulphur as an effective remedy quite rapid. Sulphur also works against other diseases and mites, so its protection against PM was but one of a number of benefits.

PM is one of the few fungal diseases that are worse in dry years than they are in wet ones and unlike most fungal diseases, it does not require water to convey it from one part of the vine to another. Air with sufficient humidity is enough. It prefers warm weather (18°-30°C or 64°-86°F) and still, humid conditions and thrives inside shaded canopies as the spores are inactivated by bright sunlight. It overwinters on old wood and given the right conditions, will often start producing spores which are spread by the wind and will attack any part of the vine early in the season, especially tender tissue such as young leaves and inflorescences. If untreated or if treatments are ineffective, the first signs of PM will be a slight discoloration on the leaves and if allowed to progress the leaves will be dusted with a white powdery covering. In the UK, leaves often remain in quite good condition and the first signs of PM will be a dusty mauve-white covering to the berries, especially those inside the most shaded part of the canopy. Quite why this should be is an interesting question and it has been suggested that a combination of our relatively low temperatures, coupled with leaves that are often wet, means that the disease is not able to attack the leaves as

easily as it does in warmer, drier and more humid climates. Depending on the state of development of the bunch, the grapes will either just wither away or, if large enough, they will split open and the seeds will pop out like two eyes – what I call the 'Mekon' look.[7] Usually, as PM attacks early in the season, damaged berries never reach the point where they ripen. In machine harvested vineyards and where there are a large number of PM infected berries remaining on the vine, there is always the danger of the juice and/or wine becoming tainted.

Unless you are growing a variety such as Seyval blanc, which is almost totally resistant to PM, it is safe to assume that your vines will get the disease. Some varieties are very susceptible, Chardonnay being one of them. When to start spraying will depend on whether you have bud mites to control, in which case you should get two applications of sulphur at a high rate on to the canes pre-bud burst. Otherwise, aim to get the first application on when the first leaves are open and keep on spraying on a 10-14 day cycle until just before flowering. By this time, you should have gained the upper hand. Delaying spraying until you see the first signs of the disease is unwise as by the time you see the disease, it is too late to prevent it and you will have to use more expensive curative products. Sulphur's effectiveness is temperature related and below around 15°C is far less active that in the 20-25° range typically seen in UK vineyards. Therefore early applications, when temperatures may be lower, may not be as effective as later applications when temperatures have risen.

There are several products, including sprays based upon strobilurins[8], available to spray against PM and which product you choose will depend upon several factors. However, given that sulphur is (a) cheap, (b) effective, (c) helps control mites and other insects, and (d) is often deficient in soils, it is the first choice of many vinegrowers. The other thing to remember when using sulphur is not to skimp on the volume of water used. Sulphur is a contact material and has no systemic action and can only work if the product, in solution, gets to all the parts of the vine it is trying to protect. It is therefore very important that spray rates are high enough, especially when the canopy reaches its full size, so that all parts of the vine are fully wetted. The most important sprays are those that go on to the open inflorescence during flowering and up until fruit-set. In countries warmer than the UK, it is usual to avoid using sulphur directly in the open flower as it is claimed that it can burn foliage and soft tissues, i.e. inflorescences. Given that temperatures during flowering in the UK seldom rise above 30°C (86°F), let alone the 38 °C (100°F) at which sulphur is said to damage vines, it is probably quite safe to continue using sulphur throughout the flowering period. However, on the basis of better safe than sorry, if temperatures are high, it is probably safer to switch to another material during the flowering and immediate post-flowering period.

As has already been pointed out in the section on *Harvest intervals* earlier in this chapter, sulphur applied to grapes in the UK used to have a HI of between 21 and 56 days depending on the exact product used, but now it has been re-classified as a fertliser and there is no HI. But, please note that in other European winegrowing countries, sulphur still has a 56 day HI on wine grapes and it is advisable that applications of sulphur should finish in good time before the harvest. In any event, if you haven't got good control of PM by 56 days before harvest, it is probably too late. The maximum rate of sulphur allowed in UK vineyards is far lower than in other European countries and you cannot use higher rates than allowed by UK legislation except under certain conditions. The UK rate is 250 g per 100 l (which is only 3 kg-ha at high volume) whereas in Germany for instance, 900 g per 100 l (11 kg-ha at high volume) is permitted at certain growth stages. However, if you are in a sulphur deficient area or can show, by reference to soil samples, that sulphur is deficient in your soil, and can persuade a FACTS advisor that your vines need more sulphur, then 10 kg-ha can be applied. Potassium Bicarbonate, which has EAMU approval for control of PM (and a zero day HI) can also be used.

There are also quite a wide range of 'alternative' materials that can be used for 'nutritional purposes' but which also may help with PM control. These include Potassium Sulphite, Monopotassium Phosphate, dilute solutions of Hydrogen Peroxide and various oils. All of these materials have little protective or residual activity, but can help with eradicating the disease and reducing the number of active spores on the plant. They need to be sprayed on a more frequent basis than other materials – probably on a seven day programme – and, as with sulphur, need to be sprayed on with sufficient water volume to thoroughly coat every part of the vine.

The main point to remember about PM is that it is relatively easy to prevent the disease from starting, but relatively difficult to eradicate it once it has got going. If you leave spraying until you see the first signs of the disease, you are probably two sprays behind the curve and you will have to use more expensive, curative, rather than cheaper, protective materials. An open canopy will greatly aid fungicide applications and deleafing immediately following flowering will allow pre-bunch-close sprays to reach all parts of the bunch.

## Downy Mildew

Downy Mildew (DM), also known as *Plasmopara viticola,* Peronospora and (in France) *le Mildiou,* originated, like PM, in North America. It was first seen in Europe in 1878 and quickly spread and is now endemic to almost all the world's vineyards. It overwinters on fallen leaves and, once present in a vineyard, is impossible to eradicate, although with regular sprays it can be kept under control. It likes warm, damp conditions, between 20°-25°C is considered optimal, and will attack any green part of the vine once the weather warms up. The first signs of DM are either light discolorations on the surface of the leaves which in time will turn darker – the so-called 'tar spots' – or small patches of mould on the underside of the leaf. Inflorescences can also be infected, shrivelling and turning brown with white mould on the stem of the inflorescence. On the berries, DM will show itself as a white fungal covering or later on in the season, will shrivel the grapes and turn them leathery (hence the German name for the disease *lederbeeren* - leatherberry). If present in sufficient numbers at harvest time and if machine harvested, infected berries can impart a characteristic mouldy taint to the wine. A common pattern to the spread of the disease is that chemical control is gained by the grower in the early and middle parts of the growing season, but, as the leaf-wall increases in thickness and density and spray penetration into, and air movement within, the canopy becomes more difficult, late season outbreaks of the disease occur. In this instance the leaves, especially the younger ones at the top of the canopy, which by this time are contributing significantly to the overall level of photosynthesis, become severely damaged and sugar production is reduced. This leads to a slowing down of the ripening process and it is therefore important to keep up protection against DM until as near to the end of the season as HIs will permit.

Control of DM is helped by the usual physical ones – opening up the leaf-wall to light, air and drying winds – but these alone will not eradicate the disease and spraying will be necessary. In 1885 it was discovered that sprays containing copper were effective against DM and Bordeaux Mixture (a blend of slaked or hydrated lime and copper sulphate), was developed.[9] Bordeaux Mixture is still a potent protective spray against the disease and its characteristic blue/mauve dusty traces can be seen in vineyards throughout the world, although it is not permitted in commercial vineyards in the UK (although it can still be bought in garden centres for domestic use). The disadvantage of Bordeaux Mixture is that it needs preparing freshly each time it is used and can, if over-used, lead to increased levels of copper in the soil, which is toxic to worms and other soil flora and fauna. Copper in the form of copper oxychloride is permitted in UK vineyards, although most growers will only use it for a post-harvest winter wash, or early pre and post-budburst 'clean up' sprays. Several other products are available, both protective and curative, and the choice of which material to use will depend upon your spray regime and disease status of the vineyard. Copper-containing products have no HI in the UK, whereas on wine grapes in many other countries – Germany for instance – an HI of 35 days is typical. This is because of the danger of traces of copper getting into the fermentation, something to be avoided.

## Botrytis

*Botrytis (Botrytis cinerea),* also known as Grey Rot or Sour Rot, is a very common fungus that occurs widely in nature and attacks all manner of vegetable, salad and fruit crops. Lettuces that turn brown and start to liquefy and strawberries and raspberries that subside into a mass of grey/mauve mould are all being attacked by *Botrytis*. It particularly likes wet and damp conditions and thrives where sugar is present, hence it's liking for grapes, especially when grown in climates with summer and autumn rain. It is also a problem for table grape growers if they have to store their grapes and for nurserymen who store wood for grafting. *Botrytis* is also one of the most damaging of diseases in vineyards as, given its preference for sugar-rich and decaying fruit, it often only appears late in the season when grapes are in their final stages of ripening. This makes chemical control difficult, as most anti-*Botrytis* chemicals have at least a 14-day HI and many have a 21-day or even 28-day one. Having said the above, I actually believe that the UK suffers fewer problems with *Botrytis* than in vineyards in warmer climates. Why? Our

temperatures, especially night-time temperatures during the month before harvesting, are lower; grape sugars are lower giving the fungus less to live on; acid levels are higher; and pH levels lower. All of these tend to make the growth of *Botrytis* less than it would otherwise be in warmer climates with sweeter, lower acid grapes. In many vineyards, with good canopy management and good chemical control, the incidence of rampant, grape-devouring *Botrytis*, such as we used to see in crops of Müller-Thurgau and Reichensteiner in the 1980s and 1990s, is a thing of the past. Having said that, some varieties, especially early ripening varieties such as Optima, Ortega and Siegerrebe (where sugar levels are high when temperatures are higher), may well be attacked.

*Botrytis starting to affect ripe bunches*

In the winery, if white grapes are heavily infected, some $SO_2$ in the picking bins, better pre-fermentation settling and a prompt fermentation using a high dose of active yeast, may well produce a wine without any noticeable *Botrytis* taint, although some fruit aromas and flavours will have been lost, the colour may well be a shade or two darker and more $SO_2$ will be required in the finished wine in order to achieve a good level of stability. In red wines, where fermentations take place in the presence of skins and pulp, more serious problems may arise including off-flavours and mouldy taints which will need charcoal fining to remove them. Wines made from *Botrytis* infected grapes will also be more difficult to filter and clarify because of the presence of glucans.

The damage *Botrytis* can do if left to develop is not to be underestimated, not only to the current year's grapes, but also to the buds holding next year's crop. It is my belief that one of the reasons why Seyval blanc crops so much better than *Botrytis*-prone *vinifera* varieties is that it never suffers bud loss from this disease. In the UK we also used to see a lot of stem-rot (Bunch Stem Necrosis), especially in years with high yields. *Botrytis* would attack the stem of the bunch so that the bunch would eventually drop on to the ground. It was not untypical to see the ground beneath the vines carpeted with healthy-looking bunches that had had their stems destroyed. Mineral deficiencies (especially of calcium and magnesium) can help weaken stems, so vineyard nutrition also plays a part in the control of *Botrytis*.

The control of *Botrytis* is helped by creating an open canopy, by shoot removal and deleafing in the fruiting zone, and by good air movement beneath the vines. Spores are transmitted from one part of the vine to the other by running or dripping water, so the quicker the leaves and shoots dry out, the less the disease will spread. An open leaf canopy will also allow chemical sprays to reach their target more easily.

*Botrytis* is a disease that has a reputation for becoming resistant to certain chemicals. In the late 1960s and well into the 1970s, as has already been mentioned, the main products used against *Botrytis* contained an active ingredient called *benzimidazole* (marketed as Benlate or Benomyl) which for some years were very effective. However, growers found that after using them for several years on the same fields, not only did their worm populations start to dwindle, but also the effectiveness of the products fell away and it was realised that their particular strain of *Botrytis* (it has a habit of becoming site specific) had become resistant.

The next generation of anti-*Botrytis* products were based upon active ingredients called *dicarboximides* – Ronilan, Rovral WG and Sumisclex were the three best known – and these proved reliable for a decade or more until, once again, their effectiveness tailed off and resistant strains of *Botrytis* surfaced, although Rovral WG, which has a 14 day HI, can still be used in conjunction with other products up to a maximum of four applications per season. In 1995, a completely new product called *Scala*, based upon an active ingredient called *pyrimethanil*, was introduced. This is a systemic product (all the previous products are contact only) and its use is restricted to a maximum of only two applications per year. It is, however, one of the most effective materials against *Botrytis*, but it has a 21 day HI (although outside Europe it only has a 7 day HI). Other products based upon different active ingredients, such as Teldor and Switch (both of which are also limited to two applications per season), are also permitted for use in the UK.

In addition to the pesticides listed above, three other products are also permitted for use against *Botrytis* on grapes in the UK. Serenade ASO is a bio-fungicide based upon *Bacillus subtilis* and has no HI, making it useful for the final anti-*Botrytis* spray, although it is one of the most expensive products on the market. Prestop is another bio-fungicide, based upon *Gliocladium catenulatum* which also has a zero day HI. How effective these bio-products are is open to question and not everyone who has tried them has been totally happy.

There is also an anti-*Botrytis* recommendation for a growth regulator called Regalis which, if sprayed towards the end of the flowering period, will open up the bunch by reducing the number of berries on the bunch. In years with good flowering conditions, where bunches are expected to be large, and especially with tight-bunched varieties (Chardonnay and some clones of Pinot noir for instance),

this could be considered. Growth regulators are nothing new in grape growing, and all table grapes are sprayed with them to produce the large, perfectly shaped bunches of disease-free grapes that we expect to see in supermarkets.

*Botrytis* is usually present in the vineyard throughout the year. It overwinters in the shape of *sclerotia* (hard, dark-brown encrustations of the dormant fungus) which are present on old wood and on grapes that have not been picked or have fallen to the vineyard floor. As soon as spring conditions are suitable, the *sclerotia* will provide the nucleus for the fungus to infect the young green tissue in the vineyard. Given that the UK has relatively damp growing conditions and most of our varieties are susceptible, spraying against *Botrytis* using a general, broad-spectrum fungicide should start when the first one or two leaves are expanded to about 25 mm across. There will be years when two or three pre-flowering sprays, followed by perhaps one during flowering and two to three after will still be too few; there may on the other hand be years, especially when growing conditions are dry and when the variety in question has a degree of in-built resistance, when two sprays prior to flowering and two after will suffice. As most anti-*Botrytis* products are relatively expensive, their use needs to be carefully targeted in terms of timing.

As with many diseases, the damage *Botrytis* can do early in the season, if uncontrolled, will make life much harder later on. *Botrytis* will infect the flowers and in a year with wet flowering conditions, especially when the flower caps struggle to detach themselves from the flowers, the disease can remain trapped in the centre of the bunch. As the grapes expand and the bunch closes, the disease will be deep inside and no amount of spraying will have any effect. In varieties with tight bunches – the Pinots and Chardonnay for instance – berries can actually burst inside the bunch due to the pressure from expanding grapes and this is often where internal *Botrytis* starts and is impossible to control. This will lead to classic *Botrytis* bunch rot and may result in substantial crop loss. The most important single spray to help control *Botrytis* is the one applied as flowering finishes. This will hopefully do two things: blow out and disperse any fragments of flower caps and stamens left within the bunch and coat the remainder with a protective spray. *Botrytis* is also a secondary invader and will take advantage of grapes that have been damaged by such things as machinery, hail, insects or birds. In these situations, where the skin of the grape has been split and the pulp exposed, *Botrytis* will develop and gradually infect the whole bunch.

The use of *Botrytis* to produce sweet wines (Sauternes, Tokay, German sweet wines etc) through the action of what the UK wine trade calls Noble Rot (and known as *Pourriture Noble* in France and *Edelfäule* in Germany) is certainly rare in UK vineyards, although not unknown. Most of the very good, even excellent, sweet wines made in the UK have been made using high-sugar varieties such as Ortega, Optima and Huxelrebe, and many have been outright accidents where growers have seen rampant *Botrytis* devour their crop, but realised that what they were witnessing was classic Noble Rot. The best have a luscious fruit character with a backing of superb acidity.

Once grapes reach a potential alcohol level of around 7 per cent (56°OE), *Botrytis* will affect the grape in a different way. Feeding on the skin of the berry, the fungus will puncture the skin without splitting it and will allow water to leach out. This happens in a slow controlled manner and over time – perhaps up to six weeks – individual grapes on the bunch will shrivel considerably. Such juice as is left in the grape will be much lower in volume, but in terms of sugar content will be much higher. Acids will also be preserved, something really sweet wines need plenty of if they are to be balanced on the palate. For Noble Rot to happen, several things are necessary: the crop must be clean up until the point where the sugar level rises to the correct level; the weather should be warm, even hot; and humidity is required for the *Botrytis* spores to develop. In the UK, we quite often have two of these – the rising sugar level and the humidity – it is just the hot weather that sometimes eludes us.

## Other diseases

If control of the mildews and *Botrytis* has been achieved, then there are few other diseases that will make life difficult for UK vineyard owners. *Phomopsis* (dealt with in *Chapter 17: Trunk diseases*) and what the Germans call *Roterbrenner* (caused by *Pseudopezicula tracheiphila*), plus Black Rot (caused by *Guignardia bidwellii*) and Anthracnose (Black Spot) are all occasional visitors, but cannot be classed as 'important' in UK vineyards and will all be controlled by the same fungicides already being used.

## Viruses

Jack Ward, in his 1984 book *Vine Growing in the British Isles*, saw fit to devote a whole chapter on 'virus diseases' listing *Court-noué*, Yellow Mosaic, *Flavescence Dorée*, Grape Leaf Roll Virus, Pierce's Disease, Yellow Vein, Asteroid Mosaic and Vein Banding as being of danger and there were also another seven which had been 'identified and reported' (although not, I assume, in UK vineyards)! How times have changed. Today, you would have to look quite hard to find many virus infected vines in UK vineyards, such has been the improvement over the last thirty years in virus control throughout the whole production process of vines. Both rootstock and scion varieties have been subjected to 'heat treatment' (which is not the same as Hot Water Treatment – HWT – of which more later) to remove viruses from a single vine of each rootstock variety and each scion variety and then using that single vine as the basis for all future mother blocks of that variety. This technical measure, together with the enforcement of the Plant Passport system and the ELISA[10] tests for viruses, has reduced the incidence of vine viruses to a point where, in many European regions, they are almost unknown. Insects such as mealy bug and various types of sharpshooter, plus nematodes (of which there are several types), all of which can act as vectors for both viruses and diseases, are luckily absent from the UK, mainly on account of our relatively low temperatures and our isolation.

In other parts of the world where temperatures are higher and controls are not so strict and in *Phylloxera*-free areas where the practice of taking wood from vineyards in order to produce rooted cuttings is common, viruses, especially ones like Leaf Roll and Corky Bark, can cause problems. I have in the past seen instances of Crown Gall and occasional leaf and shoot deformities (flat, double bud canes) which might suggest virus problems, but these were very isolated and did not appear to spread. It would be brave to say that UK vineyards do not suffer and will not suffer in the future from viruses and, as we have seen with TDs, these problems seemingly can come from nowhere. Once a vine is virus infected, there is no cure, and removal and replacement is the only solution.

1 BASIS is an organisation that manages the Professional Register for qualified pesticide advisors. www.basis-reg.com
2 The French firm Albuz are the leaders in nozzle technology. http://www.albuz-spray.com/en/
3 See www.englishwine.com/wgigb.htm for this document.
4 www.lipco.com/english/products/TUNNEL_Sprayers/tunnel_sprayers.htm
5 The 'Green Book' is officially called: Full Label and Extension Approvals and is published by the UKVA.
6 Dusting of sulphur is preferred in warmer regions as it is less likely to cause scalding or russeting of the grape's skin. Dusting is often carried out very early in the morning when there is still dew on the grapes so that the sulphur sticks to the skin, before being absorbed as the skin dries out.
7 The Mekon was the evil leader of the Treens (from northern Venus) in the Dan Dare story in *The Eagle* comic of the 1950s and 1960s.
8 Strobilurins are sprays developed from a toadstool called *Strobilurus tenacellus*.
9 It is said that growers with vineyards by the roadside would spray their vines and grapes with copper sulphate (which is both visible and bitter to the taste) in order to stop passers-by helping themselves. Once Downy Mildew appeared, it was noticed that these vines did not get the disease.
10 ELISA stands for Enzyme-Linked ImmunoSorbent Assay and is a test for viruses in many different areas: plants, food and human tissue.

# Chapter 17

# Trunk diseases

## Trunk diseases

**Note:** The discussion of trunk diseases in the confines of this book can only hope to provide an overview of the subject and to offer some practical advice to vineyard owners. Links to further reading on the subject can be found throughout this chapter.

In the summer of 2011, UK winegrowers were alerted to a new threat to their vines, a collection of conditions generically known as Trunk Diseases (TDs). Dr Richard Smart, as a WineSkills mentor, had visited 'around 30 vineyards' and had found 'symptoms of *Botryosphaeria* [one of the major TDs] in all but one'. Smart also reported that in most vineyards the level of infected vines was 'less than 5 per cent ', but in a few 'the disease had spread rapidly with over 50 per cent of vines infected'. Whilst there were some who thought he was being unnecessarily alarmist and many whose vineyards appeared to be unaffected by TDs, the fact is that they are a worldwide problem, and becoming more so, especially in young vines (Young Vine Decline), and therefore need to be discussed in some detail.

Many perennial species suffer from diseases which affect their permanent woody parts and in recent decades in the UK we have been introduced to Dutch elm disease, sudden oak death, red band needle blight, horse chestnut bleeding canker, and the latest, ash dieback, all of which affect woody plants, namely trees. Exactly why UK trees have been invaded by these new threats is, in many cases, still uncertain, although most authorities believe that climate change plays a part. We therefore need to be aware that vines have not been singled out for special treatment and view TDs in the light of other changes in our environment, learn their causes and learn how to manage them.

TDs of vines of course, are far from new and one of the major diseases, *Esca* (also known as Black Measles in the USA), was noted by Pliny the Elder in his book on natural history – *Naturalis Historia* published in AD 77-79 – and has been with us ever since. In slightly more recent times, the late 1800s and early 1900s, the famous French viticultural researchers Pierre Viala and Louis Ravaz carried out studies on *Esca*, then causing widespread problems in the Midi, France's great bulk wine producing region. Eutypa dieback (*Eutypa lata*) is another similar TD which has been present in vineyards for many centuries. Historically, TDs tended to affect older vines for a variety of reasons. The build-up of older wood and the presence of large pruning wounds probably allowed pathogens to enter the plant and slowly destroy it. Plus older vines are typically less vigorous than younger ones and are therefore more likely to succumb to problems which in their youth they might have survived. Before vines were grafted, the practice of layering[1] vines to replace a dead vine or even to re-invigorate a fading one, was commonplace (and still is in regions without *Phylloxera*) and this tended to obscure the problem of TDs. In more recent times however, TDs seem to have been making something of a comeback in vineyards all around the world and are today a source of concern, especially as they appear to be responsible for the already mentioned Young Vine Decline. The major TDs, as well as *Esca* and Eutypa, are *Botryosphaeria* canker, the most widespread of the many TDs, also known as Bot Canker or Black Dead Arm; Black Foot, caused by *Cylindrocarpon* fungi; Petri Disease, also known as Black Goo, Young *Esca* or black xylem decline, and caused by *Phaeoacremonium* and other fungi; and *Phomopsis viticola* also known as Excoriose and Dead Arm. Associated with *Esca* and Eutypa is also 'apoplexy' (sudden death of vines) which the French refer to as *folletage* or *tylosis*.

Exactly why TDs have become a modern problem in vineyards worldwide is a question to which there is no simple answer. One contributory factor may be viruses – or to be more precise – the lack of them, plus a general improvement in the pest and disease status in most vineyards. In the decades immediately after the Second World War, one of the most widespread problems in grapevines, which could not be tackled anywhere else but at source, i.e. in mother blocks and in nurseries where vines were produced, were viruses. Since the introduction (in the EU at least) of Plant Passports and mandatory ELISA testing for viruses, plus mandatory HWT for vines produced in regions where *Flavescence dorée* (Grapevine Yellows) is a problem, the overall health of vines has improved hugely. Higher quality grapevines, plus other viticultural improvements such as better trellising, better canopy management, better weed control and – probably most importantly – much better chemical pest and disease control in almost all vineyards, has, somewhat paradoxically, allowed TDs some space in which to work. This is somewhat like the increase in cancers affecting humans. Now that we no longer die of smallpox, polio and several other once common ailments, and life expectancy has risen (at least in most first world countries), cancer rates have also risen. Another often cited reason why *Esca* in particular has become a major problem in some regions is the banning, in 2001, of sodium arsenite, a fungicide which, when applied as a winter wash, reduced the incidence of *Esca* (as well as *Phomopsis*), and was widely used in mother blocks.

To understand and to try and get to grips with the problem of TDs, I have divided the topic into three areas:

• The source of TDs and what can be done to reduce the incidence of infected vines being brought into a new vineyard.
• The measures that should be taken when establishing a new vineyard that will allow newly planted vines to survive TDs and thrive.
• What practical steps can be taken in an established vineyard to reduce the likelihood of TDs becoming a problem, and dealing with vines suffering from TDs?

## The source of trunk diseases

There can be no doubt that infected mother blocks of both scion and rootstock wood are two of the major sources of infected material. Whilst it is a simple matter to state, the solution is not so easy to find. Having spoken to several French, German and Italian nurseries on the subject, some of whom deny knowing anything about the subject at all – 'what, my vines, trunk diseases?' – the facts are that the organisms causing TDs are, in many instances and to a greater or lesser extent, present in all mother blocks.

What nurseries will tell you is that NO vine is sterile and is 'infected' by many different organisms and even if it was sterile, it would soon be colonised by organisms, beneficial and non-beneficial, once planted in its final resting place. What nurseries will also tell you is that they have been selling vines for many years, many decades even, to growers whose vineyards thrive and who continue to come back for more vines – both of which are true – and whether or not their mother blocks are infected, nurseries live or die by the quality of their vines and their reputations and they do care about this.

My experience, having been buying vines from the same two nurseries since 1977, is that if correctly handled, planted and cared for, most vines survive, and losses after three years are typically below 2 per cent and often below 1 per cent. However, there is also no doubt that the TD problem is a real one and nurseries remain in the firing line as one of the main sources of infected material. To put the problem into perspective, one needs to know the process and timeline of the production of a grafted vine, a living plant that comes together from several sources and usually takes more than fifteen months to produce.

## Production process for grafted vines

The world-wide vine nursery business produces many hundreds of millions of grafted vines per year and is a multi-faceted industry. Smaller nurseries may well be growing very little of their own scion or rootstock wood, buying in what they need from suppliers, but grafting and raising all their own vines. Others will grow much of their own scion and rootstock wood, buying in what they are short of. There are also specialist rootstock producers who may sell the bulk of their production to nurseries, but who also produce grafted vines. Finally, there are specialist growers who produce grafted vines under contract and return them to nurseries who sell them as their own production. In short, it is a complex industry. One of the largest vine nurseries in the world, VCR in Italy, in 2010, produced: '55 million grafted vines, in 4,000 different combinations of variety, clone and rootstock, for distribution to 30 countries' and therefore one can imagine the complexities of keeping tabs on everything from start to finish. In Europe, most of the production of rootstocks is confined to the frost-free southern regions of France and north Italy and in regions where hail, which can seriously damage wood, is less of a problem. The production of scion wood is more widespread as varieties and clones are often only grown in certain regions.

The first stage in the production process is the obtaining of wood for the vine variety to be grafted (the scion wood) and the wood for the rootstock. The vineyards that provide this wood may be owned by, or under the direct control of, the vine nursery, or may belong to suppliers who make a living by trading in scion wood and rootstock wood. In the case of scion wood, the vineyards will typically be planted with 'propagation' grade plants which are certified to be true to the variety and clone specified and free of viruses. However, these are also producing vineyards, from which grapes will be harvested, and are managed and kept pest and disease free in the normal way. These vineyards are inspected at least twice during the growing season for pests (especially the leafhoppers which are the vectors for *Flavescence dorée*), signs of diseases or abnormalities – *Phylloxera,* viruses, TDs – and those vines from which cuttings may not be taken are tagged. During the dormant season, scion wood is then taken from the non-tagged vines, bundled up and by degrees, makes its way to the nursery. Whilst scion wood is typically taken before the vines are pruned, I have

known it to be taken from the wood left over after pruning, which may have been lying on the ground for some while. Once back at the nursery, the scion wood is sorted, cut into one-bud sections, disinfected, bagged and placed into cold storage.

Vineyards for rootstock wood are also planted with propagation grade plants, guaranteeing the variety and clone of the rootstock. Traditionally, vines in rootstock vineyards are not trellised, and are allowed to sprawl across the earth, forming a green mat across the surface of the vineyard. Rootstock vineyards are usually in warm to hot regions, where summer rainfall is low and therefore some are irrigated. These vineyards are, like their scion-wood counterparts, inspected and vines from which no wood may be taken, are tagged. Pest and disease control is fairly basic, given that rootstock varieties are typically quite disease resistant. In more recent years, and partially in response to problems such as TDs, some nurseries are now growing their vines lifted off the ground on 'tables' with the canes supported by wires. As the canes are not in contact with the soil, this makes air circulation better, and, after leaf-fall, they are not lying on top of a mulch of decaying leaf matter which improves their health status. However, this is a more expensive way of growing rootstocks. The amount of wood produced is lower and the cutting and collection costs are higher and nurseries are naturally reluctant to increase their costs when their competitors may not be. Vines for rootstock production can be grown on the same ground for as long as the vines are producing viable amounts of wood – twenty-five years is not uncommon – but once grubbed, the land has to remain free of vines for eleven years (at least, that is the rule in France) and for this reason, many rootstock producers lease land rather than own it. I have asked several rootstock producers whether their mother vines are ever tested for TDs and have yet to find one that does, even though some researchers believe that TDs such as Black Foot are endemic in many rootstock vineyards. Like scion wood, wood for rootstocks is then harvested after leaf-fall, taken back to the nursery, sorted, put through a de-budding machine to remove all the buds, and then disinfected, bundled up and put into a cold store to await the grafting procedure.

*Newly grafted vines in the nursery just starting to grow*

Grafting starts in the early part of the year. Almost all vines are machine grafted, the Wagner Omega machine being the most widely used, but other types of machine exist and there is even some hand-grafting still carried out. The grafting process is fairly straightforward, although the sizing of rootstock and scion wood is important so that the cambium layers (in effect the 'bark') of the two parts touch each other as much as they can. This makes the callousing better (the physical joining of the two different species of wood), the graft stronger and, most importantly, the percentage of grafted vines that will survive the whole process, and thus be available for sale, higher. What is also important is hygiene at all stages of the production process from the time that both scion and rootstock wood is harvested, to when vines are delivered out to producers. Apart from diseases picked up in the vineyards, storage conditions are important. Wood is often soaked prior to storage and/or grafting in order to make it more pliable and it has been shown that the re-use of water for soaking is probably one of the main points in the production process where disease pathogens can be transferred from one batch of wood to another.[2] During the grafting process, if the wood is too wet, it is also thought that the blades on the grafting machines, as they slice through and join the scion to the rootstock, may well be forcing TD organisms into the graft. There appears to be no way (at least, not at present) of spraying a disinfectant or fungicide on to the cut surfaces of the graft as they are joined together.

Immediately after grafting, the vines have their top 50-75 mm waxed. This helps keep the grafts together and keeps them moist and clean. After this they are placed, tightly packed together with damp sawdust and peat around their lower halves to keep them moist, into callousing boxes which are put into a heated greenhouse. The ground that the boxes are standing on will usually have soil warming cables in it which will help the roots start to grow. After a few weeks, the scion shoot will have started to grow, roots from the bottom of the rootstock will have appeared, and the graft will have calloused over. At this stage, the vines can be taken out of the callousing boxes, re-waxed and placed out in the nursery fields for the remainder of the summer. The young vines will often be planted through black polythene mulch to help weed control and aid root development. During the summer, the vines will often be irrigated and will be kept free of pests and diseases with a normal spray programme. They will also be inspected for viruses and other diseases and abnormalities and will be rogued accordingly. Land used for growing grafted vines can only be used for one season and then has to be rotated and remain free of vines for six years (again, the French rules) and using GPS, inspectors make sure that plots do not overlap from one year to the next. Again, because of this requirement, land used for this purpose is often leased rather than owned by producers.

At the end of the growing season, the grafted vines are lifted, and taken back to the nurseries. Here, they will have their roots washed and trimmed, and the growth they have made from the scion bud during the summer cut back to one bud, after which they will be re-waxed, bundled into twenty-fives, have a plant passport attached and placed back into cold store until required by producers. How they are stored (wrapped in polythene, in ventilated bags, in sealed bags), the temperatures they are stored at (and what the temperature fluctuations are), and the level of humidity, can all play their part in the development or otherwise of pathogens during storage. Then, they are taken out of cold store, loaded on to transport (for the most part not temperature controlled) and taken to the customer, which, in the case of the UK, might take several days. On arrival at the grower's premises, vines might be placed back into cold store (my preferred option) and only taken out a day or two prior to planting. Some will store them in a cool, dark place awaiting planting; others will heel them into damp soil. Eventually, after what is often an eighteen month production process, the vine will be planted in its final resting place and face its greatest challenge – a new vineyard!

In some cases, vines will not be sold in the year after production and can be put back into the nursery for a further year. Whether this is a positive or negative I have no idea, but it certainly happens on occasions. One nurseryman I know thinks he ought to charge more for two year old vines as they have more developed grafts and better roots! Nurseries will also trade with other nurseries, buying and selling scion wood, rootstock wood and finished vines. Towards the end of the ordering season, when a nursery may have run out of home-produced vines, I am quite sure that rather than turn down an order, some nurseries will buy in vines from other nurseries, adding another layer of complexity to the business.

As you can see from the above, the production of grafted vines is a multi-layered business and with respect to TDs, there are several occasions when perfectly healthy plant material can be infected by contact with less healthy material: in the scion vineyard, the rootstock vineyard, during the pre-grafting process, in the grafting process and during storage and transport. At all stages, cross-contamination could occur. One also has to remember that vines are composed of wood grown out of doors and therefore contamination from both vine and non-vine species on neighbouring land is always a possibility. The wood is also grown and harvested under conditions where natural rainfall is a common occurrence and where there are several opportunities for the wood to come into contact with soil which may well contain harmful pathogens.

In the last few years, some of the major vine nurseries have accepted that *maladies do bois de la vigne* are indeed a problem that needs addressing and it is good to see companies such as *Pépinières Guillaume* with their 'VigoRhize' process which uses both *Trichoderma* and mycorrhizal fungi in the production process and *Mercier Pépiniériste* with their 'Clean PROCESS©' system which results in what they call a 'Clean PLANT©'. This patented system is claimed to cover better traceability of the materials used in the production of grafted vines, the sterilisation and disinfection of plants and premises, where appropriate, through all stages of the production process, growing in the presence of mycorrhizal fungi, plus storage under ideal conditions. It also includes 'continuous health monitoring' of the plants. Mercier are also using a strain of *Trichoderma* (*Trichoderma atroviride I-1237*) 'to restore the microbial balance of the plant' and this they market as their 'T-FORCE®' system. Whether the use of *Trichoderma* actually does help control TDs is open to question and some researchers suggest its powers have been exaggerated.

The International Council on Grapevine Trunk Diseases[3] (ICGTD), which was formed in 1998, has been at the forefront of research into the problem and to date has held eight biennial workshops on the subject (International Workshop on Grapevine Trunk Diseases – IGWTD). After the most recent IGWTD held in Valencia, Spain in June 2012, it published a document titled 'Grapevine propagation; principles and methods for the production and handling of high quality grapevine planting material' (This document can be downloaded at www.englishwine.com/wgigb.htm). Written by the three foremost researchers on the subject, Helen Waite, David Gramaje and Lucie Morton, it is a very thorough, step-by-step, blueprint for producing, storing, transporting, and planting both rooted cuttings and grafted vines (which includes 'potted' vines) and 'is presented as a common starting point for propagators, grape growers and scientists to support the production of planting material that is of the highest quality' and should be mandatory reading for anyone contemplating buying grapevines and establishing a vineyard. However, whether all its recommendations – at least in the short term – are entirely practical is another matter. One of the most telling paragraphs in the report is the following. Note that the bold emphasis and underlining are in the original:

**'It should be noted that regardless of how well they are managed, the manner of cutting production predisposes mother vines to infection by trunk disease organisms. Infected <u>cuttings</u> have no visible internal or external symptoms. Visible symptoms are not apparent for several months after the infective agents (spores or mycelium) move into the tissue of the current season's canes. Therefore, it should be assumed that ALL cuttings have some level of infection. <u>Hot water treatment is the only control currently known to be effective.</u> The application of fungicides does not effectively control internal pathogens'.**

Much of the problem with getting nurseries to change their production methods is that many of the improvements suggested in this document are (so the nurseries will say) impractical, likely to result in a reduction in the percentage of vines that make it from grafting to sale, cause damage to otherwise viable vines and in almost all cases, raise costs. Subjecting mother blocks to annual laboratory analysis, growing rootstocks on trellises, not soaking cuttings prior to grafting, not processing finished vines in the same area where vines are being grafted, sampling of vines after lifting ('5-10 vines per 1,000 to be dissected'), and the complexities of effective HWT are all very desirable measures and I am sure, in time, that some will become standard industry practice. For the present though, I suspect they will not.

On the question of HWT in particular, which the report covers in much detail, the authors do not come out and say that it should be mandatory, or even advise that it is best practice, even though in the paragraph above, its effectiveness is underlined. In an article in *Wine & Viticulture Journal* of Nov-Dec 2013, Helen Waite points out that: 'although hot water treatment is currently the most effective control for known trunk diseases, it is not necessarily a completely effective eradication treatment. Very low levels of infection may persist in a small percentage of treated cuttings and act as a subsequent source of cross-contamination if sanitation is not maintained throughout the propagation period.' Nurseries are, except for vines going to regions where *Flavescence dorée* is a problem (as has already been mentioned), usually unwilling to carry out post-grafting HWT as the levels of losses and claims from their customers are too great. By doing it before grafting and planting out, then at least they are going some way towards lowering the risk of infection. It should also be noted that ungrafted vines, i.e. rooted cuttings, which are widely planted in countries and regions where *Phylloxera* is not present, are more successful when subjected to HWT, as they do not then have to go through the whole grafting procedure. It is interesting to note that on the question of HWT, *Mercier*, who do not use it as part of their patented vine production system, state: 'Hot Water Treatment is extremely traumatic for the young vines. It's [sic] consuming most of the vine reserves, that causes bud break delays (15-30 days) and in difficult conditions (poorly prepared soils, hydric stress, strong heat etc), the take rate can be seriously impacted.' How true this last statement is open to question. One researcher I asked about it said that this was an excuse for not being able to carry out HWT correctly, with the necessary pre-HWT acclimatisation times, post-HWT cooling times and subsequent storage conditions being adhered to.

The final chapter of the Waite, Gramaje and Morton document, under the heading 'Pre-planting care of vines' suggests that growers should:

*'Dissect a random sample of vines from each batch. Cut the rootstock, the scion and the graft union and look for dark staining and/or spotting in the tissue. Any tissue discolouration in the wood indicates that the vines have probably been infected with one or more of the fungi that cause Young Vine Decline and should not be accepted'.*

Whilst this may be 100 per cent sound advice, I suspect that there are very few nurseries and vine suppliers (probably none) which would accept an order for vines on this basis. Whilst it is possible to test for the presence of a very wide range of organisms that might cause TDs, there are no limits or levels that can be set to say if one vine is 'clean' and another vine 'infected' which is why a visual inspection is the best that the experts can recommend. The final section of the document headed 'Planting' contains some valuable advice including:

*'Vines, particularly the roots, should not be allowed to dry out during planting. However, standing vines with freshly trimmed roots in a bucket of water is detrimental, spreads disease and should be avoided. It is better to cover bundles with a clean damp cloth'.*

Given that this is the practice I have always adopted and recommended, I am pleased to see it in writing from such a group of experts.

Growers should also be aware that many of the organisms that cause TDs may well already be present in their vineyards and in the surrounding environment. Existing vines, especially if they are young (less than ten years old) may well have TD organisms in them which are not currently doing any harm. Apart from old pruning wood and general vine debris (including mummified grapes), several weed species can host TD organisms, as well as many species of hardwood trees which might be found in adjacent hedges and woodland. Given that many UK vineyards are in close proximity to trees, hedges, copses, woods and even full forests, this source cannot be discounted. TDs can be transmitted from any host (vine or other species) to another vine by both wind and rain splash and any wound or cut can be an entry point. Once present therefore, they are extremely hard to control and almost impossible to eradicate.

## Measures to be taken when establishing a new vineyard

In November 2011, following a WineSkills workshop on TDs, the UKVA issued Bulletin No. 50 'Grapevine trunk diseases' authored by Dr Richard Smart, Chris Cooper (UKVA Technical Advisor), Jim Newsome[4], a UK based viticultural researcher and Duncan McNeill, a viticultural consultant. The report highlighted the fact that 'the problem appears worse in young vineyards, less than 10 years old. Older vines appear more tolerant'. It also pointed out the part played by environmental factors saying that: 'Other stresses on the plant exacerbate the diseases. Poor drainage, poor nutrition, soil compaction, drought, frost, weeds, other diseases all make vines prone to trunk disease.' Bulletin No. 50 can be downloaded at www.englishwine.com/wgigb.htm.

Stress, therefore, is something to be avoided in the vine's establishment phase. Smart has also accepted, in an e-mail written in August 2013 and sent out via the UK's 'vine list' e-mail circulation system: 'that the UK is not the most favourable environment for vines, being generally too cool. I think that this stress, plus high rainfall which predisposes spread, is also a factor in the expression of poor health due to TDs in UK.' Smart also stated: 'there is no guarantee that any lot of grafted vines is always the same, nor that any nursery is better than another, nor that any [vine sales] agent is better than another. One lot of vines may be good, another not'.

Given that the organisms responsible for TDs prefer humidity and are spread when conditions are wet and windy, UK vineyards would seem an ideal place for them to survive and prosper. In addition, despite an improvement in our climate over the past twenty years (although 2011, 2012 and 2013 have somewhat taken the gilt off that particular piece of gingerbread), the UK must still be considered marginal for viticulture, especially when one factors in the change in vine varieties from predominantly German crosses plus Seyval blanc to Chardonnay and Pinot noir, both of which are more problematic with regard to fruit setting and ripening. Stress, therefore, in UK vineyards is an ever present threat, especially that of the poor accumulation of carbohydrates brought about by difficult conditions for photosynthesis, especially after harvest. Add to that the adverse weather conditions of recent years: the very low temperatures in December 2009 and January, February and December

2010, the damaging spring frosts of April and May 2009 and 2010, the very dry winter of 2010-11, the hot and dry spring of 2011, and the strange year that was 2013 and one can see that the last few years have placed a lot of stress upon young vines, especially those poorly sited, poorly planted and poorly managed.

Jim Newsome, who attended the 2012 IGWTD, as well as being one of the authors of the UKVA Bulletin No. 50 already referred to, has made presentations at WineSkills workshops, at the 2013 UKVA Annual General Meeting and has written a 'Grapevine trunk disease review' dated July 2012 and an 'Update on Trunk Disease Research' dated July 2013 (both available at www.englishwine.com/wgigb.htm). What appears in the next paragraph is taken from these sources:

'We know that it is possible to have two vines with the same fungal profile but a differing expression of symptoms and also that trunk disease fungi can exist latently within the vine, i.e. present but not actively damaging the vine. Therefore it is likely that there is a rôle for external factors in the expression of the symptoms that cause the vine harm. There has been some discussion of the potentially catalytic rôle of other micro-organisms such as bacteria and this is an interesting area for future research. Stress is also identified as a cause of the expression of TD symptoms in a paper by Brown et al. 2012, who showed that carbohydrate stress caused by partial defoliation of young vines increased the severity of Black Foot infections – a potential concern for the UK where a poor growing year can reduce a vine's carbohydrate stores. There is little doubt that stress can reduce a vine's ability to combat infection so especially with regard to new plantings, every effort should be made to reduce vine stress: to quote from Billones-Baaijens et al. 2013[5] *"…it seems likely that young nursery plants with latent infections can decline and die when planted into the more stressful conditions of vineyards.'* [Jim Newsome's italics and emphasis]

Newsome also wrote:

'It is also hypothesised by several authors that environmental conditions act as triggers to infections that would not otherwise have meaningful impact on vine yield and health (Bonfiglioli & McGregor 2006; van Niekerk et al. 2006) and the extent of this impact is of particular relevance in the UK where environmental stress is common. Bonfiglioli & McGregor (2006) refer explicitly to vineyards in "*sub-optimal*" areas in New Zealand with heavy, poorly drained soil that are showing the most damage from *Botryosphaeria* infections. Therefore, a logical further control method in the UK is to follow best practice in site selection to maximise drainage, exposure and other positive variables as well as utilise viticultural techniques such as canopy management to minimise negative environmental stresses such as shading.'

Much of what it takes to prepare a site for planting has been discussed in detail in earlier chapters in this book, but here is a summary of the most important factors to consider in establishing a vineyard in the UK, in relation to avoiding damage by TDs. It is largely taken from an article

I wrote for the UKVA Grape Press Volume 156 February 2012 (available at www.englishwine.com/wgigb.htm):

- Site selection   The UK is still marginal for viticulture and there is no doubt that the problems faced in many vineyards, not only of TDs, are exacerbated by planting vines on difficult sites and in challenging areas.
- Windbreaks   Vines planted on exposed sites without the benefit of wind protection will suffer in several different ways. Many sites could be improved with effective wind breaks.
- Vine variety   Not all varieties will grow on all sites and attempting to establish hard-to-ripen varieties on lower quality sites will always be stressful for them.
- Rootstocks   Selection of the correct rootstock for the pH and active calcium carbonate ($CaCO_3$) level in the soil is most important.
- Transport and storage of vines   Vines will be in cold store at the nursery and should be transported to the UK, preferably in temperature-controlled transport, and kept in cold store until just prior to planting.
- Preparation of vines   Vines should be trimmed for the planting method being used. Normally, the supplying nursery will trim the vines prior to dispatch.
- Vines should not be soaked prior to planting, but kept damp.
- Site preparation   This should start at least six months in advance of planting and twelve and even eighteen months is better.
- Bio-fumigation of sites using mustard and other brassicas has been shown to lessen the incidence of TDs in vines subsequently planted.
- Nutrition levels (including pH) must be sampled prior to planting and if necessary, adjusted with fertilisers being ploughed down to the root zone.
- Additions of humus, whether via green manures or by compost spreading – or both – will always help vine establishment and lessen stress.
- Poor drainage is without doubt detrimental to the long-term health of vines and must be addressed pre-planting.
- Subsoiling, using the correct implement and to the correct depth, must be done pre-planting, especially if planting by machine.
- Sites must be correctly cultivated, especially if being machine-planted, so that roots are in contact with the soil after planting.
- Time of planting   Many parts of the UK suitable for vine growing can experience spring frosts until the end of May and there is no doubt that frost damage and the incidence of TDs are closely correlated.
- Planting   Whether planting by hand, using a water lance or planting by machine, the vine should have its roots pointing downwards and firmly in contact with the soil. Mycorrhizal root treatments at planting may help.
- Weed control   Effective weed control is one of the major factors in getting vines established and preventing stress.
- Cultivations in young vines   The practice of grassing down, whether by natural regeneration or by sowing seed, may stress young vines more than is necessary and therefore keeping a vineyard cultivated for the first two to three years may be beneficial.

- Grow-tubes    I believe that the tall, narrow 'grow-tube' type of individual guard might not provide the best environment for the young vine and its graft, especially if vines are not correctly shoot selected and side-shooted. The situation is probably made worse if weeds are allowed to grow up inside the guard.
- Pest and disease control    Apart from pests such as rabbits, hares and deer, plus slugs and snails, which will make establishment more difficult, if not impossible, vines getting Powdery and Downy Mildew in their first few years will be stressed. Except for varieties known to be resistant to mildews, preventative sprays should be applied as soon as leaves reach a targetable size.
- Early cropping    Vines can often begin to crop in year two or year three, but this may be detrimental to their long-term health. Young fresh tissue and high nitrogen levels are all conducive to the growth of fungal pathogens. Delaying cropping until year four, when the vine is more mature, the graft is better developed and the vine's root system is more established, may well be better for the vine.

## Dealing with trunk diseases in an established vineyard

**Note:** some of the advice below is slightly contradictory, some probably impractical (or impossible) and some will involve additional expense and/or changes to working habits and practices. Which, and how many, of the measures listed you need to adopt will of course depend on the level of TDs in your vineyard.

The following is an amalgamation of the advice given in the UKVA and Newsome documents already mentioned, plus advice and recommendations I have gleaned from attending two WineSkills workshops on the subject; and the UKVA's 2013 AGM presentation mentioned above.
- Early identification. Get good at recognising the symptoms during the growing season and tag suspect vines.
- Map the distribution of infected vines from year to year so that the progress of infection can be monitored.
- Remove infected vines and burn them downwind of the vineyard.
- Reduce stress on vines by attending to drought, waterlogging, poor drainage, nutrient stress, and weeds. Weeds can potentially carry TDs.
- Do not prune during rainfall or when vines are still wet.
- Double pruning, i.e. basic pruning early in the winter with cleaning up of canes in drier spring weather.
- Prune early in the season when spore levels maybe lower.
- Prune late when wounds are less susceptible and heal more quickly at higher temperatures. Sap flow may hinder entry of spores into wounds.
- Minimize the number and size of pruning wounds.
- Always make cuts at an angle that allows water to drain from cut surfaces.

- When making a large cut on older wood, leave a 25 mm stub protruding from the trunk.
- Treat infected vines using 'Vinevax', a *Trichoderma* based product, for both dressing pruning wounds as well as vine implants/injections.
**Note:** Vinevax has no clearance in Europe (inc. UK) for use on vines as a fungicide, so its use must be as a growth enhancer or growth promoter.
- Use pruning paints (wound paints) to seal cut surfaces after pruning in areas with infected vines and on larger wounds on older vines. Note that Bezel (active ingredient: tebuconazole) will be illegal from August 2015.
- Tag suspect vines and prune them in a separate operation to pruning apparently healthy vines.
- Treat vines adjacent to vines known to be infected, as infected.
- Cut back infected vines to well below where disease is present and train up water shoots to replace trunks of infected vines.
- The use of powered secateurs will enable cuts to be made cleanly and in the most appropriate place.
- Disinfecting secateurs at the end of each day with a suitable product (Milton or propanol suggested).
- Remove and burn prunings.
- Mummified berries and infected wood, if left in the vineyard, can be a source for the TD inoculum. Good vineyard hygiene in general will be beneficial.
- Fungicidal sprays during dormancy are potentially helpful.
- Start protective fungicide spraying early in the season.
- Remove dead wood from trees in surrounding woodland.

## Ungrafted 'own-root' vines

In July 2013, Richard Smart suggested that, given the UK's relatively isolated position in the viticultural world, *Phylloxera* was not in reality a major threat and that the planting of ungrafted 'own-root' vines might be a way of avoiding TDs, given that many of the problems are associated with the rootstocks and the grafting procedure. He suggested that a UK nursery should be found that would import mother stock from Europe, maintain a 'mother garden' and produce ungrafted rooted cuttings for UK growers. Leaving aside the commercial reality of persuading a nursery to start production of vines for a market of perhaps 300,000-500,000 vines a year which are required in many different variety, clone and rootstock combinations, I think that when faced with the risk of getting *Phylloxera* versus the risk of TDs, growers with ungrafted vines would prefer the latter to the former. As I have pointed out in *Chapter 16: Pest and disease control* in the section on *Phylloxera*, once discovered, the pest must be notified to FERA and they will place a movement control on your vineyard. How then you would deal with the problem in the long-term is a question to which the only answer I can see is to grub the affected vines and replace with grafted stock.

In the early days of modern viticulture in New Zealand, vines were almost always planted on their own roots and a slight infestation with *Phylloxera* was tolerated and it was even said to help control the vigour of Müller-Thurgau which was then the dominant variety. After a decade or so of cropping, as the *Phylloxera* numbers started to rise and yields started to decline, the vineyard could be grubbed and replanted. Whether this would work in the UK today is another matter. The cost of grubbing and replanting in already established vineyards, i.e. with the trellising and wires already in position, is huge and needs to be taken into account. For small vineyards maybe, but for the larger, more commercial growers, I cannot see own-root vines as a viable alternative. With the control of TDs in the mother gardens and nurseries getting better all the time and with a better understanding of the problems from the grower's end, my hope is that the TD situation will improve to a point where it is no more of a problem than the many others that UK vinegrowers have to face.

## Replanting vines in a vineyard where trunk diseases have been identified

If you have TDs in your vineyard, have removed vines and have gaps to replant, then you must make sure that the vines are planted into as benign an environment as possible. An assessment must be made of whether the TDs in your vineyard have been exacerbated by something as basic as poor drainage, poor nutrition or some other rectifiable problem and the problem put right before replanting takes place. It goes without saying that good quality vines must be obtained and planted into well prepared soil. Some additional humus in the planting hole, maybe a mycorrhizal fungi dip and a good mulch of fine compost will all help the young vine to thrive. Avoid shading from adjacent vines by not allowing excessively long canes from neighbouring vines to extend over the newly planted vines. The use of high-graft vines could be considered which will help avoid this problem.

It has been suggested that layering of adjacent vines to fill gaps might be practiced instead of replanting with grafted vines. Whilst I can see this technique being used in small vineyards where perhaps only a few isolated vines have succumbed to TDs and been removed, on a larger scale this practice has its problems. Ignoring the threat of *Phylloxera* – which of course would be able to colonise the roots of a layered vine as there would be no rootstock involved – there is a possibility that a vine adjacent to one that has died because of a TD will also be suffering from the same problem and therefore will, in time, also die.

## Trunk diseases in the UK – a summary

There is no doubt that in some UK vineyards, TDs have been a problem, continue to be a problem and are a problem that require the correct measures to be taken in order to maintain a healthy and productive vineyard. In vineyards where TDs are affecting a majority of the vines, although there is a reluctance to accept that it is the best route, complete grubbing and replanting is probably the best solution. However, in many vineyards, vines affected

with TDs account for a very small percentage of total vines and the replacement of a small percentage of vines each year, or every other year, has always been part and parcel of managing a vineyard. If anything, the threat of TDs has brought to the fore one major factor in successfully establishing a new vineyard: the importance of selecting and developing a site so that as little stress is placed upon young vines as possible.

*A vine suffering from Esca which has been rejuvenated by taking a low-growing water shoot*

1 Layering (or *provignage* in French) is where a suitable cane from one vine is laid down on the soil and buried at the point where a new vine is required. Quite often the cane is slightly cracked and a rock placed on top of it to keep it in position. The cane then sends out a shoot which can be staked and trained and in time, the cane from the 'mother' vine can be removed.

2 A recent paper: *Soaking grapevine cuttings in water: a potential source of cross contamination by micro-organisms* by Waite, Gramaje, Whitelaw-Weckert and Hardie (Phytopathologia Mediterranea (2013) 52, 2, 359–368) has shown that soaking wood is a major source of infection and that the: 'development of nursery management strategies that avoid exposing cuttings to water during propagation is an essential first step in reducing the transmission of trunk diseases in propagation.'

3 www.icgtd.ucr.edu

4 www.veni-vidi-viti.com/blog

5 Billones-Baajiens R et al. M (2012) *Pathogenicity of Botryosphaeriaceae species from New Zealand nurseries.* ICGTD 8th International Workshop on Grapevine Trunk Disease 2012.

# Chapter 18
# Organic and biodynamic viticulture in the UK

**Note**: In my book *Viticulture* there is a chapter covering *Organic and biodynamic viticulture* which readers may also find helpful in dealing with this subject.

If the growing of vines in a challenging climate such as the UK's could be described as 'brave', then the growing of vines organically or biodynamically might be considered by some as tempting fate. However, my UK Vineyards Guide database lists twenty-three vineyards registered as organic or biodynamic, covering a total of 48-ha. Some are very small, in reality only hobby vineyards, but of the remainder, most are over 1-ha, several over 2-ha and a few over 5-ha. The grandfather of all UK organic growers is Roy Cook at Sedlescombe Organic Vineyard in Robertsbridge, East Sussex who, together with his wife, Irma, has been growing vines and making wine organically, and in recent years, biodynamically, since 1979. From their original base at Sedlescombe, they have expanded by taking over and converting to organic/biodynamic the nearby Battle and Bodiam vineyards which, in total, add up to 10.6-ha (26.2-acres). In recent years the ranks of UK organic growers have been swelled by some larger operators: Laverstoke Park in Hampshire which, at 9-ha (22.3-acres), is the largest single vineyard; Davenport Vineyards have 8.15-ha (20.1-acres) on two sites (Rotherfield, East Sussex and Horsmonden in Kent); Oxney Organic in East Sussex which will, after its 2014 plantings are finished, have 8-ha (20-acres); Albury Organic in Surrey have 4.95-ha (12.2-acres); and Ancre Hill Estates in Wales have 3.4-ha (8.40-acres). Laverstoke Park, owned by ex-Formula 1 Champion Jody Scheckter, is something of a temple to all things biodynamic and the 1,000-ha (2,500-acre) estate supports a wide range of different crops and products, as well as a large compost production plant and professional laboratory.

In the UK, there are three organisations which can convey organic status: the Soil Association which has been registering land as organic since 1973; Organic Farmers & Growers who were established in 1973 as a marketing organisation, but have been registering land as organic since 1992; and the BDA (Biodynamic Association) which was founded in 1929 and can certify land as either organic or biodynamic, the latter with Demeter, which is the only organisation that can confer biodynamic status.[1] The Soil Association has the reputation for being slightly less flexible when it comes to applying for derogations for the use of plant protection materials and Organic Farmers & Growers more down to earth in their approach to practical farming issues.

The major problems associated with growing vines in the UK organically (from here on, in this chapter, the term 'organic' can also be taken to include 'biodynamic') can be approached under three headings: vine varieties; weed control; and pest and disease control.

## Vine varieties

There is a wide range of vine varieties being grown in UK organic vineyards with many of the newer growers preferring what might now be called 'standard' *vinifera* varieties such as Chardonnay, Pinot noir, Meunier and Bacchus, but many of the older, more established growers, opting for both older hybrids and more modern interspecific crosses. For growers of *viniferas*, the problems of disease control in what is often a damp climate have to be at the top of their agendas if sustainable levels of yield are to be achieved with any regularity and over the long-term.

As for the selection of hybrids and interspecific crosses, quite surprisingly we probably have rather more experience in growing these disease resistant vine varieties than many other better known regions. Since the early days of modern UK viticulture, hybrid varieties such as Cascade, Léon Millot, Maréchal Foch, Seyval blanc, and Triomphe have always been popular, especially (but by no means only) with smaller growers for whom spraying against fungal diseases was always a chore to be avoided. Seyval blanc has always been, and remains, one of most widely grown varieties and of the white, still wine varieties grown in the UK, at 92-ha (227-acres) it remains at number two – Bacchus being first with 131-ha, (324-acres) – and occupies 6 per cent of the total planted area. For many organic growers, Seyval remains a good variety. Apart from its disease resistance which is usually excellent (I say 'usually' as in 2013 it severely misbehaved and succumbed to late season *Botrytis* as never before) it is an adaptable, high-yielding variety and one that, because of its longevity in UK vineyards, has become accepted as part and parcel of the UK's wine offerings. The fact that some of the UK's best known non-organic producers – Breaky Bottom, Camel Valley, Denbies, Monnow Valley and Stanlake Park – use it to make medal-winning still and sparkling wines is a bonus. As for the other older hybrids mentioned, all red varieties, only Triomphe remains popular, although it is very rarely planted today, mainly because of the much better red varieties now available.

As for interspecific crosses, Orion, Phoenix, Regent, Rondo, and Solaris are by far the most popular and are used by many organic UK vineyards. Villaris and Bolero are starting to be planted. Although some of them are not as disease resistant in the UK's climate as they appear to be in say Germany (from where these seven varieties originate), they are in most instances streets ahead of *vinifera* varieties. As for other non-*vinifera* varieties, as is shown in *Chapter 4: Vine varieties, clones and rootstocks for the UK* in the section on *Newer vine varieties*, there is a wide range of new interspecific crosses being developed in Europe – mainly Germany and Switzerland – and some of these are being trialled in both organic and non-organic vineyards.

## Weed control

After the selection of the grape varieties for an organic vineyard, the next problem which has to be tackled is that of weed control. Given that herbicides cannot be used, the options available are restricted to physical methods such as mulching and cultivations. Other options, such as grazing and cover crops, whilst they might be made to work in mature vineyards, are certainly not available in newly planted and young vineyards. The options available for controlling weeds in vineyards have been fully discussed in *Chapter 14: Weed control*, so there is no need to go through them in detail, but a short summary of the advantages and disadvantages of each method suitable for organic vineyards would be appropriate.

## Cultivations

Whilst under-vine cultivation would seem to be an ideal non-chemical method of keeping weeds down in an organic vineyard (or indeed in any vineyard come to that), in reality it appears to be very difficult, in UK soil and climate conditions, to put into practice. The advantages of course are that no chemicals are used, the soil is regularly aerated and weeds and grasses, as well as any compost or humus applied to the vines, will be incorporated into the soil. The disadvantages, ignoring the amounts of tractor time, operator time and fuel used, are that in young vineyards especially, the regular knocking of the young stems by the hydraulic arm of an automatic hoe must be avoided and the use of plant supports either side of the vine or the use of *tuteur trombone* plant supports is to be advised. Either of these support methods will of course add to the cost of the vineyard. However, even if the question of plant supports can be dealt with by simply using the correct materials, my main concern with using cultivations for controlling weeds is that in my experience it is very difficult to get good results. Whatever type or make of cultivator is used, and I have probably seen at least ten different variants used, there are always occasions when the soil conditions are not right, when the weed growth is the 'wrong type' (grasses are very hard to shift), or it's too wet to get on to the ground, all making the job less than satisfactory. In addition, whatever machine is used, they all leave a mound of earth around the base of the vines which in time must be hoed away by hand.

## Mulching

Mulches, made from plastic or fabric and laid on the ground with the edges buried, or loose mulches of various natural materials spread around the vines, have been described in *Chapter 14: Weed control* in some detail and there is no need to discuss them in this chapter. From an organic grower's perspective, mulches would seem to be an ideal solution since they are static and do not involve the use of herbicides and vines may well benefit from their use. However, the main problem with using mulches, a problem which affects both organic and non-organic growers, is the 'edge' problem. Keeping the edges of any mulch weed-free, without the use of herbicides, involves mowing or cultivating, sometimes both, and this gets problematical if the edges are not to be disturbed or damaged. Inevitably a degree of hand weeding has to take place which can be an expensive process.

## Pest and disease control

The first approach to pest and disease control in an organic vineyard must be in the planning stage. Apart from their choice of varieties, growers must plan, plant and trellis their vineyard so that it is as light and airy as possible, although that should not mean selecting a site on the top of a windswept hill so that 'diseases will be blown away' (as I once heard an organic grower explain his poor choice of site). Once established, the canopy management in the vines has to be exemplary, with as much attention as possible paid to shoot thinning, tucking in and deleafing so that the grape zone is kept as open, light and airy as possible. The organic vineyard should also be kept as clean as possible, removing as much plant debris as possible including prunings and grapes discarded during thinning or not picked for whatever reason. Inevitably these measures all mean additional expense in running the vineyard.

Unless they have selected really good disease resistant hybrids and interspecific crosses, organic growers will be faced with the same range of pests and diseases that non-organic growers face, but without their full armoury of chemicals. However, that is not to say that they have no materials to use, as organic does not mean 'not sprayed'. In general, organic growers rely on wettable sulphur and various copper containing products[2] as their main weapons, supplemented by various preparations. These would include 'Garvine', a garlic, selenium and sulphur mix[3], Serenade, a bio-pesticide based upon *Bacillus subtilis* (and already described in *Chapter 16: Pest and disease control* under the section on *Botrytis*), Sonata, also a bio-pesticide for Powdery and Downy Mildews based upon *Bacillus pumilis* and Potassium Sulphite, Potassium Bicarbonate, Monopotassium Phosphate, dilute solutions of Hydrogen Peroxide and certain oils (Codacide and JMS Stylet Oil), none of which are classed as pesticides. For biodynamic growers there are also the various 'preparations' numbered from BD500 to BD508 which range from Cow Horn Manure and Cow Horn Silica, via Yarrow, Chamomile, Stinging Nettle and Oak Bark to Valerian and Casurina Tea. The first two of these, BD500 and BD501, and the last BD508, are diluted and sprayed directly on the vines, the others used in the preparation of biodynamic compost which is an integral part of the process of persuading the vine to fight off disease naturally. Because all of the above materials are contact materials and none are systemic, organic growers will have to use higher water volumes than non-organic growers in order to get full coverage. In addition, spray intervals will in most years have to be shorter than in non-organic vineyards as contact materials are more easily washed off by rain. Both of these will raise the cost of pest and disease control.

## Costs of organic and biodynamic viticulture

There is no doubt that the additional costs involved in keeping the vineyard free of weeds, plus the additional canopy management costs, make organic viticulture a more expensive pastime than non-organic. Whilst there might be a small saving in the products used for pest and disease control versus conventional chemicals, the additional costs of the production of composts, compost teas and the various preparations used, probably eats up any savings made.

Probably the major additional 'cost' factor in organic viticulture is that of yields, which, when compared to those in conventional vineyards will, in all probability, be lower. This will either be because increased disease levels will reduce the crop or because yield reduction is used to improve air circulation and therefore the health of the crop. My yield target in organic vineyards would depend on the varieties being grown, but for what might be called 'standard' varieties it would be around 5.0 tonnes-ha (2.0 tonnes-acre), maybe a touch more if Seyval blanc was being grown. This compares to the 8.5 tonnes-ha (3.5

tonnes-acre) I would aim for in a conventional vineyard. Davenport Vineyards, with good mixture of varieties both old and new (but no Seyval blanc) admit to a long-term yield of around 3.00 tonnes-ha (1.25 tonnes-acre). Their rows are relatively wide – 2.74-m – and if you planted with a 2.0 m row width and achieved the same yield per vine, this would equate to around 4.1 tonnes-ha (1.67 tonnes-acre).

Although accurate comparisons between organic and non-organic vineyards, both in the area of running costs and yields, are almost impossible to come by (both in the UK and overseas) it is my impression that a tonne of UK-grown organic grapes probably cost at least 50 per cent more to produce than a tonne of non-organic grapes. Whether organic wines can attract a sufficient premium over non-organic wines or whether organic wines have access to markets that non-organic wines do not, to help pay the additional costs of production, is open to question.

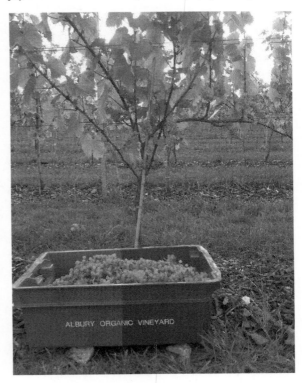

*First crop from one of the UK's largest biodynamic vineyards*

---

1 In researching this chapter I was surprised to find that Demeter own the certification mark 'Biodynamic'.

2 The use of copper is restricted to 6 kg per hectare per year for organic growers and 3 kg per hectare per year, averaged over three years, for biodynamic growers. Both limits refer to kilograms of pure copper, not kilograms of copper-containing products.

3 See www.astonhorticulture.com for more details.

# Chapter 19

# Getting started

## Getting started

Starting a vineyard in the UK is remarkably easy when compared to many other countries, especially given that we are in the European Union. No *appellation* to apply to, no planting rights to obtain, no restrictions on where to plant, what to plant or how much to plant. However, that is not to say that growing and making wine in the UK is entirely unhampered by officialdom.

Having planted your vineyard and assuming it is for the production of a 'wine sector' product, i.e. not vine leaves or some other non-potable product, within six months of planting you have to register the vineyard with the Wine Standards Branch of the Food Standards Agency who will want to know what varieties and clones of both scion and rootstock varieties you have planted, in what quantities, covering what area and where. This is so the Vineyard Register, a list of vineyards that every EU Member State must keep, can be kept up to date. The forms for doing this can be downloaded from the WSB's website whose details are in *Appendix I* or from www.englishwine.com/wgigb.htm.

In order to produce wine in the UK, you should apply to HMR&C for a licence so that you can make and store wine in a duty-free environment, export wine without payment of duty and obtain your producer's annual duty-free allowance. To register you must complete form L5 'Application for a licence to carry on an Excise Trade' and lodge this with HMR&C. Full details of this licence and all aspects of producing wine in the UK are to be found in HMR&C Notice 163 Wine Production (both available at www.englishwine.com/wgigb.htm)

When you get to the point where you wish to sell wine, you will need a Personal licence to sell alcohol, as well as a Premises Licence and these are available from the Trading Standards department of your Local Authority (LA). Full details can also be found on the Home Office's website. If you only sell wine to traders – wholesalers, retailers, restaurateurs, publicans and the like – who will be selling to the public, then you do not normally need a licence. However, you may not sell wine to the public in any quantity without a personal and premises licence. If in doubt, check with your Trading Standards department.

The erection of agricultural buildings solely for machinery and equipment for running the vineyard and any purely agricultural aspect, is, subject to siting, access and certain size and design requirements, fairly straightforward and allowed under 'Permitted Development Rights'. Annex E of Planning Policy Guidance 7 (PPG7) sets out the details. The question of planning permission for buildings on a vineyard solely for the processing of grapes grown on the land, i.e. a winery, is less clear cut, although several vineyards have persuaded their LAs that, under the precedent set by the Wroxeter Roman Vineyards case, when owner David Millington challenged the Secretary of State and won, confirming that winemaking was ancillary to growing grapes and therefore, like cider-making, an 'agricultural activity', wineries can be built under Permitted Development rights. The Millington case report and Annex E of PPG7 are available at *www.englishwine/wgigb*.

In situations where a building is used for both agricultural and other uses is never clear cut and the Planning Department of your Local Authority will, in all probability, need to be consulted. Such activities as contract winemaking, making wine from grapes not produced on the land adjacent to the winery, selling non-wine products not produced on the site, and selling tours and tastings may be allowed without full Planning Permission, but it will depend on the scale of such activities and the attitude of the LA's Planning Officer.

Applications for agricultural accommodation will always require Planning Permission and Annex I of PPG7 sets out the basis for such applications. In general applications will only be allowed on 'well-established agricultural units', which are 'financially sound', have been 'established for three years', and have 'been profitable for at least one of them'. Applications also have to show an existing functional need, i.e. the accommodation is required for the proper functioning of the enterprise and that there is no other suitable accommodation 'on the unit' or 'in the area' which is suitable. Despite these requirements, several vineyards have managed to get planning permission for houses on site and an application is always worth making if backed up with a professionally prepared financial and a functional report.

**Note**: See *Appendix VI: Vineyard pre-planting check list*

## Appendix I: Useful addresses

One of the best resources for information on specialist suppliers, consultants and contractors for UK vineyard owners and potential owners is the UKVA Commercial Database which is available from www.ukva.org.uk under 'Information' or from www.englishwine.com/wgigb.htm. The English Wine Producers' website is also worth visiting. Many of the websites listed below will contain links to additional useful websites.

| Vineyard and Wine Trade Associations and Organisations | | |
|---|---|---|
| United Kingdom Vineyards Association | UK national vineyard asscociation | www.ukva.org.uk |
| English Wine Producers | UK Vineyards marketing organisation | www.englishwineproducers.co.uk |
| East Anglian Vineyards Association | UK Regional vineyard association | www.eastanglianwines.co.uk |
| Mercian Vineyards Association | UK Regional vineyard association | www.ukvines.co.uk/mercia |
| South East Vineyards Association | UK Regional vineyard association | www.seva.uk.com |
| South West Vineyards Association | UK Regional vineyard association | www.swva.info |
| Thames and Chiltern Vineyards Association | UK Regional vineyard association | www.thameschilternsvineyards.org.uk |
| Welsh Vineyards Association | UK Regional vineyard association | www.winetrailwales.co.uk |
| Wessex Vineyards Association | UK Regional vineyard association | tim@ingramhill.co.uk |
| Wine and Spirits Trade Association - WSTA | UK Wine Trade association | www.wsta.co.uk |
| **Official Agencies** | | |
| DEFRA | Department for the Environment, Food & Rural Affairs | www.gov.uk/government/organisations/department-for-environment-food-rural-affairs |
| Food Standards Agency - Wine Standards Branch | EU Wine regulations, Vineyard Register, Labelling | www.food.gov.uk/business-industry/winestandards |
| Health and Safety Executive | Pesticdes | www.pesticides.gov.uk |
| HM Government | Wine trade regulations and documents | www.gov.uk/wine-trade-regulations |
| HM Revenue & Customs | Excise Duty, Producer's Guide and Licence | www.hmrc.gov.uk |
| Home Office | Licences to sell alcohol | www.gov.uk/alcohol-licensing |
| National Proficiency &Training Council (NPTC) | Pesticde Training Courses | www.nptc.org.uk |
| Rural Payments Agency | Single Farm Payment Scheme (SPS) | www.rpa.defra.gov.uk/rpa/index.nsf/home |
| **Commercial Wine Websites** | | |
| Drink Britain | News website | www.drinkbritain.com |
| English Sparkling Wine | News website | www.englishsparklingwine.co.uk |
| English Wine | Commercial website | www.englishwine.com |
| UK Vine | News website | www.ukvine.com |
| UK Vines | Guide to Vineyards of Britain | www.ukvines.co.uk |
| **Wine Education** | | |
| Association of Wine Educators | Wine education | www.wineeducators.com |
| Institute of Masters of Wine | Wine education | www.mastersofwine.org |
| Plumpton College | Wine education | www.plumpton.ac.uk |
| Wine and Spirit Education Trust | Wine education | www.wsetglobal.com |
| WineSkills | Wine education | www.wineskills.co.uk |

## Appendix II:  Vine varieties grown in the UK (WSB 2013) and their status for different wine categories

| 2013 Ha | Variety Name | Colour | Species | Synonym | Notes |
|---|---|---|---|---|---|
| 6.88 | Acolon | Red | Vinifera | | |
| 1.05 | Albalonga | White | Vinifera | | |
| 0.40 | Albarino | White | Vinifera | | |
| | Arbane | White | Vinifera | | |
| 9.78 | Auxerrois | White | Vinifera | | |
| 130.79 | Bacchus | White | Vinifera | | |
| | Black Hamburg | Red | Vinifera | Trollinger, Blauer | |
| 0.23 | Blauburger | Red | Vinifera | | |
| | Blaufränkisch | Red | Vinifera | Blauer Limberger, Kékfrankos | |
| 0.40 | Bolero | Red | ISC | | Not sure of legal status for PDO |
| | Cabernet blanc | White | ISC | | Not sure of legal status for PDO |
| 0.52 | Cabernet Dorsa | Red | Vinifera | | Not on DEFRA PDO/PGI lists |
| 0.69 | Cabernet Franc | Red | Vinifera | | |
| 1.50 | Cabernet Sauvignon | Red | Vinifera | | |
| 0.23 | Cascade | Red | Hybrid | Seibel 13-053 | On PDO list, but should not be |
| | Chambourcin | Red | Hybrid | | |
| 326.99 | Chardonnay | White | Vinifera | | Eligible for PDO Sparkling |
| 0.57 | Chasselas | White | Vinifera | | |
| | Comtessa | White | Vinifera | | |
| 0.01 | Dalkauer | White | Vinifera | | |
| 19.21 | Dornfelder | Red | Vinifera | | |
| 2.76 | Dunkelfelder | Red | Vinifera | | |
| 0.25 | Ehrenfelser | White | Vinifera | | |
| | Elbling, White | White | Vinifera | | |
| | Enantio | Red | Vinifera | Lambrusco a Foglia Frastagliata | |
| 4.31 | Faberrebe | White | Vinifera | | |
| | Felicia | White | ISC | | Not sure of legal status for PDO |
| 0.71 | Findling | White | Vinifera | | |
| | Gagarin Blue | Red | Hybrid | | On PDO list, but should not be |
| | Gamaret | Red | Vinifera | | |
| 1.23 | Gamay noir | Red | Vinifera | | |
| | Garanoir | Red | Vinifera | | |
| 0.95 | Gewürztraminer | White | Vinifera | | |
| | Grüner Veltliner | White | Vinifera | | |
| 1.45 | Gutenborner | White | Vinifera | | |
| 0.01 | Heroldrebe | Red | Vinifera | | |
| 17.59 | Huxelrebe | White | Vinifera | | |
| | Johanniter | White | ISC | | Not sure of legal status for PDO |
| 0.01 | Jubiläumsrebe | White | Vinifera | | |
| | Kanzler | White | Vinifera | | |
| 5.92 | Kerner | White | Vinifera | | |
| 4.92 | Kernling | White | Vinifera | | |
| 2.60 | Léon Millot | Red | Hybrid | Kuhlmann 194-2 | |
| 1.32 | Madeleine Sylvaner III 28/51 | White | Vinifera | | |
| 45.87 | Madeleine x Angevine 7672 | White | Vinifera | | |
| | Malbec | Red | Vinifera | | |
| 0.25 | Manzoni Bianco | White | Vinifera | | Not on DEFRA PDO/PGI lists |
| 0.40 | Maréchal Foch | Red | Hybrid | Kuhlmann 188-2 | |
| 2.05 | Merlot | Red | Vinifera | | |

| 2013 Ha | Variety Name | Colour | Species | Synonym | Notes |
|---|---|---|---|---|---|
| | Merzling | White | ISC | | Not sure of legal status for PDO |
| 68.55 | Meunier | Red | Vinifera | Pinot Meunier, Wrotham Pinot | Eligible for PDO Sparkling |
| | Monarch | Red | ISC | | Not sure of legal status for PDO |
| 55.99 | Müller-Thurgau | White | Vinifera | | |
| 0.01 | Muscaris | White | ISC | | Not on DEFRA PDO/PGI lists |
| | Muscat | White | Vinifera | | |
| 0.01 | Nobling | White | Vinifera | | |
| 1.05 | Optima | White | Vinifera | | |
| 10.82 | Orion | White | ISC | | |
| 34.53 | Ortega | White | Vinifera | | |
| 0.54 | Perle (from Alzey) | White | Vinifera | | |
| | Petit Meslier | White | Vinifera | | |
| 23.59 | Phoenix | White | ISC | | |
| 25.36 | Pinot blanc | White | Vinifera | | Eligible for PDO Sparkling |
| 15.17 | Pinot gris | White | Vinifera | Rülander, Pinot grigio | Eligible for PDO Sparkling |
| 305.22 | Pinot noir | Red | Vinifera | | Eligible for PDO Sparkling |
| 20.24 | Pinot noir Précoce | Red | Vinifera | Frühburgunder, Blauer | Eligible for PDO Sparkling |
| 0.10 | Portugieser, Blauer | Red | Vinifera | | |
| | Refosco | Red | Vinifera | | |
| 24.28 | Regent | Red | ISC | | |
| 4.50 | Regner | White | Vinifera | | |
| 80.49 | Reichensteiner | White | Vinifera | | |
| 3.03 | Riesling | White | Vinifera | | |
| 47.39 | Rondo | Red | ISC | | |
| | Roter Veltliner | Red | Vinifera | | |
| 4.64 | Sauvignon blanc | White | Vinifera | | |
| | Sauvignon gris | White | Vinifera | | |
| 1.91 | Scheurebe | White | Vinifera | | |
| 34.54 | Schönburger | White | Vinifera | | |
| 0.01 | Senator | White | Vinifera | | |
| 92.05 | Seyval blanc | White | Hybrid | | |
| 14.28 | Siegerrebe | White | Vinifera | | |
| | Sirius | White | ISC | | Not sure of legal status for PDO |
| 16.14 | Solaris | White | ISC | | Not sure of legal status for PDO |
| | Traminer | White | Vinifera | | |
| 14.67 | Triomphe | Red | Hybrid | Kuhlmann 319-3 | |
| 0.86 | Villaris | White | ISC | | Not sure of legal status for PDO |
| | Wrotham Pinot | Red | Vinifera | | |
| 4.54 | Würzer | White | Vinifera | | |
| | Zalagyöngye (Zalas Perle) | White | Hybrid | | On PDO list, but should not be |
| 1.71 | Zweigeltrebe | Red | Vinifera | | |
| 1,498.07 | | | | | |
| 5.44 | Miscellaneous varieties | | | | |
| **1,503.51** | **Total UK vineyard area** | | | | |

**Note:** Varieties listed above, but without a planted area, are planted on less than 0.1 ha and are included under 'Miscellaneous varieties'. PDO Sparkling Wine can only be made from Chardonnay, Meunier, Pinot blanc, Pinot gris, Pinot noir, and Pinot noir Précoce. Cascade, Gagarin Blue and Zalagyöngye are all listed on the DEFRA list of varieties eligible for PDO still wine, but as hybrids, they should not be.

Bolero, Cabernet blanc, Felicia, Johanniter, Merzling, Monarch, Sirius, Solaris, and Villaris (all ISC varieties) are all listed on the DEFRA list of varieties eligible for PDO still wine, but their UK legal status as '*viniferas*' is uncertain. Cabernet Dorsa, Manzoni Bianco, and Muscaris are all listed by the WSB as being grown in the UK, but not listed by DEFRA on either the PDO or PGI lists. See *Chapter 4: Vine Varieties, clones and rootstocks* for more detail on which varieties may be used for which wines.

## Appendix III: The story of Wrotham Pinot

The vine that Edward Hyams discovered in Wrotham in the early 1950s was in all probability the variety known as 'Miller's Burgundy' which had been widely grown on walls and in gardens in Great Britain for many years. Archibald Barron writing in his book, *Vines and Vine Culture,* the standard Victorian work on grape growing, states that the variety was: *found by* [the famous horticulturalist] *Sir Joseph Banks in the remains of an ancient vineyard at Tortworth, Gloucestershire* – a county well known for its medieval vineyards. Hyams took cuttings to Brock at Oxted who said that when compared to supplies of Meunier from France, the variety now known as Wrotham Pinot: *had a higher natural sugar content and ripened two weeks earlier*. Hyams, ever the journalist in search of a good story, claimed that this vine had been left behind by the Romans although provided no evidence for this.

Brock, in his *Report No. 3: Progress With Vines and Wines* of 1961, states that Wrotham Pinot: 'appears to be better adapted to this climate than the standard Pinot grapes' and 'is a consistent cropper, and ripens here in good years in the open vineyard', i.e. not under cloches. He continues that: 'it would probably be suitable for a really highly flavoured Burgundy type of red wine in favoured sites in the south of England, but it is not suitable where the conditions are not very good'. Brock sold cuttings and the variety became quite popular in early vineyards, although it is unlikely that any vines from the cuttings supplied by Brock survive in any of today's UK vineyards. Jack Ward, writing in his 1984 book *Vine Growing in the British Isles*, says that Wrotham Pinot: 'was given a fair trial in the Beaulieu vineyard and contributed to the production of a rosé wine' but that: 'its performance was adequate but hardly good enough, for it was later grubbed in favour of other varieties'. Gillian Pearkes, writing in the 1989 version of her 1982 book *Vinegrowing in Britain* says that Meunier: 'suffers from the same inadequacies' as Pinot noir which she states: 'is seldom if ever even a mediocre wine; it is thin, pale and lacking in intensity of bouquet and depth of flavour'. Despite the fact that today all plantings of Meunier in the UK stem from French and German nurseries, the name Wrotham Pinot is still a legally acceptable synonym for this variety, although the name is not used at all in the UK.

In 2004, a well-known grower from California, Richard Grant Peterson, (who was winemaker at Beaulieu Vineyards in Napa after the famous André Tchelistcheff) announced that he had a vineyard in Yountville in the Napa Valley, planted with Wrotham Pinot vines propagated from cuttings taken from the original Wrotham Pinot vine in 1980. At the time, Peterson was a judge at the International Wine and Spirits Competition (IWSC) and had been told about a vine growing wild against a stone wall in the village of Wrotham. He then claims to have inspected it and found that it had tiny white hairs on the upper surface of the leaves and was unlike any vine he had ever seen. In addition, this vine: 'had developed a considerable immunity to Powdery Mildew'. On his website, Peterson states that the original vine in Wrotham died in the mid-'80s, but that: *there are now at least two new wild seedlings growing a few feet from where the mother vine had stood*. This statement would appear to show that Peterson knows where the original vine was. Despite several attempts to contact Peterson, I have been unable to verify whether he personally visited the cottage in Wrotham or who the 'local winemakers' were that had made the wine he tasted. Ignoring the fact that a 'seedling' cannot possibly be the same variety as vine variety that produced the bunch of grapes from which it came, I find the whole story slightly unbelievable!

On his website, Peterson states that: 'English viticulture scholars eventually came to the conclusion the Wrotham vine was a natural seedling of Pinot noir vines that the early Romans brought to England 2000 years ago'. Ignoring the 'seedling question again, quite who these 'English viticulture scholars' were is not known, but possibly a reference to Ray Brock at Oxted, although he never mentioned this to me when I interviewed him (several times) for my UK Vineyards Guide before he died in 1999.

Peterson also states that he tasted a *Blanc de Noirs* wine from the variety made by 'local winemakers' and immediately recognised its potential. He imported cuttings into California and, 'after a quarantine of many years as required by law', vines were propagated and a 0.8-ha (2-acre) vineyard established which he grows without the need to spray them with sulphur against Powdery Mildew. Peterson had a vine analysed by the University of California's Davis wine department who pronounced the vine's DNA to be identical to Pinot noir. Peterson now makes a wine from Wrotham Pinot, a bottle-fermented rosé sparkling, which sells for $60 a bottle. Its quality is obviously excellent as the 2001 vintage recently won a Double Gold at the US National Women's Wine Competition.

The Wrotham Historical Society publishes a booklet *Farming in Wrotham Through the Ages* which I purchased for £3 in the hope that it might provide some useful information. The booklet mentions that: *there is reputed to have been a Roman vineyard on the slopes of the North Downs above Wrotham* (funny how reports about Roman vineyards always start with 'reputed' or 'thought to have been') but about the location of the cottage it gives little help. The booklet merely says that the cottage wall was *on the main road in the village* which is hardly giving the game away. The text in the booklet is more or less the same as can be found on Peterson's website: www.richardgrantwine.com.

## Appendix IV: The Agricultural Flat Rate Scheme

The Agricultural Flat Rate Scheme (AFRS) is an alternative to being registered for Value Added Tax (VAT) for most farmers and growers. Wine producers are specifically included in the scheme and HMR&C state that the scheme: 'includes the growing of grape vines and the production by vineyards of their own wine, up to and including the sale of the wine'. Full details of the scheme can be found in Notice 700/46 (available at www.englishwine.com/wgigb.htm). Farmers wishing to join the AFRS should apply using application form VAT 98. It should be noted that this is specifically not a VAT scheme and is not the same as the Flat Rate Scheme for VAT.

The essence of the scheme is that instead of being VAT registered and therefore being able to reclaim all VAT paid out on goods and services bought, but having to charge VAT on all eligible sales and pay that VAT over to HMR&C, the AFRS does not allow you to reclaim any VAT, but, on sales to non-VAT registered customers, i.e. members of the public and small traders who are below the VAT threshold for registration, you keep 100 per cent of the sales price and on sales to VAT registered customers, i.e. most wine traders, retailers, restaurants, hotels etc you can charge a 'Flat Rate Farming' (FRF) charge of 4 per cent of the invoice value which can include delivery charges. The VAT registered customer to whom you are making the sale is allowed to treat the FRF charge as if it was VAT and reclaim it in the normal way, i.e. it has no effect upon their business or the profit they can make from selling your wine. As I show below in an example where a producer sells 15,000 bottles of both still and sparkling wine a year, two-thirds to the public at full price and one-third to traders at usual discounts, this equates to additional income for the AFRS registered producer of around £30,000 per year, against which has to be set VAT spent on purchases which cannot be claimed.

AFRS registered traders are also allowed to make supplies of goods and services not produced on the farm, which would normally be subject to VAT, as long as the turnover of these supplies is below the VAT registration threshold (2013: £79,000). For a vineyard and winemaking enterprise these might include visits, tastings, meals, sales of non-wine items in a farm shop, and accommodation. This means that you can charge the same prices for these as would be charged by VAT registered providers, but retain 100 per cent of the price instead of paying 20 per cent to HMR&C. Therefore if you were selling say £40,000 worth of non-agricultural goods and services, you would be £6,667 better off than a VAT registered trader.

AFRS registered traders are also allowed to supply quite a wide range of services as long as they are 'linked' to one of the qualifying activities. Therefore a vineyard owner can supply 'technical assistance', 'storage of agricultural products' and 'hiring out of equipment' in relation to the farming activity that entitles them to be AFRS registered. As these relate to your farming activities, they do not count towards your non-farming supplies total and again, if you supply these to VAT registered customers, you can add the 4 per cent FRF charge which you retain.

One of the additional benefits of the AFRS is that for vineyard owners having wine made by another winery, no VAT is chargeable upon the winemaking charges, which can include labelling, including the cost of the labels, all storage charges and all delivery charges. This is because a business that is carried on in duty-free (i.e. tax free) premises, such as a winery, may not add a tax to its charges. If, for instance, you decided to sell all your wine abroad, or to a duty-free operator such as a cruise line or sold it in-bond to a UK supermarket, then no VAT would be payable. Therefore AFRS registered wine producers, who would not be able to reclaim the VAT were it charged, can get hold of their wine free of VAT.

Most vineyard owners will register for VAT as soon as they start and will be able to reclaim the VAT on all the equipment and supplies that they buy in order to establish the vineyard, even though they may not be making taxable supplies for some years to come. Once in production however, and making taxable supplies, i.e. selling wine, there is nothing to stop them de-registering from VAT registration and becoming AFRS registered.

The difference between being VAT registered and AFRS registered are shown in the examples below. They are based upon a producer selling 15,000 bottles a year, 50 per cent still and 50 per cent sparkling, two-thirds being sold to the (non-VAT registered) public and one-third sold to VAT registered traders, i.e. wholesalers, retailers, restaurateurs, hoteliers etc. The retail prices have been taken for this example as £10 per bottle for still wine and £24 per bottle for sparkling wine. Trade margins of 35 per cent for still wines and 30 per cent for sparkling wines, as set out in *Chapter 2: Why plant a vineyard* in the section on *Return from wine sales*, have been used. Both examples use a VAT rate of 20 per cent and Excise Duty rates of £266.72 per hectolitre for still wine and £341.63 per hectolitre for sparkling wine. As can be seen from these examples, the additional income based upon the data above, amounts to £30,275 per annum or just over £2 per bottle.

However, deducted from this would have to be the VAT paid on all goods, supplies and services used in the vineyard. These would include VAT on repairs, maintenance and fuel on tractors and other farm equipment, plus VAT on pesticides, fertilisers, farming sundries and any other farming expenses that carried VAT. Items such as rent (if the land was leased for instances), plus all wages and salaries are not subject to VAT. Taking the above example of selling 15,000 bottles a year, this might come from say 2 ha (5-acres) and the running costs attracting VAT might come to say £5,000, so a VAT charge of £1,000 to be offset against the additional income. Even allowing for some quite hefty costs of repairs to the vineyard and replacements to machinery over time, the additional income will more than compensate for this and in addition, the additional income from non-farming sales would add further income.

If the wine producer also operated a winery, then this might complicate matters as, unless you were VAT registered, you would be unable to reclaim the VAT for any expenses incurred in the production process such as materials, including bottles, packaging and labels. However, there is nothing to stop you running the farming enterprise and the winemaking enterprise as two legally separate entities. You could for instance have two separate limited companies, or run one as a sole trader and the other as a partnership. In this way, the farming enterprise could be AFRS registered and the winemaking enterprise could be VAT registered and able to reclaim any VAT.

As a slight refinement to the above, you could have one enterprise (A Ltd) that owned the vineyards and a winery and was VAT registered. It owned all the equipment necessary to operate the vineyard and winery and could reclaim VAT on all its outgoings. You could then have a separate company (B Ltd) that rented the vineyards from A Ltd and farmed them and would therefore be eligible to be AFRS registered. Its rent would include use of the farm equipment. This might be challenged by HMC&E as being somehow separate from the rent of the land (which is not subject to VAT), so there might be some VAT to pay at this stage. B Ltd would produce the grapes which would then be processed into wine by A Ltd under bond (and therefore free of VAT). All costs of production, including the cost of all labels, packaging and transport to the customer, would be part of the charge B Ltd paid to A Ltd and would be free of VAT.

## Appendix V: Vineyard running costs

The annual running costs of a vineyard will depend on many variables and it is impossible to arrive at a standard costing. The major variables are:

- Row width and vine density. A vineyard planted at 1.75 m row width with 7,000 vines-ha (2,833 vines-acre) will take a lot longer to prune, tie down, tuck-in, deleaf etc than one planted at 2.50 m row width with 3,000 vines-ha (1,214 vines-acre).

- In small vineyards, much of the work will be carried out by hand and/or with small-scale machinery. In larger vineyards, much of the work can be partially and even fully mechanised, with huge savings in time and cost.

- Both methods of, and efficiency of, the weed control will have a considerable impact upon costs of keeping the vines weed-free.

- Costs of pest and disease control will depend upon many factors: varieties being grown, condition of vineyard, quality of sprayer and spraying techniques.

- Whether the vineyard is run using family labour, directly employed, contract labour or by a contractor using his or her own machinery will greatly affect costs.

The costings below have been arrived at based upon a vineyard planted at 2.00 m row width, with vines at 1.20 m apart, a density of 4,167 vines-ha (1,686 vines-acre). The cost per hour of labour (£9.95) and of tractor and driver (£22.00) have been taken from the John Nix Farm Management Pocket Book 44th Edition (2014).

Several assumptions have been made with regard to machinery and equipment available and the costings have assumed that lower shoot removal, tucking-in and deleafing would be done by hand.

They do not include the costs of bunch thinning, although have allowed for three rounds of tucking-in, two rounds of deleafing, and ten each of mowing and spraying. This number of operations will be considered excessive by some producers, but realistic by others. I have also not included anything for fertilisers or manures.

If anything, these costings are on the high-side and in a vineyard of 5-ha (12.5-acres) or more and with suitable equipment, I would expect savings to be made. In really large, fully mechanised vineyards, I would expect the annual cost to be nearer to £6,200-ha (£2,509-acre).

These costings do not include picking costs, which are covered in *Chapter 2: Why plant a vineyard in the UK?*

| Annual growing costs per ha | Hours per hectare | Cost per hour | Cost per hectare | Cost per acre |
|---|---|---|---|---|
| **Hand work** | | | | |
| Pruning and pulling out prunings | 125 | £ 9.95 | £ 1,244 | £ 503 |
| Tying down | 50 | £ 9.95 | £ 498 | £ 201 |
| Repairs to trelliswork. Gapping up vines. | 10 | £ 9.95 | £ 100 | £ 40 |
| Removing lower shoots | 25 | £ 9.95 | £ 249 | £ 101 |
| Tucking in x 3 | 75 | £ 9.95 | £ 746 | £ 302 |
| Deleafing by hand x 2 | 175 | £ 9.95 | £ 1,741 | £ 705 |
| | **460** | | | £ - |
| **Tractor work** | | | | £ - |
| Pulverising prunings | 5 | £ 22.00 | £ 110 | £ 45 |
| Herbicide applications x 2 | 10 | £ 22.00 | £ 220 | £ 89 |
| Trimming by machine x 3 | 9 | £ 22.00 | £ 198 | £ 80 |
| Mowing. 1.5 hrs-ha x 10 | 15 | £ 22.00 | £ 330 | £ 134 |
| Spraying. 3 hrs-ha x 10 | 30 | £ 22.00 | £ 660 | £ 267 |
| | **69** | | | £ - |
| **Materials** | | | | £ - |
| Ties etc | £ 25 | | £ 25 | £ 10 |
| Herbicides | £ 200 | | £ 200 | £ 81 |
| Pestcicdes excluding herbicides | £ 1,150 | | £ 1,150 | £ 465 |
| Miscellaneous: posts, vines, secateurs | £ 125 | | £ 125 | £ 51 |
| | **£ 1,500** | | | |
| **Total cost: Labour, machinery, materials** | | | £ 7,595 | £ 3,074 |

## Appendix VI: Vineyard pre-planting check list

- **Measure up site accurately, allowing space for:**
  - Windbreaks, internal roadways, shading from boundary trees
  - Sufficient space for trimming hedges and windbreaks
  - Fencing
  - Correct headland distance for tractor and any likely (towed) equipment
  - End-posts and anchors, 1.5 m - 2.0 m
  - Sufficient turning space for rows at angles
  - Removal of internal trees, hedges etc not required
  - Area for stacking and loading of crop
  - Parking for worker's and picker's vehicles
  - Rest and/or changing room and WC facilities

- **Calculate number of vines required**
  - Decide on row width based upon tractor width +700 mm depending on pruning system
  - Decide upon inter-vine distance depending on pruning system
  - Divide area to be planted by row width and inter-vine distance to arrive at vine numbers

- **Vines**
  - Order required number of vines
  - Decide where vines are to be stored after they arrive in the UK and before planting
  - Decide whether vines are to be treated with dip (mycorrhizal or *Trichoderma*) at planting and get materials on order
  - Book planting contractor for early May
  - If hand planting, make sure team available for early May and assemble equipment: tape measure, measuring strings and stakes, individual vine position markers, spades, vine carrying boxes etc

- **Windbreaks**
  - Decide whether you need windbreaks
  - Measure up for number of trees allowing for appropriate spacings
  - Order windbreak trees. Bare rooted whips (600-900 mm) are best
  - If windbreaks are not to be inside rabbit fencing, order rabbit guards
  - Plant windbreaks in advance of vines if possible
  - Make sure windbreaks are looked after, kept weed-free, fertilised and if possible mulched with compost
  - Stake windbreaks until they grow a trunk strong enough to support themselves

- **Nutrition**
  - Take soil samples and send to laboratory
  - Ask for BS (Broad Spectrum) analysis plus Active Calcium Carbonate if pH over 7.5
  - Alternatively (or as well as) have site EC mapped (SoilQuest from Agrii)
  - Depending on soil analysis, decide upon fertliser and lime requirements
  - Lime best applied before any work done to the site
  - Other fertliser applied at suitable times, typically half before sub-soiling and half before final cultivations
  - Would the site benefit from green manure?
  - Would the site benefit from manure or compost applications?

- **Machinery requirements for establishment phase**
  - Tractor with sufficient power for sprayer, mower etc
  - Pesticide sprayer
  - Mower or cultivator for between rows
  - Weed control equipment

- **Other equipment**
  - Secateurs – Felco No.2
  - Max Tapener tying machine, plus appropriate tape, staples and spare blades

- **Site preparation**

  - **Drainage**
    - Does the site require draining?
    - Contact drainage contractors for drainage survey and quotes
    - Book drainage contractor and get date confirmed allowing enough time between drainage and remainder of site preparation
  - **Levelling**
    - Are there humps and depressions on the site that would be best ironed out?
    - If yes, find contractor with suitable tracked bulldozer to carry out work
    - Major earthworks best carried out before drainage work
  - **Trees and hedges**
    - Trim up or remove trees around site if these are likely to impede planting machine and/or cast shadows on vines
    - Remove any internal trees and hedges
    - Make sure trees and undergrowth are open up at the bottom of a slope if this is relevant to frost problems
  - **Fencing**
    - Decide upon fencing requirements
    - Get quotes based upon correct specification. See Forestry Commission and British Deer Society data sheets on rabbit, hare and deer fencing
    - Make sure rabbit netting is correct height and gauge
    - Make sure posts are of correct quality for designed life of fencing
    - Allow for sufficient gates for machinery and entrances for personnel
    - Place order with contractor
    - Work to be completed within 2 weeks of vines being planted
    - If site is not to be fenced, decide how vines are to be protected from rabbits and hares and order vine guards
  - **Water**
    - Is there a requirement for water on the site? It will be needed for both pesticide and herbicide applications
    - If not already present or nearby, make provisions for a connection to the mains
    - Install spray tank
  - **Cultivations**
    - Spray area to be planted, including headlands, with suitable weedkiller
    - Apply lime and fertilisers
    - Apply composts or manures
    - Subsoil to a depth of at least 600 mm. Ideally this requires a tracked machine
    - Plough, disc, rotary harrow to seedbed quality. Before rotary harrow, apply balance of fertliser
    - If it has been decided to grow green manure crop, then plant it for overwintering. Site will require probably need spraying off again, re-ploughing and cultivating prior to planting.
    - **Note:** All cultivations want to be up and down the slope in the direction of the vine planting

- **Trellising**
  - Based upon planting density, decide upon number of end-posts, intermediate posts and planting stakes required and place on order
  - If using contractor, get quotes based upon trellising design, number of vines and number of posts, end-posts etc
  - Also order required number of end-post anchors, anchor wires, trellising wire, chains, spreaders, clips for planting stakes
  - After planting, order end-post tags with details of row number, variety, clone and rootstock (Daltons ID Systems)

- **Planting**
  - ○ Make sure vines are on-site or nearby a day or two before planting
  - ○ Have available 100-200 bamboo canes (1.20 m) for marking out ends of rows
  - ○ Welcome planting machine and get planting
  - ○ Put rabbit guards on if using these
  - ○ Spray pre-emergent weedkiller once vines settled and before bud-burst
  - ○ Consider using strip-spread compost on sites with poor humus content

# Bibliography

Basler P, Scherz R, *PIWI Rebsorten* Stutz Druck, Wädenswil, Switzerland, 2011.

Bishop J, McKay H, Parrott, D and Allan, J *Review of international research literature regarding the effectiveness of auditory bird scaring techniques and potential alternatives.* DEFRA, 2003.

Campbell, Christie *Phylloxera*. HarperCollins, London, 2004.

Coombe, B. G, and Dry, P. R., (eds), *Viticulture Volume 1, Resources,* Adelaide, Winetitles, 1992 and 2nd edition,    2005. *Viticulture, Volume 2, Practices.* 1995.

Crossen, Tom *Venture into Viticulture*. Country Wide Press, Australia. 2003.

DEFRA *Code of practice for using plant protection products* (PB 11090). DEFRA, London, 2006

Dry, Nick *Grapevine Rootstocks*, Lythrum Press. Adelaide in association with the Phylloxera and Grape Industry Board of South Australia 2007.

Galet, Pierre, *A Practical Ampelography – Grapevine Indentification,* translated by Lucie T. Morton, London, Cornell University Press, 1979.

Goode, Jamie. *Wine Science. The Application of Science in Winemaking*. London, Mitchell Beazley, 2005.

Iland P, Dry P, Proffitt T, Tyerman S, *The Grapevine, from the science to the practice of growing grapes for wine*    Patrick Iland Wine Promotions Pty Ltd, Adelaide, 2011.

Jackson, David, *Monographs in Cool Climate Viticulure – No.1. Pruning and Training,* Christchurch, New Zealand, Lincoln University Press, 1997.
    *Monographs in Cool Climate Viticulure – No.2. Climate,* Wellington, New Zealand, Daphne Brazell Associates Ltd with Gypsum Press, 2001.

Kliewer, W. M. *Grapevine Physiology. How does a grapevine make sugar?* University of California, Division of Agricultural Sciences, Berkeley, California, USA. 1981.

Landers, Andrew *Effective Vineyard Spraying* www.effectivespraying.com New York, 2010.

Lott, Heinz and Pfaff, Franz, *Taschenbuch der Rebsorten*, 13th edition, Mainz, Germany, Fachverlag Dr Fraund GmbH, 2003.

Lytle, S. E., *Vines Under Glass and in the Open,* Liverpool, Horticultural Utilities Ltd, ca 1951.
    *Successful Growing of Grape Vines,* ca 1954.

MacGregor, C.A. *Cool climate crop size estimation: Site specific*. Fifth International Symposium on Cool Climate Viticulture and Oenology. Melbourne, 2000.

May, Peter *Flowering and Fruitset in Grapevines*. Phylloxera and Grape Industry Board of South Australia with Lythrum Press. Adelaide. 2004.

McGrath, M. T. *What are Fungicides?* The Plant Health Instructor. The American Phytopathological Society 2004

Ministry of Agriculture, Fisheries and Food (MAFF)
    *Cane Fruits, Bulletin 156,* 1975
    *Soils and Manures for Fruit, Bulletin 107,* 1975
    *Outdoor Grape Production, HSG 22,* 1978
    *Grapes for Wine, Reference Book 322,* 1980
    *Lime and Fertliser Recommendations No: 3, Fruit and Hops* 1978
    *Weed control in bush and cane fruit HGG 25,* 1979, London, Ministry of Agriculture, Fisheries and Food.

Mollah, Mahabubur, *Practical Aspects of Grapevine Trellising*. Winetitles. Adelaide. 1997.

Nicholas P, Margery P, and Wachtel M, *Diseases and Pests,* Winetitles, Ashford, South Australia, 2011.

Nix, John, *Farm Management Pocketbook 44th Edition* Agro Business Consultants Ltd, Melton Mowbray, 2014

Ordish, George, *The Great Wine Blight,* London, J. M. Dent and Sons Ltd, 1972, 1986.

Pearkes, Gillian, *Vinegrowing in Britain,* London, J. M. Dent and Sons Ltd, 1982, 1989.

Pearson R, and Goheen A, *Compendium of Grape Diseases,* APS Press Minnesota, USA 1988.

Robinson, Jancis, *Oxford Companion to Wine* (ed.), Oxford University Press, 1994, 1999, 2006.

Robinson J, Harding J and Vouillamoz J, *Wine Grapes* Allen Lane, London, 2012.

Rousseau J, Chanfreau S, Bontemps E, *Les cépages résistants aux maladies crptogamiques. Panorama européen*, Groupe ICV, 34970 Lattes, France, 2012.

Skelton, Stephen P., *Viticulture – an introduction to commercial grape growing for wine production,* London, S. P. Skelton, Edition 011c, 2009.

Smart, Richard and Robinson, Mike, *Sunlight into Wine – A Handbook for Winegrape Canaopy Management*, Adelaide, Winetitles, 1991.

Trought, M.C.T, Howell, G.S, Cherry, N. *Practical Considerations for Reducing Frost Damage in Vineyards* Report to New Zealand Winegrowers 1999, Lincoln University.

Trout, R.C. and Pepper, H.W. *Forest Fencing. Forestry Commission Technical Guide,* Forestry Commission, Edinburgh, 2006.

van Leeuwen, C, Trégoat O., Choné X, Gaudillère J-P, and Pernet, D. *Different environmental conditions, different results: the role of controlled environmental stress on grape quality potential and the way to monitor it*. Proceedings. 13th Australian Wine Industry Technical Conference 2007, AWITC inc, Glen Osmond,    Australia.

Waldin, Monty *Biodynamic Wines*. Mitchell Beazley. London. 2004.

Ward, Jack, *The Complete book of Vine Growing in the British Isles*, London, Faber and Faber, 1984.

White, Robert E., *Understanding Vineyard Soils*, New York, Oxford University Press, 2009.

Wilson, James E. Terroir. *The Role of Geology, climate and Culture in the Making of French Wines*. Mitchell Beazley. London. 1998.

Wrotham Historical Society, *Farming in Wrotham Through the Ages – The Wrotham Grape*, Wrotham Historical Society, 2004, pp. 56–8.

## Stephen Skelton – Biography

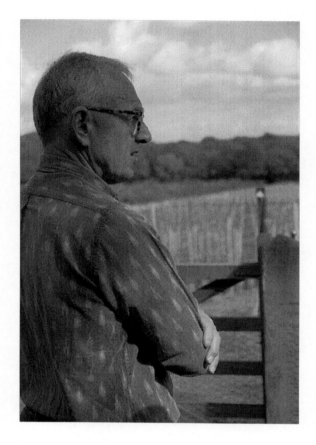

*Stephen contemplating some young vines!*

Stephen Skelton has been involved with growing vines and making wine since 1975. He spent two years in Germany, working at Schloss Schönborn in the Rheingau and studying at Geisenheim, the world-renowned college of winegrowing and wine-making, under the late Professor Helmut Becker. In 1977 he returned to the UK to establish the vineyards at Tenterden in Kent (now the home of the UK's largest wine producer, Chapel Down Wines), and made wine there for 22 consecutive vintages. From 1988 to 1991 he was also winemaker and general manager at Lamberhurst Vineyards, at that time the largest winery in the UK. He now works as a consultant to vineyards and wineries in the UK, setting up new vineyards for the production of both still and sparkling wine and helping existing growers expand.

In 1986 Stephen started writing and lecturing about wine and has contributed articles to many different publications. He has written several books on the wines of the UK: *The Vineyards of England* in 1989, *The Wines of Britain and Ireland* (Faber and Faber) in 2001 - which won the André Simon Award for Drinks Book of the Year - and the *UK Vineyards Guide* in 2008 and 2010. He is the English and Welsh vineyards contributor to the annual wine guides written by Hugh Johnson and Oz Clarke and writes the section on English and Welsh wine in both Jancis Robinson's *Oxford Companion to Wine* and Hugh Johnson and Jancis Robinson's *World Atlas of Wine.*

Stephen was a director of the English Vineyards Association (EVA) from 1982–1995 and of its successor organisation, the United Kingdom Vineyards Association (UKVA) from 1995–2003. He was Chairman of the UKVA from 1999–2003. He was also at various times between 1982 and 1986 Treasurer, Secretary and Chairman of the South East Vineyards Association, Secretary of the Circle of Wine Writers between 1990 and 1997 and has served on various EU committees in Brussels representing UK winegrowers.

In 2000 he completed a BSc in Multimedia Technology and Design at Brunel University. While at Brunel, Stephen was awarded the Ede and Ravenscroft Prize for his final year project. In 2011 he was awarded an Honorary Doctor of Business Administration from Anglia Ruskin University and in 2012 he completed an MA in Creative Writing at the University of East Anglia.

In 2003 Stephen became a Master of Wine, winning the prestigious Robert Mondavi Trophy for gaining the highest marks in the Theory section of the examination and in 2005 won the AXA Millésimes Communicator of the Year Award for services to the MW education programme. Between 2003 and 2009 he served on the MW Education Committee and was Course Wine Coordinator and since 2009 has served on the Council of the Institute of Masters of Wine.

Stephen is the UK wines panel Chairman for the Decanter World Wine Awards and has judged in the past for the International Wine Challenge, the International Wine and Spirit Competition, the Japan Wine Challenge and the Veritas Wine Awards

Printed in Great Britain
by Amazon.co.uk, Ltd.,
Marston Gate.